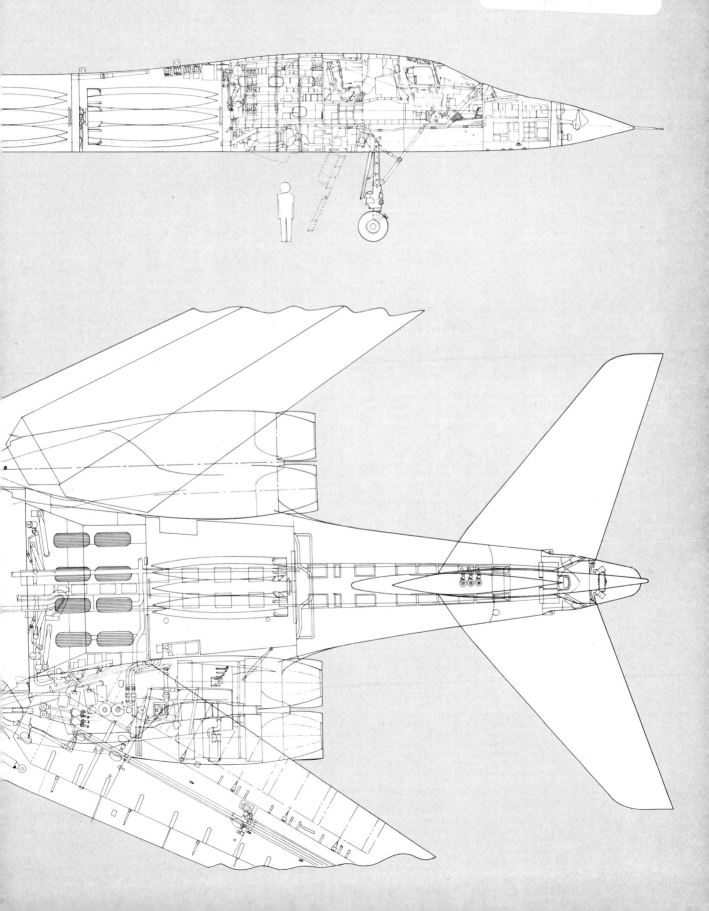

The Illustrated Encyclopedia of 20th Century
WEAPONS AND WARFARE

The Illustrated Encyclopedia of 20th Century

WEAPONS AND WARFARE

COLUMBIA HOUSE/New York

Editor: Bernard Fitzsimons
Consultant Editors: Bill Gunston (Aviation)
Ian V. Hogg (Land Weapons)
Antony Preston (Naval)
Deputy Editor: Suzanne Walker
Copy Editor: Michael Maddison
Assistant Editors: Will Fowler, Richard Green,
Corinne Benicka, John
Liebmann, Michael de Luca
Editorial Assistant: Julie Leitch
Art Editor: David Harper
Assistant Art Editor: John Bickerton
Design Assistants: Jeff Gurney, John Voce
Production: Sheila Biddlecombe
Picture Research: Jonathan Moore
Contributors: David Brown, Norman Friedman, Ian Friel,
Michael J. Gething, Bill Gunston, Mark Hewish,
Ian V. Hogg, John Jordan, David Lyon, Pamela D.
Matthews, Kenneth Munson, Malcolm Passingham,
Antony Preston, John A. Roberts, C. J. Ware,
Anthony J. Watts, John S. Weeks, M. R. Wilson
Illustrator: John Batchelor

Cover Design: Harry W. Fass
Production Manager: Stephen Charkow

"Courage is rightly esteemed the first of human qualities because it is the quality which guarantees all others."
—Winston S. Churchill

INTRODUCTION

Although the Italian **Vilar Perosa** is widely held to be the first ever submachine gun, on the grounds that it was the first automatic weapon to fire pistol-caliber ammunition; its absurdly high rate of fire, which emptied its 25-round magazine in less than one second, meant that it was actually used as a twin-barrelled light machine gun. Its shortcomings, though, were overwhelming. The **Thompson**, on the other hand, is rightly renowned as one of the most reliable and effective weapons of its type ever produced, and after a long period of rejection by military authorities—contrasting with its enthusiastic adoption by gangsters—it came into its own during the Second World War, when some 1,750,000 were produced. A more recent submachine gun which enjoys a similarly high reputation is the Israeli **Uzi,** while the **Vickers** machine gun, developed from the original Maxim, was another outstandingly reliable automatic weapon.

In spite of the notable small arms mentioned above, naval warfare is predominant in Volume 23 of *The Illustrated Encyclopedia of 20th Century Weapons and Warfare.* Not only the first part of our coverage of **Naval Ordnance,** which outlines some of the particular problems and requirements of ships' guns and begins a survey of the principle weapons used in the various calibers, but also **Torpedoes,** a different type of naval weapon, and the vessels with which they are often most commonly associated, the German **U-Boats** of the two World Wars, are included here.

The perfection of the Whitehead torpedo in the 1880s was one of the main spurs to the development of the submarine which until then had been hamstrung by the lack of a suitable weapon. Germany was among the last countries to display any interest in the new weapon, but made up rapidly for lost time. During the First World War the U-boats' campaign against merchant shipping came within an ace of winning the war. This campaign was repeated during the Second World War, and again came close to success.

Of course, just as the torpedo is not used exclusively by submarines, submarines are not just torpedo carriers. Germany evolved mine-laying and transport U-boats, and the profusion of different types of torpedoes, including sophisticated homing types, have been carried by ships and aircraft.

Statistics can often be misleading, if not actually meaningless, but the bare figures describing the exploits of the Republic P-47 **Thunderbolt** are nothing less than awe-inspiring. In Europe alone, in less than a year, Thunderbolts are credited with dropping 119,748 tons of bombs, firing 135,000,000 rounds of .5-in ammunition, and launching 60,000 rockets; in the process they destroyed no less than 86,000 rail cars and 9000 locomotives, as well as 68,000 motor vehicles and 6000 armored vehicles. The "Thunder" series of fighter-bombers begun by the P-47 has been continued by the F-84 **Thunderjet** and its F-8F **Thunderstreak** and RF-84F **Thunderflash** photo-reconnaissance derivative and the F-105 **Thunderchief.**

Finally, some notable products of the North American aircraft company are included in Volume 23. The T-6 **Texan** and its many variants, including the British Harvard, were responsible for training the vast majority of Allied pilots during the Second World War—a reminder of the often neglected part played by trainers. North American went on to produce the replacement for the Texan, in the shape of the T-28 **Trojan;** a more novel means of replacing a successful aircraft was applied in the case of the successor to the P-51 Mustang to produce the F-82 Twin Mustang, a name which succinctly sums up the technique of combining two Mustang fuselages.

T-35

Soviet heavy tank. The Soviet concept of a heavy tank in the late 1920s was a massive vehicle capable of independent operations like a land battleship. The heavy T-32 and medium T-28 reflected this doctrine with their multiple turrets armed with low- and high-velocity guns and machine-guns. The T-32, which appeared in 1930-31, had five turrets; an improved tank, the T-35, followed two years later. Tracks, armour and suspension were modernized but it retained the five-turret design. The total armament consisted of one 76.2-mm (3-in) and two 37-mm (1.46-in) guns with five 7.62-mm (0.30-in) machine-guns. The T-35 carried 96 rounds of 7.62-mm ammunition and 220 of 37-mm with 10 000 for the machine-guns. With this armament it is hardly surprising that the T-35 required a crew of ten.

The M-17 engine drove through four forward and one reverse gears in a mechanical gearbox. The suspension consisted of units of two bogies with rubber tires. Armour was only bullet-proof.

Experience in Finland led to further work on the suspension and the replacement of the 37-mm guns by 45-mm (1.77-in) guns. A flame-throwing version was also produced with a flame gun in the machine-gun turret.

By the time the Germans invaded the Soviet Union, some 20-30 T-35s had been produced and some were encountered around Lvov in Poland. Most had run out of fuel, but some were caught by Stukas as they moved up to the front and their thin armour proved no protection against dive-bomber attacks.

(T-35-1) *Weight:* 45.7 tonnes *Length:* 9.6 m (31 ft 6 in) *Width:* 3.2 m (10 ft 6 in) *Height:* 3.43 m (11 ft 3 in) *Armour thickness:* 30-11 mm (1.2-0.4 in) *Armament:* 1 76.2-mm (3-in) L/16 or L/24; 2 45-mm (1.77-in); 5 7.62-mm (0.30-in) machine-guns *Powerplant:* M-17M V-12 gasoline, 500 hp at 2200 rpm *Speed:* 29 km/h (18 mph) on road *Range:* 151 km (94 miles) on road *Crew:* 10

T-37, **Cessna** US basic trainer aircraft
See **Dragonfly**

T-38, **Northrop** US advanced trainer aircraft
See **Talon**

T-44

Soviet medium tank. The T-44 was built at the close of the Second World War and saw limited action in Europe and later during the Hungarian uprising in 1956. It was derived from the T-34/85 with a longer version of the 85-mm (3.35-in) gun and a T-34 rear drive sprocket. With the war in Europe drawing to its finish there was considerable pressure to produce the T-44 in time to be combat tested. The result was that though it was an advance in tank design with its low silhouette, powerful gun, thick armour and transversely mounted engine, it suffered from deficiencies which would have been weeded out in a peacetime development programme. The torsion-bar suspension was particularly troublesome and eventually the T-44 was only issued in small numbers with production stopping in 1949.

The T-44 reverted to a crew of four by eliminating the assistant driver/hull-gunner. This allowed the ammunition to be stowed more conveniently in the hull-gunner's position. It also produced a stronger 90-mm (3.5-in) glacis plate, with no driver's hatch or machine-gun mounting, at an angle of 45° as opposed to 60° on the T-34/85. The hull was box shaped, with vertical sides with a flat roof joined to a long sloping glacis plate. The hull was welded throughout with two small openings in the glacis plate for the vision slit for the driver and the hull machine-gun. The machine-gun was electrically fired and intern-

ally mounted so that the muzzle was flush with the armour. The position of the driver's hatch on the roof made waterproofing quicker.

The turret was similar to the T-34/85, hexagonal with angular corners sloped between 10° and 20°. There were two periscopes for the commander and the loader, with a commander's cupola and loader's hatch. The turret was larger than the T-34/85 but retained the same gun mounted in a curved external mantlet with a cylindrical sleeve. The transverse engine occupied less space in the hull and allowed the turret to be positioned centrally. Some later models were fitted with a 100-mm (3.9-in) gun which lacked the external armoured sleeve.

(T-44/85) *Weight:* 32.4 tonnes *Length:* 7.65 m (25 ft 1 in) *Width:* 3.1 m (10 ft 2 in) *Height:* 2.39 m (7 ft 10 in) *Armour thickness:* 75-20 mm (3-0.8 in) *Armament:* 1 85-mm (3.35-in) M-1944 ZIS-S53 L/51.5 DP; 3 7.62-mm (0.30-in) machine-guns *Powerplant:* V-2-44 V-12 diesel, 512 hp at 2000 rpm *Speed:* 51 km/h (32 mph) on roads *Range:* 233 km (145 miles) on roads with extra fuel tanks *Crew:* 4

T-54/T-55

Soviet medium tanks. Mechanical problems with the T-44 prompted more work on a new medium tank in the late 1940s, and by 1947 a new prototype, the T-54, had been produced. It used the best features of the T-44 and was mechanically reliable. However, during immunity trials the original turret showed a tendency to trap shells and deflect them towards the turret ring. It was replaced by one based on the Joseph Stalin heavy tank. The combination of the JS-III 'frying pan'

The Soviet T-54A, first seen in 1956, is one of the variants of the T-54 which is still in service with Warsaw Pact and Soviet oriented countries. It has seen action in Africa and the Middle and Far East

type turret with an improved T-44 produced an outstanding medium tank. The turret was a smooth one-piece casting with an internal mantlet extending slightly beyond the hull sides. To the rear were the commander's cupola, loader's hatch, periscopes and ventilator which were attached to two plates welded into the turret roof.

The suspension was torsion-bar with five wheels on each side. Western intelligence experts noted a slightly larger gap between the front and second road wheels which became an identification feature. The rear drive sprocket had two rows of teeth which engaged track links bolted to both edges of the track blocks.

The engine was the same V-2 type fitted to the T-44 and, as in the earlier tank, it was mounted transversely.

The 100-mm (3.9-in) D-10T gun had an internal mantlet and telescopic sight on the left with coaxial machine-gun on the right. The commander had a rotating cupola with three episcopes and two periscopes in the turret roof. The loader had a 12.7-mm (0.5-in) DShK AA machine-gun mounted on the turret forward of his hatch. The driver had a 7.62-mm (0.30-in) machine-gun firing through a slit in the glacis plate.

The first T-54s were still fairly simple vehicles with no fume extractor, and infrared equipment for the driver alone. Retrofitting infrared equipment for the commander and gunner with other improvements produced the T-45(M). A new model appeared in the streets of Budapest in 1956 which had a fume extractor and elevation stabilizer. The T-54A had snorkel equipment and a gun derived from D-10S M-1944 from the SU-100 which was redesignated D-10TG. Tanks fitted with infrared equipment for the commander and gunner were designated T-54A(M).

The third model had a bore evacuator at the end of the gun barrel, a two-plane stabilizer, commander's and gunner's infrared and a raised cupola for the loader and his DShK AA gun.

The T-54B became the fourth production model, entering service in 1958. It had full snorkelling equipment and a D-10T2S gun which was stabilized in both planes.

The T-55 was the fifth version of the T-54. The turret was recognizable by the absence of a cupola for the loader and no AA machine-gun. The 100-mm gun was an improved D-10T2S with a two-plane stabilizer and 43 rounds of stowed ammuni-

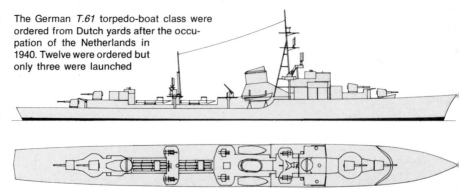

The German *T.61* torpedo-boat class were ordered from Dutch yards after the occupation of the Netherlands in 1940. Twelve were ordered but only three were launched

tion, an increase of nine on the T-54. The turret was fitted with gyroscopic controls, built-in computer and factory-fitted infrared and snorkel equipment. The 12-cylinder diesel engine was more powerful and made the T-55 over 5 km/h (3 mph) faster. A reworked T-55 appeared in 1961 with a fairing around the commander's hatch and thicker hatches for the loader and driver. The infrared equipment in these tanks is composed of a main 350-mm (13.8-in) light mounted coaxially with the gun with ranges of 800-1000 m (875-1100 yards), the tank commander's 200-mm (7.9-in) searchlight mounted on the turret with a range of up to 400 m (440 yards) and a driver's light mounted on the left-hand side of the hull.

The T-54/T-55 has been built in Poland and Czechoslovakia, and in China where it is known as the T-59. It is in service with Afghanistan, Algeria, Bulgaria, Cuba, East Germany, Egypt, Finland, Hungary, India, Iraq, Israel, Libya, Mongolia, Morocco, North Yemen, Pakistan, Romania, Syria, and Yugoslavia. Since its first appearance in Hungary the T-54/T-55 has seen action in the India-Pakistan conflicts, the Middle East wars, Vietnam and, in Cuban hands, in Angola. Its performance has varied according to the training of the crews and the quality of the opposition. The Israeli tanks were captured from the Syrians and Egyptians, have been regunned with the British 105-mm (4.1-in) gun and re-engined, but the cramped

conditions make them unpopular with their new crews. The Chinese T-59 has been supplied to Albania, North Korea, Vietnam, Sudan and Tanzania, who have also received Soviet tanks. The Chinese version is a rather crude copy of the Soviet original which lacks infrared equipment and CBW protection. It is slightly lighter at 35 tonnes.

The T54 chassis has been used for mine-clearing, for a combat bulldozer, bridge-layer, amphibious armoured recovery vehicle and probably also as a flame thrower. The mine-clearing tank PT-54 is fitted with two small hydraulically operated mine rollers. The bulldozer version can also be adapted to a mine-clearing role, and proved very effective against the simple nuisance mines found in Angola. Designated T-54 BTU, the bulldozer blade is fitted with a hedge clearer or plough when it is used as an antimine vehicle. The bridge-layer carries a 12×3.5-m (40 ft×11 ft 6-in) lattice-type bridge which is winched forward over the front of the tank. It is designated T-54/MTU or MST-54 (mostovy tank).

(T-54) *Weight:* 35.6 tonnes *Length:* 9.04 m (29 ft 7 in) *Width:* 3.28 m (10 ft 9 in) *Height:* 2.4 m (7 ft 10 in) *Armour thickness:* 210-20 mm (7.9-0.8 in) *Armament:* 1 100-mm (3.9-in) D-10T L/54 dual-purpose gun; 1 12.7-mm (0.5-in) DShK AA machine-gun; 2 7.62-mm (0.30-in) DT machine-guns *Powerplant:* V-2-54, V-12 diesel, 570 hp at 2000 rpm *Speed:* 50 km/h (31 mph) on roads

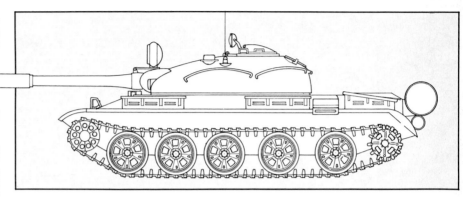

Range: 350 km (220 miles) on roads; (T-54[M]) 00 km (310 miles) *Crew:* 4

(T-55) *Weight:* 35.6 tonnes *Length:* 8.52 m (27 ft 1 in) *Width:* 3.28 m (10 ft 9 in) *Height:* 2.39 m (7 ft 10 in) *Armour thickness:* 210-20 mm (7.9-0.8 in) *Armament:* 1 100-mm (3.9-in) D-10T2S L/54 dual-purpose gun; 1 7.62-mm (0.30-in) DT machine-gun *Powerplant:* V-2-55 V-12, diesel, 80 hp at 2200 rpm *Speed:* 55 km/h (34 mph) on roads *Range:* 350 km (220 miles); (T-55-2) 770 km (477 miles) *Crew:* 4

T.61

German torpedo-boat class, built 1941-45. Twelve large torpedo-boats were ordered late in 1940 from Dutch shipyards. The design differed considerably from the contemporary T.1, T.13 and T.22 Classes in having a raised forecastle, and had to be tailored to materials available in the Netherlands. The layout was that of a conventional destroyer, with two gun positions forward and two aft, and uptakes from three boilers trunked into a single capped funnel. The armament comprised single 12.7-cm (5-in) SK C/34 guns in single C/34 mountings, and two quadruple torpedo tubes firing G7a torpedoes. Antiaircraft defence was provided by two twin 3.7-cm (1.46-in) SK C/30 AA mountings and four 20-mm (0.79-in) Flak 38 Vierlings, two abreast on the midships searchlight platform and two in the bridge wing.

Assiduous sabotage by the Dutch Resistance coupled with a lack of materials meant that only eight had been laid down by 1942. The orders were divided between Wilton-Fijenoord (T.61-62, T.67-68), Rotterdam dry dock (T.63-64, T.69-70) and de Schelde (T.65-66, T.71-72). Only three were launched, T.61, T.63 and T.65, of which T.61 capsized on taking to the water. She was salved but later sunk by Allied air attack while in tow. T.67-68 and T.71-72 were never laid down, and the others were destroyed on the slip. T.63 and T.65 reached Kiel but were scuttled there in May 1945.

Displacement: 1960 tons (standard), 2604 tons full load) *Length:* 114 m (374 ft) oa *Beam:* 11.3 m (37 ft) *Draught:* 3.8 m (12 ft 6 in) *Machinery:* 2-shaft geared steam turbines, 49 500 shp=35

knots *Armament:* 4 12.7-cm (5-in) SK C/34 (4×1); 4 3.7-cm (1.46-in) SK C/30 (2×2); 16 20-mm (0.79-in) Flak 38 AA (4×4); 8 53-cm (21-in) torpedo tubes (2×4) *Crew:* 224

T-62

Soviet medium tank. The T-62 evolved from the T-54/55 tanks and has many similar features. It entered production late in 1961 and was first seen in public in 1964. It is slightly larger than the T-55 and has a new turret in a central position which mounts a 115-mm (4.52-in) U-5TS smoothbore gun which fires an APFSDS (armour-piercing fin-stabilized discarding-sabot) round.

The hull is similar to the T-55 with external fuel cells located on the track guards. The driver's hatch is to the left of the gun and he does not have a hull machine-gun. The T-62 can carry two large fuel drums attached to the rear hull for refuelling on the march, but like the external cells these are vulnerable to tracer fire.

The turret has two hatches for the commander and loader with a small one to the rear for disposal of empty shell cases. An infrared searchlight is mounted and a 12.7-mm (0.5-in) DShK AA machine-gun can be located by the loader's hatch in the T-62A. A larger infrared light is positioned on the right of the main armament with a smaller one on the left side of the glacis plate. A coaxial 7.62-mm (0.30-in) PKT machine-gun is mounted in the turret. The 115-mm gun has a fume extractor fitted and can fire at a maximum rate of five rds/min. Ranging is by a stadiametric rangefinder in the turret, though a laser system is believed to be under development. The T-62 carries 40 rounds of HE, HEAT and APFSDS but the fin-stabilized AP ammunition is believed to be less effective at ranges over 1500 m (1600 yards). These ranges are less likely to be encountered in Europe, but during the Middle East war of 1973 they were a feature of tank actions in the Sinai desert where the T-62 was deployed by Egypt. The T-62 has the same limited gun depression (−4°) which dogged the T-55, which made it hard to engage targets from a hull down position.

The T-62 is protected against CBW and can wade up to 1.4 m (4 ft 6 in), and with the snorkel fitted up to 3.96 m (13 ft).

In 1978 it was in production in the Soviet Union and in service with Afghanistan, Bulgaria, Czechoslovakia, East Germany, Egypt, Hungary, India, Iraq, Libya, Poland, Romania, and Syria. In addition, Israel has pressed into service T-62s captured during fighting with Egypt and Syria.

(T-62) *Weight:* 36.5 tonnes *Length:* 6.86 m (22 ft 6 in) *Width:* 3.35 m (11 ft) *Height:* 2.4 m (7 ft 10 in) *Armour thickness:* 210-20 mm (8.3-0.8 in) *Armament:* 115-mm (4.52-in) gun; 1 7.62-mm (0.30-in) machine-gun *Powerplant:* V-2-62, V-12 water-cooled diesel, 700 hp at 2200 rpm *Speed:* 55 km/h (34 mph) *Range:* 480 km (300 miles) *Crew:* 4

T-72

Soviet medium tank. The T-72 appeared in the mid-1970s and was for a time shrouded in some mystery, but it proved to be a fairly conventional well-armed medium tank.

Its 125-mm (4.9-in) gun equipped with a fume extractor is mounted in a low pear-shaped turret which tapers to the rear. There are two hatches: the commander's with a cupola, and the gunner/radio operator's with the 12.7-mm (0.5-in) AA machine-gun. Stowage bins are located on the right and rear sides with what is probably a factory-fitted snorkel on the left. The commander has a small infrared searchlight, while a larger one is mounted coaxially with the main gun on the right with a 7.62-mm (0.30-in) machine-gun on the left.

The T-72 has a three-man crew, which suggests that the 125-mm gun is fitted with an automatic loader. It fires semicombustible rounds which include 22 HE, 12 APFSDS and 6 HEAT and has a range in excess of 2500 m (2730 yards).

The driver's position is protected from mud and spray during cross-country driving by a V-shaped ridge on the glacis plate and by small mudguards extending from the track guards to the glacis plate. The T-72 is equipped with a toothed shovel/dozer blade for digging in and assault-engineer work. Fuel cells are located along the length of the right track guard and the rear half of the left. Tracks and suspension are of a new design consisting of a rubber-bushed single-pin suspension with a rear-mounted 14-tooth sprocket, front idler wheel and three return rollers. The six road wheels are evenly spaced. Like the T-62, the T-72 is equipped with a snorkel for deep fording, and can wade up to the height of the driver's entrance hatch with very little preparation time.

(T-72) *Weight:* (not known) *Length:* 6.4 m (21 ft) *Width:* 3.3 m (10 ft 10 in) *Height:* 2.2 m (7 ft 3 in) *Armour thickness:* (not known) *Armament:* 125-mm (5.9-in) gun, 40 rounds; 1 12.7-mm (0.5-in) AA machine-gun; 1 7.62-mm (0.30-in) coaxial machine-gun *Powerplant:* Diesel *Speed:* 100 km/h (62 mph) *Range:* 500 km (310 miles) approx *Crew:* 3

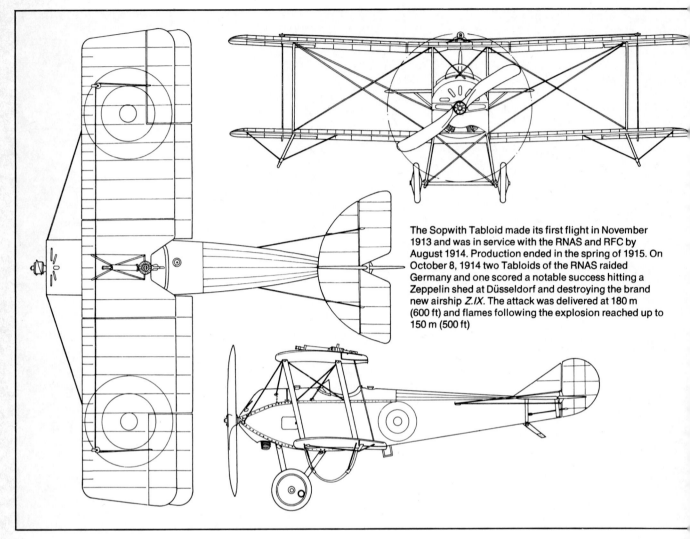

The Sopwith Tabloid made its first flight in November 1913 and was in service with the RNAS and RFC by August 1914. Production ended in the spring of 1915. On October 8, 1914 two Tabloids of the RNAS raided Germany and one scored a notable success hitting a Zeppelin shed at Düsseldorf and destroying the brand new airship *Z.IX*. The attack was delivered at 180 m (600 ft) and flames following the explosion reached up to 150 m (500 ft)

T-100

Soviet heavy tank. The T-100 and its derivative the SMK grew from specifications for a new heavy tank which were laid down in 1938. When Stalin saw the proposed three-turret tank he suggested that one turret should be removed and the saving in weight be used to increase the armour. Stalin approved three designs, two with twin turrets and the third with only one. This last tank was to become the KV1, but the other two, the T-100 and SMK, were useful testbeds.

The T-100 and SMK (Sergius Mironovitch Kirov) were almost identical in appearance. They had an upper central turret mounting a 76-mm (3-in) gun with a 360° traverse and a lower turret in the front with a 180° traverse and a 45-mm (1.77-in) gun. This combination was intended to give an effective AP and HE capability with high- and low-velocity guns. The T-100 had a crew of six and the SMK seven.

Armour protection, which was entirely cast, was designed to give protection against 37-mm (1.46-in) AP shot at all ranges, which was a considerable improvement on earlier heavy tank protection. The most important innovation, however, was the track and suspension. The chassis had a torsion-bar suspension with eight independently sprung small-diameter bogie wheels on each side,

each with a resilient rubber-bushed hub. The upper track was supported by four return rollers on each side. The track itself was very wide with heavily spudded small-pitch links; the resulting reduction in ground pressure allowed the tank to cross soft ground and snow without bellying down.

The T-100 and SMK were deployed in small numbers in the Soviet-Finnish War without notable success.

(T-100) *Weight:* 58 tonnes *Length:* 8.9 m (29 ft 2 in) *Width:* 2.97 m (9 ft 9 in) *Height:* 3.26 m (10 ft 8 in) *Armour thickness:* 60-30 mm (2.4-1.2 in) *Armament:* 1 76-mm (3-in) L/24; 1 45-mm (1.77-in) L/45; 3 7.62-mm (0.30-in) DT machine-guns *Powerplant:* BD-2 V-12 gasoline, 400 hp at 2000 rpm *Speed:* 30 km/h (18.7 mph) on roads *Range:* 150 km (94 miles) on roads *Crew:* 6

Tabloid, Sopwith

British scout aircraft. The prototype of the Tabloid was a two-seat single-bay biplane of 1913 powered by an 80-hp Gnome engine and originally intended as a racer and demonstration aircraft. Its performance, both speed and rate of climb, proved exceptional; the prototype was subsequently used for demonstrations in Australia, while a modified floatplane version powered by a 100-hp Gnome Monosoupape went on to win the 1914 Schneider

Trophy at an average speed of 87 mph over 28 laps of the 10-km (6.2-mile) course. One consequence of the Tabloid's outstanding performance, at least equal to that of contemporary monoplanes of comparable power, was the reinforcement of the prejudice against monoplanes which had led to their being banned from military use by the British authorities in 1912 after a number of fatal crashes, and which persisted to the extent that only one monoplane, the Bristol M.1C, was built in Britain during the First World War.

A small number of single-seat Tabloids were built for the RFC and RNAS during the first half of 1914, and these went to France after the outbreak of war. Highlight of their early service was the bombing raid made by the two RNAS machines based at Antwerp on October 8 which resulted in the bombing of Cologne railway station and the destruction of the brand new Zeppelin airship *Z.IX* in its shed at Düsseldorf. Four Tabloids, two of them aboard the seaplane carrier *Ark Royal*, were sent to the Dardanelles in early 1915 but saw no action there.

In fact, although a further 36 Tabloids were built between October 1914 and the following June, the type saw very little action. Having been designed as a high performance sporting aircraft it proved rather light for military service, and was in any case hampered by the universal defect of the first fighting aircraft, namely the lack of a suitable armament. A small number were fitted with Lewis guns, either above the upper wing centre section or mounted on the port side of the forward fuselage to fire between the propeller blades, which were protected with steel deflector plates, and a few 9-kg (20-lb) bombs could be carried, but apart from the destruction of *Z.IX* the Tabloid's only other notable success was achieved by Lieutenant Norman Spratt, RFC, on August 28, 1914. Carrying a few steel darts as makeshift armament, Spratt succeeded in forcing down an enemy aircraft by circling round it in mock attacks. After the spring of 1915 the Tabloid was withdrawn from military service, although small numbers of seaplane derivatives remained in service until 1918.

Span: 7.72 m (25 ft 6 in) *Length:* 6.2 m (20 ft 4 in) *Gross weight:* 508 kg (1120 lb) *Maximum speed:* 148 km/h (92 mph)

Tabun

German war gas. In the 1930s much German research went into the development of insecticides and weed-killers for agricultural purposes, during the course of which a team headed by Dr Gebhard Schrader became aware of the potentialities of some organophosphorus compounds as war gases. Instead of attacking the lungs or eyes, as was general with poison gases, this class of gas attacked the body's central nervous system. The body depends upon this system to transmit impulses, and these impulses lead to the formation of a compound called acetylcholine at the nerve junctions. This is neutralized by an enzyme so as to 'cancel' the signal and leave the nerve path open to receive a fresh signal. Tabun (ethyl dimethyl amidophosphorcyanidate) attacks the enzyme, converting it into a compound which has no effect on the acetylcholine, so that the nerve junctions remained blocked and fresh signals cannot pass. The body's functions are no longer under the brain's control, and within a short time the victim dies.

Once the powers of Tabun were realized, a factory was built at Dyhernfurth on the River Oder. The engineering problems which arose in converting the laboratory process into a full-scale production process were formidable, particularly given the lethal nature of the material, but by 1942 the factory was in operation with a planned eventual production figure of some 1000 tonnes per month. Some 15 000 tonnes are believed to have been produced before the advancing Soviet army overran the factory. Since that time, nothing has been heard of it; reports indicate that the entire factory was dismantled and shipped to the USSR, and certainly nothing remains at Dyhernfurth today. About half a million shells and over 100 000 aircraft bombs were filled with Tabun and were found in dumps throughout Germany when the war ended. According to authoritative German statements, this had been done simply to get the stock of gas out of Dyhernfurth before the Soviets arrived, and there was no intention of using the substance in battle. The Germans believed that the Allies were in possession of the same type of gas, since mention of similar compounds in technical papers in the West

had been censored during the war, though this had occurred for other completely different reasons.

Sarin (isopropyl methyl phosphorfluoridate) was also discovered by Schrader's research team. It proved to be extremely difficult to produce in quantity, and although a pilot plant was eventually built, no satisfactory production was achieved before the war ended. Soman (pinacolyl methyl phosphorfluoridate), the third of the German nerve gases, was discovered in 1944 but was never taken beyond the laboratory stage.

In postwar years much more research into this field has been done, and Tabun, Sarin and Soman are now generally referred to as the G Agents, since the German terminology was GA, GB and GC for the three gases.

Tachikawa Japanese aircraft See Ki-9, Ki-17, Ki-36, Ki-54, Ki-70, Ki-74

Taifun, EMW

German unguided surface-to-air rocket. Taifun was designed by Dipl Ing Scheufeln, range officer at the Peenemünde research and test establishment, as a cheap but effective alternative to the Wasserfall surface-to-air missile, and was the last weapon to be developed at that establishment. Development began in September 1944 and Elektromechanische Werke started production of the Taifun F version in the following January. The weapon was planned to equip 400 batteries by September 1945, and each battery was to have 12 30-round launchers based on 88-mm (3.46-in) antiaircraft gun mountings, but only about 600 rounds out of the 10 000 ordered in the initial batch had been completed by the time the war ended in May.

The rocket was powered by hypergolic (self-igniting) propellants—Salbei (fuming nitric acid) oxidizing Visol (vinyl isobutyl ether)—and carried a small contact-fuzed warhead, which was more effective than the proximity-fuzed blast charge fitted to Wasserfall. Prototypes of various other models using different propulsion systems and of varying sizes were also built under the designations Taifun 1 to 4.

Length: 1.93 m (6 ft 4 in) *Diameter:* 10 cm (4 in) *Weight:* 21 kg (46 lb 5 oz) *Maximum speed:* 3500 km/h (2200 mph) approx *Maximum altitude:* 15 000 m (50 000 ft) *Warhead:* 0.5 kg (1 lb 2 oz) high-explosive

Taiho

Japanese armoured fleet carrier. In 1939, influenced by the knowledge that the Royal Navy was building a class of carriers with an armoured flight deck, the Imperial Japanese Navy took the radical decision to follow suit. By the time that *Taiho* (great phoenix) was laid down in 1941, both HMS *Illustrious* and HMS *Formidable* had proved the value of the armour, and two more ships of the class were ordered in 1942, followed by five more in a supplementary programme in the same year. None of the later ships was laid down.

Unlike the British, in whose armoured carriers the hangar was a protected box, with sides and ends at least as thick as the top, the

Japanese provided only the last—an armoured flight deck with a thickness of 75-80 mm (2.9-3.1 in) between the two lifts (an amidships lift would have reduced the strength of the deck). Two hangar decks were incorporated, the lower deck being of 32-mm (1.3-in) armour, all machinery, magazines and gasoline stowages being within the length covered by the armour. Waterline belt armour was 152 mm (6 in) abreast the magazines and 55 mm (2.2 in) outside the machinery spaces.

In an attempt to preserve stability, in spite of carrying so much armour high up, the designers gave a total of just over four decks' depth to the hull above the full-load waterline, so that the lower hangar deck was just above the waterline and the bottom of the lift wells were actually below it. A large island, with a canted funnel, increased the resemblance to British Fleet carriers, and for the first time the Japanese also gave the ship an enclosed bow to improve seaworthiness and the airflow over the flight deck. The machinery was the most powerful ever installed in a Japanese warship, producing 180 000 shp on trials, to give the ship a speed of 33.34 knots at a displacement of 28 300 tons.

The main gun armament also marked a departure from Japanese practice, the long-established 127-mm (5-in) Type 88 gun giving way to the excellent high-velocity 100-mm (3.9-in)/65-cal Type 98 dual-purpose guns, in twin enclosed mountings, three of which were fitted on each deck edge. Fifteen triple 25-mm (1-in) AA guns initially and an additional 26 barrels, in triple and single mountings, were provided later. Air-warning radar was fitted on the island, one antenna ahead of the funnel and the other abaft.

The intended aircraft capacity was 84, but shortage of trained aircrew reduced this number. Thirty Yokosuka Judy non-folding dive-bombers, (including three of the reconnaissance variant), 27 Mitsubishi Zero Model 52 fighters and 18 Nakajima Jill torpedo-bombers were embarked.

Built by Kawasaki at Kobe, *Taiho* was launched on April 7, 1943, and completed exactly 11 months later. She was immediately allocated to Carrier Division 1, together with *Shokaku* and *Zuikaku*, and despatched to the Singapore area to work up. The air unit allocated to the division was designated the 601st Air Group on May 5, shortly before the carriers sailed to join the 1st Mobile Fleet at Tawi Tawi in the southern Philippines. The fleet lay at this anchorage, awaiting the US Pacific Fleet's next move, from May 16 until June 13, when it became evident that the Marianas were the objective.

Taiho launched just one full deck-load as her contribution to Carrier Division 1's 130-aircraft first strike on June 19. These were forming up when the submarine USS *Albacore* fired six torpedoes at *Taiho*, scoring one hit right forward, almost in line with the forward lift, which fell 2 m (6 ft 6 in) and jammed. The forward aviation fuel tanks ruptured and the ship went down about 1.2 m (4 ft) by the bow. Some flooding occurred, filling the lift wells with a mixture of water and gasoline. Speed was reduced by only about one knot and *Taiho* remained in formation, and with the forward lift aperture planked over, looked set to continue operating. But inflammable vapour from the spilled gasoline spread fumes throughout the ship, and it ignited some five hours after the hit with shattering effect. The armoured flight deck was split down the centre, the hangar sides blew out and, apparently, so did a large proportion of the ship's bottom. The huge fires, fed from the ruptured gasoline tanks, were beyond all control and less than 500 of her crew were able to get clear. *Taiho* sank about 90 minutes after the explosion, taking with her over 1000 men and the 13 aircraft which she still had on board.

Displacement: 29 300 tons (standard), 37 270 tons (full load) *Length:* 260.5 m (854 ft 8 in) oa *Beam:* 27.7 m (91 ft) wl, 33.6 m (110 ft 3 in) oa *Draught:* 9.6 m (31 ft 6 in) *Machinery:* 4-shaft geared steam turbines, 180 000 shp=33.3 knots *Aircraft:* 75 *Armament:* 12 10-cm (3.9-in) AA; 71 25-mm (1-in) AA *Crew:* 1751

Taildog British air-to-air missile See **SRAAM**

Taiyo

Japanese escort carrier class. In late 1940 both the Royal Navy and the Imperial Japanese Navy initiated conversion of merchant ships into auxiliary aircraft carriers intended for trade protection. In Britain this took the form of the simple addition of a flight deck in place of the superstructure on a 5500-ton diesel freighter, which commissioned as HMS *Audacity* in June 1941. (USS *Long Island*, also commissioned in June 1941, was the US Navy's response to a British request for *Audacity* type conversions.) The Japanese, short of shipbuilding capacity and raw materials, decided quite independently to undertake even more elaborate conversions of bigger, faster ships.

A class of three 17 100-grt, 22-knot NYK Line passenger liners, all built by Mitsubishi, Nagasaki, was selected of which two were already in service. The third, *Kasuga Maru*, had been launched on September 19, 1940, and she was towed to the Sasebo navy yard on May 1, 1941, and there converted as a flush-deck carrier, commissioning under the same name on September 15, 1941. Shortly afterwards, *Yawata Maru* (launched October 31, 1939) was taken in hand at the Kure navy yard and when she was commissioned (again under her original name) on May 31, 1942, her place was taken at Kure by *Nitta Maru* (launched May 20, 1939).

A 91-m (300-ft) hangar was erected one deck above the original upper deck, two centreline lifts being installed at the ends of the hangar; at the forward end of the 'box' under the flight-deck overhang were communications offices and the navigating bridge. The wooden flight deck was over 171 m (560 ft) long and was equipped with eight arrester wires and a barrier, but no catapult. A large aircraft crane was located on the port side of the flight deck amidships, but the deck was otherwise uncluttered. The original two-shaft steam turbine machinery was retained, the boiler uptakes being routed across to the starboard side to exhaust downwards from the deck edge through a single funnel. All three ships could attain 21 knots and had the high cruising speed of 18 knots.

Armament in the first ship, *Kasuga Maru*, comprised six single 120-mm (4.7-in) AA guns, three on each side; in the later ships, *Yawata Maru* and *Nitta Maru*, the two mountings on the forecastle were omitted, and those further aft were replaced by twin 127-mm (5-in) dual-purpose mountings, giving a total of four guns on each broadside. Light AA armament consisted initially of four twin 25-mm (1-in) AA mountings, but this was later increased to between 22-64 25-mm and five-ten 13.2-mm (0.52-in) AA machine-guns were added.

Kasuga Maru's first operation was to have been in support of the Luzon landings in December 1941, for which she, *Ryujo* and *Zuiho* were to have embarked the Tainan Air Group's Mitsubishi Zero fighters. Fuel-consumption trials showed that the fighters were capable of reaching the Philippines from Formosa and the carriers' contribution was therefore cancelled and the newly completed escort carrier began what was to be her main task, ferrying aircraft. As early as March 1942, *Kasuga Maru* transported Zeros to Rabaul, and as the New Guinea and, later, the Solomons campaigns intensified, so she and *Yawata Maru* became more essential in this role, bringing short-range aircraft forward from Truk or the Philippines to the combat zone and delivering them to the airfields. As the Japanese navy experienced between 20% and 30% losses on long-distance ferry flights overseas, the use of the carriers represented a considerable saving in aircraft and pilots.

Kasuga Maru and *Yawata Maru* were renamed *Taiyo* (great falcon) and *Unyo* (falcon of the clouds) on August 31, 1942. On September 28 *Taiyo* was torpedoed and damaged 64 km (40 miles) off Truk by USS *Trout*. By the time that she was repaired, the third ship was operational, *Chuyo* (ocean falcon) (ex-*Nitta Maru*) having commissioned on November 20, 1942.

Throughout 1943, the three carriers transported not only navy but also army aircraft between Japan and Truk. Although allocated to the General Escort Command in December 1943, their task remained the same and they did not operate on trade protection duties. *Chuyo* did not survive to join the new Command, for on December 4, 1943, six days before allocation, she was torpedoed and sunk off Hachijojima by USS *Sailfish*, going down with all hands after a brilliant attack in a storm by the US submarine.

Just over a month later, USS *Haddock* damaged *Unyo* as she was ferrying aircraft to Saipan. The carrier was badly damaged and had to be towed back to Japan for repairs. During the passage, two submarines made unsuccessful attacks on her. *Taiyo*, with *Shinyo* and *Kaiyo*, supported the build-up for the decisive Marianas campaign during the spring of 1944, but on August 18 she was attacked while in a convoy off Luzon by USS *Rasher*, which scored two hits. *Taiyo* caught fire, burned for 20 minutes and then blew up violently.

A month later, on September 16, 1944, *Unyo* was found in convoy in the South China Sea by USS *Barb*. The submarine fired a six-torpedo salvo which sank a 10 000-dwt tanker and scored three hits on the carrier. *Unyo* sank in less than three minutes, following a huge explosion.

The *Taiyo* Class was undoubtedly usefully employed throughout their careers, but had they been used for convoy protection, in the manner so effectively demonstrated by the Allies, they might well have been able to check the activities of the daring US submarine commanders who, in the end, were responsible for the sinking of all three.

Displacement: 17 830 tons (standard) *Length:* 180.14 m (591 ft) oa *Beam:* 22.5 m (73 ft 10 in) wl, 35.7 m (117 ft) oa *Draught:* 7.8 m (25 ft 6 in); (*Taiyo* 8 m [26 ft]) *Machinery:* 2-shaft geared steam turbines, 25 200 shp=21.4 knots (*Taiyo* 21.1 knots) *Aircraft:* 27 *Armament:* (*Unyo* and *Chuyo*) 8 127-mm (5-in) DP (4×2); 8-24 25-mm (1-in) AA; 5-10 13.2-mm (0.52-in) AA; (*Taiyo*) 6 120-mm (4.7-in) AA (6×1); 8 25-mm AA; 10 13.2-mm AA *Crew:* 850 (*Taiyo* 747)

Takao

Japanese cruiser class. These four cruisers were laid down under the 1927 Reinforcement Programme. They were designed as heavy cruisers of an improved *Myoko*-type design. In appearances the two classes were very similar, but the *Takao* Class had a more extensive bridge structure housing all the fire and damage control, communications and ancillary equipment. In spite of the size of the bridge (the largest of any of the Japanese cruisers) it was much more streamlined than in previous vessels. Extensive use was made of electric welding in an effort to cut down weight, and light alloys were used wherever possible. The *Takao* Class had greatly increased armour protection around the magazine, a total thickness of 127 mm (5 in) being carried in this area.

The vessels were very heavily armed with a total of five twin 8-in (203-mm) turrets having a maximum elevation of 70°. It was decided to develop these mountings in order that the secondary 4.7-in (120-mm) AA armament could be reduced to four guns, the weight saved being used to mount the extra 8-in turret. With a 70° elevation the 8-in guns were capable of engaging air as well as surface targets. The vessels carried four twin 24-in (61-cm) torpedo tube mounts on the upper deck. They were sited high up to minimize the possibility of an accidental explosion breaching any watertight compartments. With efficient crews, a salvo of torpedoes could be fired every three minutes.

During August 1938 *Atago* and *Takao* went into dock for an extended refit and modernization. The mainmast was resited from just aft of the after funnel to a position just in front of X turret, and a new superstructure was built just abaft the funnels. At the same time the twin 24-in torpedo tube mounts were replaced by quadruple mounts, and magazines holding a total of 24 torpedoes extended in the superstructure. The AA armament was modernized and increased in firepower, the 4.7-in mounts being replaced by twin 5-in DP mounts. A new rangefinder and main gunnery director were also fitted. In addition to the new 5-in a total of eight 25-mm (1-in) and four 13-mm (0.51-in) were also added. During the refit, facilities were built in to enable an extra seaplane to be carried, the two catapults on either beam forward of X turret being retained. The beam had to be increased to 20.7 m (68 ft) and, with all the alterations, displacement rose to 13 400 tons the draught increasing to 6.5 m (21 ft 4 in).

The *Chokai,* one of four Japanese *Takao* Class cruisers, in Kagoshima harbour in April 1939

Chokai and *Maya* did not undergo a refit at the same time as *Atago* and *Takao*. *Chokai* was a very popular ship, and being a flagship could not easily be spared from operational duties. She retained her original specifications until lost on October 25, 1944 at the Battle of Leyte Gulf.

Maya underwent a minor refit just after the start of the war, twin 5-in DP guns replacing the single 4.7-in and eight 13-mm being added. Following severe damage received in an air raid on Rabaul on November 5, 1943, *Maya* received extensive repairs. During these repairs C turret was replaced by two twin 5-in AA turrets (bringing the total to 12 5-in) and a total of 39 25-mm were fitted. The seaplanes were also landed at this time. Subsequently *Maya* carried a total of 66 25-mm AA. *Maya* was finally torpedoed and sunk by the submarine *Dace* on October 23, 1944.

Atago and *Takao* received further armament alterations in March 1944. *Atago* was torpedoed by the submarine *Darter* on October 23, 1944, while on her way to take part in the Battle of Leyte Gulf. *Takao* was badly damaged by limpet mines laid by the British midget submarine *XE.1* in Singapore. She was surrendered and sunk by the Allies in the Malacca Straits on October 27, 1946.

Displacement: 9850 tons (standard) *Length:* 201.6 m (661 ft 6 in) wl *Beam:* 18 m (59 ft) *Draught:* 6.1 m (20 ft) *Machinery:* 4-shaft geared steam turbines, 130000 shp=35.5 knots *Protection:* 102-76 mm (4-3 in) main belt, 3.5 in (89 mm) decks and turrets, 127 mm (5 in) magazine *Armament:* 10 8-in (203-mm) (5×2); 4 4.7-in (120-mm) (4×1); 8 24-in (61-cm) torpedo tubes (4×2); 2 seaplanes *Crew:* 722

Takasago

Japanese cruiser. *Takasago* was laid down in April 1896 by the British firm of Armstrong at their Walker yard; she was launched in May 1897 and completed in April 1898. She was built to a design prepared by Sir Philip Watts and was a typical Elswick cruiser of the period with a forecastle and poop which stood well clear of the water. However, the single 8-in (203-mm) guns mounted fore and aft gave rise to a lively behaviour in heavy seas and she gained a reputation for rolling. In spite of these problems she was a fast ship with a speed of over 21 knots. In fact, on her three-hour steaming trial at a displacement of 4392 tons, she recorded a speed of 22.9 knots at an indicated horsepower of 12990.

She was reasonably well protected for her

Name	completed	builder
Atago	3/32	Kure navy yard
Chokai	6/32	Mitsubishi
Maya	6/32	Kawasaki
Takao	5/32	Yokosuka navy yard

time, the Harvey steel armour being capable of withstanding a direct hit by 8-in armour-piercing shot. She was designed with a total of 109 watertight compartments, of which 18 were sited in the double bottom. Her entire armament consisted of quick-firing guns which made her a powerful adversary: the 8-in weapons were capable of a rate of fire of 4 rds/min. In addition to the 8-in guns, *Takasago* carried ten 4.7-in (120-mm) guns of which the fore and aft weapons were below the forecastle and poop, with the remainder sited behind the low bulwark amidships. To reduce topweight and improve stability the fighting tops were mounted low down, their vulnerability to shell fire being an accepted hazard to ensure the safety of the vessel. Each fighting top carried two 2½-pdr guns.

Takasago saw service during the Russo-Japanese War, taking part in the Battle of the Yellow Sea. She was lost off Port Arthur on December 12-13, 1904 when she struck a mine and sank with the loss of 274 men.

Displacement: 5260 tons (full load) *Length:* 118.1 m (387 ft 6 in) oa *Beam:* 14.78 m (48 ft 6 in) *Draught:* 6.2 m (20 ft 6 in) *Machinery:* 2-shaft vertical triple-expansion, 10850 ihp=22 knots *Protection:* 114-64 mm (4.5-2.5 in) deck and turrets *Armament:* 2 8-in (203-mm); 10 4.7-in (120-mm); 12 12-pdr (75-mm); 6 2½-pdr (42-mm); 5 18-in (46-cm) torpedo tubes *Crew:* 425

Takatsuki

Japanese destroyer class. *Takatsuki,* the first of the four destroyers of this class, was ordered under the 1963 Programme. They are designed for A/S duties, and at the time of completion were the largest warships in the Japanese Maritime Self-Defence Force. They are well-armed vessels carrying an extensive range of antisubmarine weapons which include an eight-barrelled Asroc launcher mounted immediately in front of the slab-sided bridge. Amidships, on either beam and just aft of the forefunnel, are two triple Mk32 A/S torpedo tube mountings with homing

torpedoes. There is also a four-barrelled A/S rocket launcher mounted right forward on the forecastle. Aft on the quarterdeck is a clear space for operating the three DASH helicopters, and their hangar is forward of this and just aft of the 5-in (127-mm) gun. The DASH helicopters were removed during 1977 and replaced by two HSS-2 A/S helicopters.

The ships carry a comprehensive array of radar and sonar equipment; in 1979 SQS-35 (J) variable-depth sonar was carried only by *Takatsuki* and *Kikuzuki,* but it was planned to equip the other two vessels with VDS at their next major refit. The hull-mounted sonars are SQS-23 and OQS-3. Air-warning radar is an OPS-11, surface-warning an OPS-17 and fire-control is by a US Mk 35 radar. The gunfire-control system is the US Mk 56. The vessels are equipped with Mitsubishi machinery and the radius of action is 7000 nautical miles at 20 knots.

Displacement: 3100 tons *Length:* 136 m (446 ft 2 in) oa *Beam:* 13.4 m (44 ft) *Draught:* 4.4 m (14 ft 6 in) *Machinery:* 2-shaft geared steam turbines, 60000 shp=32 knots *Armament:* 2 5-in (127-mm); 1 8-barrel Asroc launcher; 1 4-barrel A/S rocket launcher; 6 21-in (53-cm) torpedo tubes; 2 helicopters *Crew:* 270

No and name	completed	builder
DD.164 *Takatsuki*	3/67	Ishikawajima
DD.165 *Kikuzuki*	3/68	Mitsubishi
DD.166 *Mochizuki*	3/69	Ishikawajima
DD.167 *Nagatsuki*	2/70	Mitsubishi

Taksin

Italian cruiser class, built 1939-43. In 1938 the Royal Thai Navy ordered a pair of small cruisers from the Cantieri Riuniti dell' Adriatico shipyard, Trieste, to be named *Taksin* and *Naresuan*. They would have been single-funnelled ships with one twin 152-mm (6-in) turret forward and two aft, and a catapult between the funnel and the mainmast.

Work stopped on both ships in December 1941, but the following August the Italian navy took them over and renamed them *Etna* and *Vesuvio* respectively. *Naresuan* had been launched on August 6, 1941, and *Etna* was launched on May 28, 1942. They were redesigned as antiaircraft ships, but also capable of transporting a number of troops and stores. As recast they would have had twin 135-mm (5.3-in) dual-purpose guns, no catapult and a close-range AA armament of 65-mm (2.56-in) and 20-mm (0.79-in) guns. The funnel would have been faired into the forward bridgework and given a pronounced rake, and the pole mainmast would have been reduced to a stump.

Work proceeded very slowly for lack of steel and labour, and when the armistice was negotiated in September 1943, *Etna* and *Vesuvio* were only 60% complete. Both hulls

Talon, Northrop T-38A

fell into German hands but nothing was done to complete them, and they were scuttled in Zaule Bay near Trieste at the end of the war. Although refloated in 1946 they were scrapped in 1949.

Displacement: 5500 tons (standard) (increased to 6000 tons as revised) *Length:* 153.8 m (504 ft 7 in) *Beam:* 14.47 m (47 ft 6 in) *Draught:* 5.25 m (17 ft 3 in) (increased to 5.95 m [19 ft 6 in] as revised) *Machinery:* 2-shaft geared steam turbines, 45 000 shp=30 knots *Protection:* 60 mm (2.4 in) belt, 30 mm (1.2 in) deck *Armament:* (As designed) 6 152-mm (6-in) (3×2); 6 76-mm (3-in) AA (6×1); 4 40-mm (1.57-in) AA (4×1); 6 45-cm (17.7-in) torpedo tubes; 2 aircraft, 1 catapult (As AA cruisers) 6 135-mm (5.3-in)/45-cal DP (3×2); 10 65-mm (2.56-in)/45-cal AA (10×1); 20 20-mm (0.79-in)/65-cal AA (20×1); 2 aircraft, 1 catapult *Crew:* not known

---

Tallin Soviet name for ex-German heavy cruiser *Lützow*   See *Lützow*

Talon, Northrop T-38A

US supersonic advanced training aircraft. In service with the United States Air Force since the spring of 1961, the Talon originated as a parallel development of Northrop's N-156 Freedom Fighter, which became the F-5. Primarily a supersonic successor to the air force's veteran Lockheed T-33A, it is capable of covering all stages of advanced and tactical training previously carried out by the T-33A, the Cessna T-37 and two-seat versions of such jet fighters as the F-100 Super Sabre. The first training aeroplane to be designed from the outset for level supersonic flight, it flew for the first time on April 10, 1959, following a USAF contract for three prototypes placed in December 1956. The first two of these YT-38s were powered by two General Electric non-afterburning YJ85-GE-1 turbojets, but all subsequent Talons had 1746-kg (3850-lb) st J85-GE-5 reheat engines. Under successive contracts from 1958 to 1970, Northrop built a total of 1187 Talons, of which 1112 were for USAF training units. Forty-six of the remainder, delivered in 1967, were for the Federal German Luftwaffe, but were delivered in USAF markings to bases in the US and employed there for the advanced training of Luftwaffe pilots. Five were procured by the US Navy for its Test Pilot School at Patuxent River, and the remaining 24 were acquired by the National Aeronautics and Space Administration to provide spaceflight-readiness training to the first generation of US astronauts. The last Talon was delivered in January 1972.

The T-38A is an unarmed tandem two-seater. Although it clearly has considerable airframe commonality with its stablemate, the F-5A/B fighter, the T-38A lacks the leading-edge flaps of the latter and has lower-powered engines. Nevertheless, it is capable of Mach 1.3 at altitude, and achieves the outstanding initial rate of climb of 10 241 m/min (33 600 ft/min). It has also been used by the US Air Force's Thunderbirds aerobatic display team.

Span: 7.7 m (25 ft 3 in) *Length:* 14.12 m (46 ft 4 in) *Gross weight:* 5466 kg (12 050 lb) *Maximum speed:* 1385 km/h (860 mph)

Top: A Talos long-range SAM lifts off from a launcher during trials. *Above:* Talos mounted aboard a US Navy warship. The missile has alternative nuclear or high-explosive warheads

Talos

US Navy surface-to-air missile. Talos is probably the longest-running surface-to-air missile project in the world. It was the first product of Project Bumblebee which also produced the Tartar, Terrier and Typhon surface-to-air weapons. In 1979 Talos remained in service aboard a few US Navy missile carriers, but was being phased out in favour of the extended-range version of Standard (SM-2); it remained, however, the most powerful US naval surface-to-air weapon. It is one of the few US naval missiles to have been fired in anger: in 1968 the missile cruiser *Long Beach* shot down two MiG fighters over North Vietnam at an officially claimed range of over 105 km (65 miles).

Project Bumblebee began officially in December 1944, in response to a July 1944 suggestion by the Bureau of Ordnance (navy) to the group at the Applied Physics Laboratory at Johns Hopkins University, which had developed naval proximity fuzes. A missile was required to counter German bombers launching such stand-off devices as the FX 1400 guided bomb and the Hs 293 antiship missile; Bumblebee was to attack bombers flying at 645 km/h (400 mph) at 9150 m (30 000 ft) outside conventional attack range of 18 300 m (60 000 ft). The Johns Hopkins group proposed a 907-kg (2000-lb) ramjet to carry a 272-kg (600-lb) warhead; it would be launched at 560 m/sec (1850 ft/sec) by a 907-kg rocket booster. This radical approach would be combined with a new beam-riding guidance system proposed by the Naval Research Laboratory. Although the kamikaze threat of 1945 made missile research urgent, the Bureau of Ordnance saw in Bumblebee a weapon of great potential postwar significance, and in January 1945 decided specifically against building a makeshift device.

The first Bumblebee ramjet, a 15.2-cm (6-in) type called Cobra, flew in April 1945 and demonstrated supersonic performance that June. In 1946 Bumblebee produced a 45.7-cm (18-in) ramjet test vehicle (RTV), and by that September enough progress had been shown to convince the navy to extend the project to a long-range surface-to-surface version, named Triton. Problems in booster design delayed the ramjet missile programme, so in order to press ahead with work on missile guidance a rocket-propelled supersonic test vehicle (STV) was developed. The STV-2 made its first successful supersonic beam-riding flight on March 22, 1948, remaining within a fixed beam for 24 seconds. The navy immediately initiated a study to examine a modified version as a short-range antiaircraft weapon, which became Terrier.

The original Bumblebee effort remained oriented along ramjet lines; it had been hoped that an experimental prototype missile (XPM) could be produced by 1948. The XPM was to be used to train the fleet and to gather data concerning missile performance and would incorporate telemetry gear. In 1948 the XPM was intended to reach a range of up to 36 600 m (120 000 ft) and in its ultimately developed form an altitude of 18 300 m (60 000 ft), with a maximum speed of Mach 2. By this time warhead size had shrunk to 136 kg (300 lb). XPM became Talos, but by the mid-1950s Triton had been dropped.

Progress was not nearly as swift as the Johns Hopkins team had hoped. The first Talos prototype (ATV-N-6a3) flew in March 1951 and the first homing intercept RTV-N-6a4 was made in October 1952. At the same time the first true Talos weapon prototype flew, designated SAM-N-6. By 1956 Talos had made several intercepts, and the first destruction of a drone by a Talos with a warhead was made in March 1957. By that time several ships had been assigned Talos batteries; operational evaluation of the Talos system aboard the missile cruiser *Galveston* began in May 1957.

Talos is a very large missile: its standard Mark 5 launching system, which could fire 46 missiles in succession, weighed about 180 tonnes; the later Mark 12, with 52 missiles, weighed 320 tonnes. Talos was installed aboard the converted light cruisers *Galveston*, *Little Rock*, and *Oklahoma City*, the nuclear-powered cruiser *Long Beach*; and the converted heavy cruisers *Albany*, *Chicago* (CG-11) and *Columbus*. Further installations aboard three more heavy cruisers were planned, but the programme was terminated in favour of Super Talos which became the abortive Typhon. Other proposed Talos platforms included converted merchant ships, for antibomber patrol off the North American coastline, and *Iowa* Class battleships. The US Army also tested Talos as an alternative to the air force Bomarc missile.

The Talos guidance system was unusual. It was recognized early that beam-riding alone would not suffice for a very-long-range weapon, since the guidance beam would spread out with distance. It was, therefore, necessary for the missile to have some form of terminal guidance. This could not involve a large radar dish in the missile nose since most of that nose area was required for the air intake feeding the big ramjet. The solution adopted was interferometric semiactive homing. The needle antennae evident in the nose of a Talos pick up pulses reflected by a target, which in turn is illuminated by a specialized fire-control radar. In most semiactive systems the missile flies along a path determined by this reflected illumination, but Talos flies along a programmed beam generated by a secondary beam-forming radar, the small SPW-2; its target is illuminated by the big microwave lens of an SPG-49. Talos can, therefore, fly along an up-and-over trajectory.

Alternative nuclear and high-explosive warheads were specified quite early: the nuclear Talos is beam-riding throughout its flight, and was originally considered primarily as an antiship weapon. At first nuclear and high-explosive versions were not interchangeable, the nuclear type being designated Talos W and being distinguishable by its lack of interferometer 'horns'. Within the Talos programme it was designated 6bW; the 6a series had been test vehicles, as noted above, and 6b was the first generation high-explosive weapon; 6c1 was a unified nuclear/non-nuclear Talos. (This series of designations accorded with the Defense Department's SAM-N-6 designator.) However, in 1962 a new series of missile designations was introduced, in which the three letters indicated, respectively, launch platform, mission, and type of weapon, and Talos became RIM-8 (ship-launched intercept missile). Final versions were RIM-8G and RIM-8H,

the latter being an antiradar homing weapon developed to destroy North Vietnamese coastal radar stations (alternatively designated RGM-8H, signifying its surface-to-surface role). Production, which was by Bendix, ended in 1968. Some early Talos have been used as target drones in tests of antimissile defence systems.

Length: 10.1 m (33 ft) including booster *Span:* 2.9 m (9 ft 6 in) *Diameter:* 76 cm (2 ft 6 in) *Weight:* 3540 kg (7800 lb) including booster *Range:* over 120 km (75 miles) *Speed:* Mach 2.5 *Warhead:* continuous-rod or nuclear

Tambor

US submarine class. This class of 12 submarines was very similar to the previous *Salmon* Class. The main differences between the two classes concerned the machinery and torpedo armament, the latter being increased to six bow tubes. This class reintroduced the direct-drive propulsion system with the diesel engines arranged in tandem. This arrangement led to difficulties in coupling the engines together, and were used more than the forward diesels and consequently wore out more quickly. This meant that only half the power was normally available on one shaft for recharging the batteries.

The vessels were modified during the Second World War, and the conning tower was rebuilt so that two single 20-mm (0.79-in) mounts could be fitted forward and aft of it. In addition the 3-in (76-mm) gun was removed and a 5-in (127-mm) weapon mounted instead.

The 12 submarines were all launched in the space of just over one year, between December 1939 and January 1941.

Triton, Trent, Grayling, Grenadier—built by Portsmouth navy yard
Tambor, Tautog, Thresher, Gar, Grampus, Grayback—built by Electric Boat
Tuna, Gudgeon—built by Mare Island navy yard

Tuna was scuttled as a target off San Francisco on September 25, 1948.

The remaining vessels were all war casualties. *Triton* was sunk by three Japanese destroyers on March 15, 1943. *Trout* was sunk on February 29, 1944. *Grampus* was

probably sunk by the destroyers *Minegumo* and *Murasame* on March 6, 1945. *Grayback* was sunk in collision with the Japanese freighter *Hokuan Maru* on September 9, 1943. *Grenadier* was sunk by Japanese aircraft on April 20-21, 1943. *Gudgeon* was lost some time between April and May 1944. Four ships survived the war to be sold for scrap: *Thresher* (1948), *Tambor* and *Gar* (1959), and *Tautog* (1960). *Tuna* was sunk as a target on September 25, 1948.

Displacement: 1475/2370 tons (surfaced/submerged) *Length:* 93.8 m (307 ft 9 in) oa *Beam:* 8.3 m (27 ft 3 in) *Draught:* 4.2 m (13 ft 9 in) *Machinery:* 2 shafts, 4 direct-drive diesels/2 electric motors, 5400 bhp/2740 hp=20/8.75 knots (surfaced/submerged) *Armament:* 1 3-in (76-mm); 4 machine-guns; 10 21-in (53-cm) torpedo tubes (6 bow, 4 stern), 24 torpedoes *Crew:* 85

Tang

US submarine class, built 1949-52. The design of these six submarines was based largely on information derived from captured war records and German Second World War submarines. They were designed to have a high submerged speed and the propulsion machinery consisted of a vertically mounted 16-cylinder four-row radial diesel which was half the weight and two-thirds the size of engines previously used to power submarines. Under operational conditions they did not prove satisfactory and the boats were re-engined with a lightweight horizontally mounted diesel during the 1950s. This involved cutting the boats in half and adding a 2.7-m (9-ft) section to accommodate the new diesels. The vessels were further modernized during the 1960s when another extra section was added to house improved electronics and other equipment. The final length was 87.5 m (287 ft).

The *Tang* Class were the first postwar submarines to be designed and built for the US Navy, and *Gudgeon* was the first US submarine to circumnavigate the earth. The submarines were equipped with the BQG-4 PUFFS (passive underwater fire-control feasibility system) fire-control sonar used as an A/S targeting system. This was housed in small fin-like structures on top of the deck casing.

USS *Tang* off the coast of Oahu, Hawaii in February 1961. She was launched in June 1951

US Navy

'Tango'

No and name	laid down	launched	completed	builder
SS.563 *Tang*	4/49	6/51	10/51	Portsmouth navy yard
SS.564 *Trigger*	2/49	6/51	3/52	Electric Boat, Groton
SS.565 *Wahoo*	10/49	10/51	5/52	Portsmouth navy yard
SS.566 *Trout*	12/49	8/51	6/52	Electric Boat, Groton
SS.567 *Gudgeon*	5/50	6/52	11/52	Portsmouth navy yard
SS.568 *Harder*	6/50	12/51	8/52	Electric Boat, Groton

Trigger and *Harder* were transferred to Italy in 1973-74 and renamed *Livio Piomarta* and *Romeo Romei*. *Tang* was used on acoustic research during the late 1970s.

(As modernized) *Displacement:* 2050/2700 tons (surfaced/submerged) *Length:* 87.5 m (287 ft) oa *Beam:* 8.3 m (27 ft 4 in) *Draught:* 5.8 m (19 ft) *Machinery:* 2-shaft diesels (3 mounted)/2 electric motors, 4500 bhp/5600 hp=15.5/16 knots (surfaced/submerged) *Armament:* 8 21-in (53-cm) torpedo tubes (6 bow, 2 stern) *Crew:* 83

'Tango'

Soviet submarine class. The first of the class took part in the Navy Day review at Sevastopol in July 1973, since which time a further three boats of the class have been completed. It is possible that the 'Tango' Class may succeed the 'Foxtrot' Class as the standard Soviet conventionally powered submarine. Length is identical to that of the earlier boats,

A Soviet 'Tango' Class submarine. 'Tangos' are conventionally powered and have a crew of 62

although there has been a slight increase in beam. The propulsion plant is thought to be of similar power and performance, with the slight increase in speed probably the result of a more streamlined hull form. Like the 'Foxtrot' Class they are equipped with six bow tubes for 53-cm (21-in) torpedoes, although the stern tubes of the latter have been omitted. There has been a significant reduction in complement from 78 to 62, indicating increased automation.

The major external difference from their predecessors lies in the raised bow section, which is about 1 m (3 ft) higher forward of the conning tower than it is aft of it.

Displacement: 2100/2500 tons (surfaced/submerged) *Length:* 90.5 m (297 ft) oa *Beam:* 8.6 m (28 ft 3 in) *Draught:* 6.4 m (21 ft) *Machinery:* 3-shaft diesel/3 electric motors, 6000 bhp= 20/16 knots (surfaced/submerged) *Armament:* 6 53-cm (21-in) torpedo tubes (bow) *Crew:* 62

Tarasnice

Czech recoilless antitank gun. The Tarasnice or Type T-21 was a simple smoothbore gun which could be fired from a man's shoulder or from a small two-wheeled carriage. The projectile was a fin-stabilized hollow-charge bomb resembling a mortar bomb in general appearance, which was attached to a perforated cartridge case. The weapon was breech-loaded. On firing, a portion of the propellant gas escaped through the perforations in the side of the cartridge case into an annular space around the chamber, and was then vented through the breech block to eliminate recoil. The bomb was claimed to be capable of piercing up to 228 mm (9 in) of armour.

The Tarasnice was in Czech army service in 1960-72 and numbers were sold to Middle East countries. It has been replaced in Czech service by the Soviet B-10 82-mm (3.23-in) recoilless gun.

Calibre: 82 mm (3.23 in) *Weight in firing position:* 17.3 kg (38 lb 2 oz) *Length:* 147 cm (58 in) *Weight of bomb:* 2.13 kg (4 lb 11 oz) *Muzzle velocity:* 267 m/sec (876 ft/sec) *Maximum range:* 475 m (520 yards)

Tarawa

US amphibious assault ship class. Five ships were laid down between 1969-71, but four further ships were cancelled in 1973. Cancellation led to compensation being paid to the builders, the Ingalls Shipbuilding division of Litton Industries, as the original contract price was based on nine ships being built using modular construction methods at the company's specially built facility at Pascagoula.

The *Tarawa* Class, designated LHA, were intended to combine the features of an amphibious assault ship (LPH), amphibious cargo ship (LKA), and amphibious transport dock (LPD) into a single hull. The ships therefore have a full-length flight deck, with a half-length hangar deck beneath that runs from amidships aft. The latter is connected to the flight deck by a port-side elevator and a large stern lift, an arrangement which gives them maximum hangar space for up to 26 troop-carrying helicopters or marine AV-8 Harrier V/STOL aircraft. The forward half of the ship is taken up by vehicle storage and

The USS *Tarawa*, one of five amphibious assault ships in service or building for the US Navy

No and name	launched	commissioned
LHA.1 *Tarawa*	12/73	5/76
LHA.2 *Saipan*	7/74	1977
LHA.3 *Belleau Wood*	1977	1978
LHA.4 *Nassau*	1978	1979
LHA.5 *Da Nang*	1978	1980

maintenance facilities for tanks, trucks and jeeps. Cargo can be moved automatically by conveyors and there are seven further lifts for the movement of cargo and vehicles. Beneath the hangar deck is a docking well capable of accommodating four of the large LCU-1610 type landing craft. The ships have sophisticated internal and external communications. In addition to the main propulsion system, a bow thruster is provided for holding position while the landing craft are being floated out.

On either side of the bow and on the port side of the stern three single 127-mm (5-in)/54-cal lightweight guns are carried just below flight-deck level. The director for these is the Mk 86 fire-control system, which is carried on the mainmast. On the starboard side of the stern and on the forward end of the large block-like superstructure are two octuple launchers for the Basic Point Defense Missile System (BPDMS). Target data for this is provided by an SPS-52 three-dimensional planar radar on the mainmast. Surface-search is provided by an SPS-10 scanner, and aircraft-navigation by a dome-covered SPN-35 radar fitted above the flight deck on the after corner of the superstructure.

Extensive automation has resulted in considerable manpower savings, enabling a marine battalion landing team of 1800 men and all their equipment to be carried.

In January 1975 *Saipan* was damaged dur-ing a storm and grounded, delaying her completion. Labour and construction problems have resulted in further delays in the building programme.

Displacement: 39300 tons (full load) *Length:* 250 m (820 ft) oa *Beam:* 32.3 m (106 ft) *Draught:* 7.9 m (26 ft) *Machinery:* 2-shaft steam turbines, 70000 shp=24 knots *Armament:* 16 CH-46 helicopters; 6 CH-53 helicopters; 4 UH-1E helicopters or AV-8 Harrier V/STOL aircraft (in place of some helicopters); 3 127-mm (5-in)/54-cal (3×1); 16 BPDMS Sea Sparrow launchers (2×8) *Crew:* 902

Tarhe, Sikorsky CH-54

US flying-crane helicopter. The Tarhe was developed by Sikorsky, under the company designation S-64 Skycrane, as a heavy-lift military helicopter of the flying-crane type, consisting basically of a rotor system, power-plant and minimal airframe, to which could be affixed interchangeable container pods to carry the passengers, cargo or other payload. The first of three company-funded S-64A prototypes was flown for the first time on May 9, 1962, and subsequently these were evaluated by two armed services: one by the US Army at Fort Benning, Georgia; the other two by the West German army.

No orders were placed by the latter service, but the US Army ordered six more (designated YCH-54A) in 1963 to investigate further the compatibility of the heavy-lift concept with the increased mobility that it required in the battlefield. Powered by two 4500-shp Pratt & Whitney T73-P-1 turboshaft engines to drive the six-blade main and four-blade tail rotors, they were followed by about 60 generally similar CH-54As, which received the US Army name Tarhe. In service with the US Army's 478th Aviation Company, they operated in Vietnam in support of the First Cavalry Division (Airmobile), retrieving more than 380 damaged aircraft and transporting heavy loads of vehicles and equipment.

The CH-54A carries a crew of three, including a second pilot who can take over control during loading and unloading. Payload is carried in a UMP (universal military pod) measuring 8.36 m (27 ft 5 in) long, 2.69 m (8 ft 10 in) wide and 1.98 m (6 ft 6 in) high, the nominal capacity of which is 45 combat troops, 24 stretchers or an equivalent weight of cargo for an all-up pod weight of 9072 kg (20000 lb). The operative word is 'nominal', for Tarhes in Vietnam often carried a pod payload equivalent to that weight, and in 1965 one aircraft lifted an earlier-type container with 87 combat-equipped troops inside.

In 1968 Sikorsky received an army contract to increase the payload capacity of the Tarhe to 11340 kg (25000 lb), and to improve its operating capability in 'hot and high' conditions. Among the changes necessary to achieve this were a switch to 4800-shp T73-P-700 engines, a new rotor system with wider-chord blades and higher-capacity gearbox, twin-wheel main landing gear units, general strengthening of the structure, and provision of automatic flight controls. Under the new designation CH-54B, ten of this improved version were delivered between 1969-71, equipping the army's 291st Aviation Company. During October 1970 one of these lifted a test load of 18497 kg (40780 lb), and in 1971-72 the CH-54B set nine international helicopter records for payload to height, time to height, and height with payload.

(CH-54A) Rotor diameter: 21.95 m (72 ft) *Length:* 21.41 m (70 ft 3 in) fuselage *Gross weight:* 19051 kg (42000 lb) *Maximum speed:* 203 km/h (126 mph)

Tartar

US Navy surface-to-air missile. The third and, in a sense, the most successful of the three operational products of the Bumblebee missile development programme, Tartar has surpassed the performance of the far larger Terrier in a missile half the size of the earlier type, and has been exported to the Australian, French, Italian, Japanese, Spanish and West German navies; Standard Missile is a direct development. The basis of Tartar was the requirement that it be suitable for destroyers and smaller ships, to form a direct replacement for the standard 5-in (127-mm) gun mount. The Bureau of Ordnance set this requirement in 1951, and the Applied Physics Laboratory at Johns Hopkins University, responsible for Talos and Terrier, studied it

A Sikorsky CH-54 Tarhe heavy lift helicopter. The Tarhe saw service in Vietnam with the US Army's 478th Aviation Company. Loads are carried in a UMP (universal military pod) which can accommodate 45 combat troops or 24 stretchers, though this capacity is often exceeded

through 1954, submitting a weapons proposal in 1955. The Applied Physics Laboratory received a contract in May 1955, and full-scale development began in the second half of that year.

Progress was relatively swift; by this time the US Navy wanted large numbers of missile ships, and the high cost of missile cruisers made weapons which destroyers might be able to carry very attractive. Tartar was designed from the first to use semiactive homing, which required simpler shipboard radars than did the beam-riding of the other two standard missiles, but this appeared to duplicate the system used by the army Hawk missile, and Tartar funds were frozen in October 1955 while the Department of Defense evaluated the two missiles. Tartar development was then approved, and the first Tartar test vehicle flew in November 1956. The first Tartar control-test vehicle flew at the Naval Ordnance Test Station in July 1957, and the Tartar prototype flew at the Naval Ordnance Test Station in August 1958. Meanwhile, a class of Tartar-armed destroyers had been ordered, the *Charles F Adams* series, the name-ship having been laid down on June 16, 1958.

The keys to Tartar development were a new two-pulse rocket motor and semiactive homing. In the earlier Terriers the booster provided a first pulse to fire the missile into the vicinity of its target; the motor in the missile proper then providing power for terminal manoeuvres. The only way to achieve a really compact missile, which could fit aboard a destroyer in some quantity, was to do away with the booster; that in turn required a two-pulse motor, since no single motor could burn long enough to power the missile throughout its flight. Nor was it necessary for the missile to accelerate to a speed which so long a burn might guarantee.

As for semiactive homing, that was important in view of the simplification which could be achieved in the guidance radar. The SPG-51 of Tartar is a relatively simple dish, whereas both Talos (SPG-49) and Terrier (SPQ-5 and SPG-55) required heavy microwave lenses or other elaborate systems. Semiactive homing was also effective against low-level attackers and, by extension, against surface targets.

Yet another important feature of Tartar was that its tail fins could unfold automatically as it was placed on the launcher: previous missiles had required manual fitting of wings and tail surfaces, and spaces for such fitting had enlarged the launcher and magazine areas. Terrier and Talos installations had employed horizontal stowage for their relatively long missiles; in Tartar launchers the missiles stood upright, in concentric rings which (at least in theory) permitted a kind of modular launcher design. Thus the smallest Tartar launcher, the Mark 22 for destroyer escorts (now designated missile frigates), carried only 16 missiles; the larger Mark 11 (twin rail) carries 42, and the Mark 13 (single rail) carries 40. It was the very high rate of fire attainable per rail which permitted the replacement of the formerly standard twin-rail launcher, as in earlier missile systems, with the single-rail Mark 13 and 22; the adoption of twin rails in the new Mark 26 is not an indication of some problem with the single-rail system, but rather an attempt to increase the rate of missile fire to deal with saturation attacks.

Tartar production, by General Dynamics, Pomona, began in 1960 and was completed in 1968, as the compatible Standard replaced it. The missile was designated RIM-24; no SAM-N designator appears to have been used, possibly because it was very similar to the upper stage of the Advanced Terrier. The original production version was RIM-24A, followed by the RIM-24B Improved Tartar, which was somewhat heavier and had a longer range. RIM-24C, Tartar Retrofit, was a modified version of the -24B with improved electronics.

The US Navy thought of Tartar as a missile-age equivalent of the 5-in gun, ie a primary destroyer weapon and a cruiser secondary one. Thus the *Long Beach* and the three *Albany* Class missile cruisers carried it as their secondary batteries. The *Charles F Adams* Class missile destroyers are in some ways modifications of the *Forrest Sherman* Class in which one 5-in mount has been replaced by a Tartar launcher, and in the *Brooke* Class missile frigates one of the two 5-in guns has been replaced by a 16-missile Tartar launcher. A very similar launcher, with a capacity of 40 Standard Missiles (and compatible with Harpoon) arms the new *Oliver Hazard Perry* Class missile frigates. Abroad, the Australian and West German navies purchased *Adams* Class missile destroyers, with their Tartar systems. France employed Tartar to refit the *Surcouf* Class fleet destroyers, and Italy, Japan and the Netherlands mounted these weapons in new destroyers. Spain mounted Tartar in place of one 5-in mount on six frigates she built, otherwise similar to the US *Knox* Class.

(RIM-24B) *Length:* 4.52 m (14 ft 10 in) *Diameter:* 35 cm (13.5 in) *Weight:* 646 kg (1425 lb) *Speed:* Mach 2.5 *Range:* over 16 km (10 miles) *Warhead:* continuous-rod

Tashkent

Soviet flotilla leader or large destroyer, built 1937-39. Intended to be the prototype for a class of four built in Soviet yards, this unusual and handsome ship was ordered from the Odero-Terni-Orlando shipyard at Livorno, and has the distinction of being the only Soviet ship blessed by a Roman Catholic archbishop at her launch on November 21, 1937.

Without armament the ship made 44 knots on trials with 116 000 hp. After delivery to the Black Sea she received a temporary armament of four single 130-mm (5.1-in) guns but in 1940-41 these were replaced by three twin mountings.

Tashkent led a short but hectic life as a fast transport carrying troops and ammunition into beleaguered Sevastopol, making 40 round trips. Her luck finally ran out and she was badly damaged by bombs off the Crimea on June 28, 1942. She crawled into Novorossiisk with 1900 tons of water aboard and sank in the harbour. The wreck fell into German hands and was partly dismantled by them, though two of the turrets had been removed and installed in the destroyer *Ognyevoi* before the USSR abandoned the port.

The rest of the class, to be named *Kiev, Yerivan, Ochakov* and *Perekop* were to be built by the Marti and 61 Kommunar yards at Nikolaiev. The incomplete hulls of *Kiev* and *Yerivan* were towed from Marti to Poti and Batum respectively in August 1941 but were never completed. The other two were scrapped on the slipway.

Displacement: 2893 tons (standard), 3200 tons (full load) *Length:* 139.75 m (458 ft 6 in) oa *Beam:* 13.7 m (44 ft 11 in) *Draught:* 3.7 m (12 ft 2 in) *Machinery:* 2-shaft geared steam turbines, 110 000 shp=42 knots *Armament:* 6 130-mm (5.1-in) DP (3×2); 6 45-mm (1.77-in) AA (6×1); 6 53-cm (21-in) torpedo tubes (2×3) *Crew:* 250

Tatra

Austro-Hungarian destroyer class, built 1911-18. Six destroyers were laid down in 1911-12 by the Ganz & Danubius shipyard, Porte Re (now Kraljevica); *Tatra, Balaton, Csepel, Lika, Triglav* and *Orjen.* These were completed between October 1913 and July 1914 and so were the latest destroyers in the Kuk Marine. *Lika* and *Triglav* were both mined off Durazzo (Dubrovnik) on December 29, 1915. *Lika* sank immediately and although her sister was taken in tow she had to be scuttled later that day off Cape Rodoni. In 1917 two of their 66-mm (2.6-in) guns were replaced by AA guns of the same calibre.

Six more units were authorized under the 1914 naval estimates but were suspended in August 1914. In 1916 four were laid down in the same yard to replace losses—*Triglav, Lika, Dukla* and *Uzsok.* They were completed between July 1917 and January 1918, and a further four of an improved type were ordered in December 1917. Although the names *Lovcen* and *Honved* were chosen for the first two they were never laid down. Work proceeded on the machinery but insufficient steel was available to start work on the hulls.

Tatra, Balaton, Csepel, Orjen, Triglav, Lika and *Uzsok* were ceded to Italy in 1920 and as the *Fasana, Zenson, Muggia, Pola, Grado, Cortelazzo* and *Monfalcone* served in the Italian navy. The first two lasted only three years before being scrapped; the *Muggia* was sunk in a typhoon off Amoy in the China Sea on March 25, 1929; *Pola* was renamed *Zenson* in 1931 and was scrapped with her sisters in 1937-39.

Displacement: 870 tons (normal), 1050 tons (full load) *Length:* 84 m (275 ft 7 in) wl *Beam:* 7.8 m (25 ft 7 in) *Draught:* 2.5 m (8 ft 2 in) *Machinery:* 2-shaft steam turbines, 20 600 shp=32.5 knots *Armament:* 2 10-cm (3.9-in) L/50 (2×1); 6 66-mm (2.6-in) L/45 (6×1); 4 45-cm (17.7-in) torpedo tubes (2×2) *Crew:* 104

Tatra

Czech military vehicles. The Czechoslovakian firm Zavody Tatra AS of Koprivnice was formed in 1923 by the merger of two older motor companies and has since produced a wide variety of civil and military vehicles. The most notable design feature of Tatra vehicles has been that the chassis consists of a central 'backbone' to which all the mechanical components are attached; the swing axles employing this give all Tatra vehicles a noticeable inward camber of the rear wheels. Prior to and during the Second

World War the company produced several types of command cars and cargo trucks for the Czech and German armies. Tatra vehicles used by the Czech army include 1.5-tonne 4 × 4 trucks and the 8 × 8 Kolos heavy prime mover. The company is involved in the manufacture of the OT-64 eight-wheeled APC, which was designed jointly with the Polish army in the early 1960s. This vehicle uses a Tatra tubular chassis with a welded armoured hull and eight independently suspended wheels. The driver and commander are at the front with the Tatra diesel engine behind them and the personnel compartment behind that. Eighteen fully equipped infantry can be carried inside the body, which has two rear doors and four or five roof hatches. Early models merely had a light machine-gun on a pintle mount available at one of the hatches, but later models are fitted with the turret of the Soviet BRDM-2 MICV at the front of the personnel compartment. This mounts a 14.5-mm (0.57-in) machine-gun and a 7.62-mm (0.30-in) machine-gun side by side, and some vehicles have a modified turret permitting the guns to be used as antiaircraft weapons. The OT-64 (which is known as the SKOT in the Polish army) has been widely exported to India, the Middle East and Africa.

(OT-64) *Weight:* 14.5 tonnes *Length:* 7.44 m (24 ft 5 in) *Width:* 2.49 m (8 ft 2 in) *Height:* 2.67 m (8 ft 9 in) *Armour thickness:* 10 mm (0.4 in) *Armament:* 1 14.5-mm (0.57-in) machine-gun; 2 7.62-mm (0.30-in) machine-guns *Powerplant:* 8-cylinder Tatra diesel or multifuel, 180 bhp at 2000 rpm *Speed:* 95 km/h (60 mph) *Range:* 650 km (400 miles) *Crew:* 2 (+18 passengers)

Taube, Etrich/Rumpler

Austro-Hungarian observation and training aircraft. The military Taube (dove) of the First World War is associated more with the Rumpler Flugzeug-Werke of Germany, but it was in fact a design of the Austrian engineer Dr Igo Etrich, whose first flying machine was a model tailless glider built in 1904 in association with Franz Wels. After testing this, Etrich and Wels progressed to a full-size, man-carrying glider which they flew in Bohemia in 1907, but their early attempts at powered aircraft were not very successful, despite use of the excellent little 24-hp Antoinette engine. Etrich, working alone, eventually achieved a successful powered machine in 1909, and in November of that year at Wiener-Neustadt he flew the forerunner of what was to become the Taube.

The Taube prototype, which first flew in July 1910 and was powered by a 120-hp Austro-Daimler engine, had a physical resemblance to a flying bird that has probably never been equalled by any other aeroplane in history, though it was botany rather than ornithology that was its inspiration. Etrich modelled the planform of its wings on the winged seed pod of a palm tree, *Zanonia macrocarpa*, believing this to have a near-perfect aerodynamic shape. This seemed to be borne out by the 1909 aircraft, which could fly for almost 4.75 km (3 miles) and reach a speed of 70 km/h (43 mph). Not geared to produce the Taube in quantity, Etrich negotiated manufacturing licences at the end of 1910 with the Lohner company in Austro-Hungary and Rumpler in Germany, and the latter produced most of the Taubes between 1910-14, most with 100-hp or 120-hp Mercedes or Argus engines.

When war broke out the Taube was already in service for observation and training duties with the Austro-Hungarian, German and Italian air forces. By this time, after a dispute with Rumpler, Etrich had relinquished his rights in the design, with the result that numerous other German manufacturers now also began to build variations of the basic design. Among these were Albatros (whose other early aircraft were much influenced by the Taube), DFW and Jeannin (whose aircraft were usually known as Stahltauben, because of their steel-tube fuselages), Gotha, Halberstadt, Kondor, Krieger, LVG, and Lübeck-Travemünde. Lohner-built Taubes for the Austro-Hungarian air service were given the military designations A.I and A.II, with 85-hp and 120-hp Austro-Daimler engines respectively, and others were built by the KuK Flieger arsenal at Fischamend.

Stable and pleasant to fly, the Taube had a reasonable performance for 1914, considering that it was then a four-year-old design. It was unarmed (except for any small-arms carried by the crew), but could—and occasionally did—serve as a 'nuisance' raider with a modest load of small bombs. It was withdrawn from front-line duties by the spring of 1915, but remained a useful trainer for at least another year after that. Overall production is thought to have reached 500.

(1912 Rumpler military Taube) *Span:* 14 m (46 ft) *Length:* 10.3 m (33 ft 10 in) *Gross weight:* 540 kg (1190 lb) *Maximum speed:* 95 km/h (59 mph)

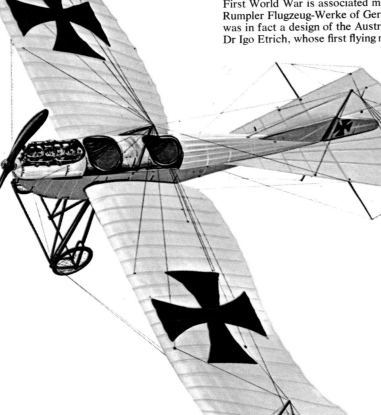

The Etrich/Rumpler Taube (dove) first flew in 1910 and was in service as an observation and training aircraft at the beginning of the First World War. Although normally unarmed, it was used in some of the early 'air raids' with a small load of bombs or hand grenades, and the crews went aloft with pistols or rifles to engage enemy aircraft. Nevertheless it was withdrawn from front-line service in the spring of 1915

TB-1, Tupolev

Soviet heavy bomber. The fledgling Soviet aircraft industry came of age when the prototype TB-1 took to the air on November 26,

TB-3, Tupolev

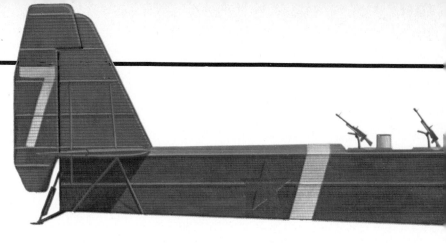

1925. Here for the first time was a twin-engined low-wing cantilever monoplane of Soviet design which could be truly said to be ahead of its time. The corrugated KA metal sheet utilized for covering the wings and fuselage was characteristic of the designs of Andrei N Tupolev, head of the TsAGI (Central Aero- and Hydrodynamic Institute) in Moscow, who was responsible for the TB-1 under bureau designation ANT-4. Of all-metal construction, the Soviet-developed KA (kolchugaluminium) duralumin alloy was used throughout the structure.

Power on the first prototype was provided by two 450-hp Napier Lion water-cooled engines. Later tests were made with Lorraine Dietrich engines. Finally German BMW VI engines were fitted and the fuselage nose shape modified.

The fixed undercarriage of TB-1 was of split-axle type. TB-1 featured a large single fin and rudder, and the horizontal tailplane was supported on either side by a single strut. Fuselage and wing were each built up in three sections, the centre section of the wing being integral with the main (central) section of the fuselage. The thick-section wing was designed by V M Petlyakov, who was later to become a successful aircraft designer in his own right.

Tests with the prototype were successful, but the first series TB-1s only appeared in June 1929, following delays in manufacturing its 730-hp M-17 in-line engine with a nose radiator, which was based on the BMW VI. Nevertheless, no fewer than 216 TB-1s had been completed by the time the last aircraft was rolled out in 1932. They provided the world's most effective heavy bombing force for the period.

The aircraft's nose contained a gunner's cockpit with a twin 7.62-mm (0.30-in) DA-2 machine-gun mounting. Below was a glazed section for the bomb aimer, and in the upper fuselage just in front of the wing leading edge were located side-by-side open pilots' cockpits with instrument dashboards for the engines immediately behind. A bridge led from the pilots' cockpits through the internal weapons bay, between cassette-type racks for up to 1000 kg (2205 lb) of bombs, to the two rear dorsal gunners' positions. Each dorsal gunner had a twin DA-2 ring mounting with 7.62-mm machine-guns, which could be moved across the fuselage, thus enabling defensive fire to be concentrated when TB-1s were flying in formation. A twin-float version, the TB-1P, built at Taganrog, went into limited service as a torpedo-bomber with Soviet naval aviation.

During August and October 1929, TB-1 *Strana Sovetov* (land of the Soviets) crewed by S A Shestakov, F E Bolotov, B V Sterligov and D V Fufayev made an impressive flight to New York. The first stages to Khabarovsk were made on a wheeled undercarriage, which was then changed to twin floats for the Pacific stages to San Francisco. The wheels were fitted again for the flight across the United States which ended in New York on October 30, 1929. The publicity which accompanied this momentous achievement provided the first taste of Soviet air power for many US citizens.

After being retired from the bombing role many TB-1s were utilized as transport aircraft by the air force, civil aviation and Soviet Arctic aviation. A TB-1 piloted by A V Lyapidevsky was the first rescue aircraft to make a successful landing on the drift ice near the trapped Soviet icebreaker *Chelyuskin* in March 1934. The TB-1 was also employed in the Zveno satellite-fighter experiments. It carried a pair of· I-4 (ANT-5) fighters into the air attached above its wings for subsequent release in flight.

Span: 28.7 m (94 ft 2 in) *Length:* 18 m (59 ft 1 in) *Gross weight:* 6810 kg (15013 lb) *Maximum speed:* 178 km/h (111 mph)

TB-3, Tupolev

Soviet heavy bomber. The first TB-3 four-engined low-wing all-metal bomber achieved its maiden flight on December 22, 1930. It had been planned by Tupolev and his AGOS design team at TsAGI five years earlier and had been under active development for some four years. Powered by US Curtiss Conqueror engines, the original prototype had given every sign, despite some technical problems, of being an outstanding bomber. In less than a year quantity production was underway at two major Moscow aircraft factories, GAZ Nos 22 and 39. The initial series version was powered by the M-17, the Soviet-built version of the German BMW VI engine of 730 hp. After factory tests, the first production aircraft was delivered for state trials in January 1932. Others soon followed, and nine TB-3s (design bureau designation ANT-6) took part in the 1932 May Day fly-past over Red Square. The following year 50 TB-3s participated.

These early bombers had a loaded weight higher than any other contemporary land-plane in service anywhere, and had the heavy defensive armament of eight 7.62-mm (0.30-in) DA machine-guns. There were twin DA-2 mountings in the nose cockpit and in two tandem dorsal cockpits. These had a layout similar to those on TB-1 and the gun rings, fitted on sliders, could be operated from either the port or starboard sides of the wide, angular fuselage. The remaining guns were installed in semiretractable turrets in the underside of the wings, just inboard of the outer engines. As with the TB-1 the fuselage and wing covering was largely corrugated duralumin sheet. As in its predecessor, the thickness of the wings permitted 'crawlways' giving access to the engines in flight.

The lower section of the nose was glazed for bomb aiming, and there were several side windows to the navigator bomb aimer's cabin in front of the pilots' open cockpit. Seating of the pilot and copilot was unusual. They were not side by side, but at the port and starboard ends of the cockpit, each with a separate windscreen. The independent main undercar-riage units each had twin tandem wheels and there was a large tail skid. The high tail fin had a balanced rudder and the tailplane was strut-braced.

As mass production got underway, tests were made with the new 830-hp M-34 engines in March 1933, and this version was phased into production towards the end of that year. Wheel brakes were fitted for the first time and the separate wireless operator's compartment of the earlier machines was dispensed with. By this time the Soviet government had investigated the possibility of building aerodromes for the TB-3s in Eastern Siberia. With fears of Japanese aggression, particularly after Japan had occupied Manchuria, three of the first special TB-3 heavy bomber brigades to be formed (each with four squadrons of aircraft) were sent to support the Soviet Far Eastern army. In 1936 the strategic special air arm or AON was formed, largely with TB-3s.

Meanwhile, in 1934, TB-3s were being built with M-34R engines fitted with reduction gear and offering a considerably improved performance. The following year 970-hp M-34RNs with superchargers were fitted to production TB-3s. In 1935 the wing area and span were increased, and the fuselage was lengthened behind the fin and rudder to accommodate a new tail gunner's position, the underwing turrets having been deleted some time earlier. Aerodynamic refinements included covering the skin of the wing and tail areas with fabric and fitting a large fairing between wing and fuselage. The net result was a greatly improved maximum speed and better high-altitude performance and overall controllability. Engine maintenance was eased by ingenious platforms formed by sections of the wing leading edge either side of each engine which were hinged to fold downwards.

Internal bombload of the TB-3 was carried on 26 racks mounted horizontally and vertically in the bomb bays. Bombs weighing 100 kg (220 lb), 80 kg (176 lb) or 50 kg (110 lb) could be carried. Improved power permitted increased loads over shorter distances, and external racks were frequently installed: two under the fuselage for four bombs each, plus four underwing racks. The load could include up to three 1000-kg (2205-lb) bombs, but the maximum-weight combination was eight 500-kg (1102-lb) bombs externally plus 18 100-kg (220-lb) bombs internally, a total of 5800 kg (12790 lb).

Final versions of the TB-3, produced in 1937, were powered by M-34FRN engines which increased maximum speed to 300 km/h (186 mph). Major redesign introduced huge single main undercarriage wheels and a tail wheel, a new smooth skin covering and enclosed manually operated nose and dorsal

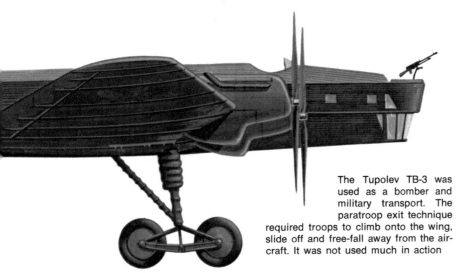

The Tupolev TB-3 was used as a bomber and military transport. The paratroop exit technique required troops to climb onto the wing, slide off and free-fall away from the aircraft. It was not used much in action

turrets. Defensive armament now comprised single 7.62-mm ShKas machine-guns in nose, dorsal and extreme tail positions, with a rate of fire and accuracy much higher than the original twin DA weapons.

The strategic air arm AON was not only concerned with bombing, but with the use of airborne forces. From 1935 three paratroop brigades were in service, all based on use of the TB-3, and by the 1936 Red Army manoeuvres, parachute troops dropped by TB-3s played a key role. Other TB-3s were used to transport artillery and light tanks.

The military transport version of the TB-3 was designated G-2 and a special version for Aviaarktika (Soviet Arctic aviation) had fully enclosed crew accommodation and usually operated on skis. The G-2 achieved fame during the Otto Schmitt polar expedition in 1937, and formations of TB-3s made a number of goodwill flights abroad, with gun positions discreetly covered and civil registrations applied to wings and fuselage. Among European capitals visited were Warsaw, Paris and Prague.

TB-3s took part in the fighting against the Japanese in the Lake Sasan area in summer 1938 and over the Khalkin Gol a year later. The AON was abolished in 1940, after the TB-3 had shown its obsolescence in the Winter War with Finland, and most TB-3s were brought under the control of the newly formed DBA-GK (Long-Range Bomber Command of General HQ). Many TB-3s of this force were lost in the first two months after the German invasion of the Soviet Union in June 1941, and by October 22 it had only 92 TB-3s left. Most surviving TB-3s were subsequently relegated to transport duties with occasional night-bombing forays. Little was heard of them in the paratroop-carrying role and most parachute units were pressed into service alongside the infantry.

In all, 818 of all versions of the TB-3 were built over an eight-year period. Among the more exotic activities of the TB-3 was its use in a series of experiments conducted by Vladimir Vakhmistrov in which it acted as a mother ship for a number of single-seat parasite fighters. In August 1934 Zveno 2 comprised a TB-3 with two I-5 biplane fighters attached to the upper wing surfaces. The TB-3 took off with the fighters attached and in due course launched them in mid-air, thus giving them additional fighting range. Later Zveno combinations utilized the specially developed Grigorovitch I-Z fighter, carried between the TB-3's undercarriage legs, plus two I-5s above the wing and two I-16 monoplane fighters slung underwing. The ultimate development was a special unit established in 1940, based on six TB-3s each carrying two SPB dive-bombers, modified from I-16s. After the German invasion a number of operations were mounted in which the TB-3s air-launched SPBs, each carrying two 250-kg (550-lb) bombs. Attacks were made on bridges over the Danube and the Dnieper, against the Ploesti oil refineries and the Romanian naval base at Constantsa. The unit was based in the Crimea and was disbanded when the Germans reached the Perekop Isthmus. The German invasion also put an end to tests with radio-controlled TB-3s directed onto the target by mother SB bombers.

(Later version with M-34RN engines) *Span:* 41.85 m (137 ft 4 in) *Length:* 25.18 m (82 ft 7 in) including tail turret *Gross weight:* 18 877 kg (41 617 lb) *Maximum speed:* 288 km/h (179 mph)

TBD, Douglas US Navy torpedo-bomber
See **Devastator**

TBF, Grumman US Navy torpedo-bomber
See **Avenger**

TBM, General Motors US Navy torpedo-bomber
See **Avenger**

TBU, Vought US Navy torpedo-bomber
See **Sea Wolf**

TBY, Convair US Navy torpedo-bomber
See **Sea Wolf**

T.B.8, Bristol

British coastal patrol and trainer aircraft. A 1912 monoplane designed by Henri Coanda was converted in the summer of the following year with two-bay biplane wings to become the T.B.8 (tractor biplane, 80-hp Gnome). The new biplane was tested in July and August and again in September after conversion to a twin-float seaplane. The Admiralty ordered two more modified T.B.8 floatplanes, though these were never delivered, and went on to buy a total of 45 of the landplane version, including 12 ordered for the RFC but rejected by that service after trials. As well as the 80-hp Gnome, 80-hp Le Rhône and Clerget and 100-hp Gnome Monosoupape engines were used. Six T.B.8s were also sold to the Romanian army in 1913. Later T.B.8s had ailerons instead of the original wing-warping system of lateral control, new engine cowlings, modified undercarriage and a new tailplane. The single example of the G.B.75 variant was bought by the RFC.

A few T.B.8s served in France in the early stages of the First World War, while the first flight of No 1 Squadron, RNAS, was formed with T.B.8s in October 1914. This flight carried out coastal patrols off north-east England from the following month, but the type was more widely used as a trainer, the last 24 of the machines delivered to the RNAS being ordered for this purpose in August 1915. These were used at the Eastchurch and Hendon training schools. One of a pair of RNAS T.B.8s which followed the original conversion had been fitted with a bomb sight and rack for 12 bombs, but little use was made of these devices.

Span: 11.48 m (37 ft 8 in) *Length:* 8.92 m (29 ft 3 in) *Gross weight:* 755 kg (1665 lb) *Maximum speed:* 121 km/h (75 mph)

Tellier French aircraft   See **T.3**

Tempest, Hawker

British fighter-bomber. The Tempest was developed from the Typhoon (and was initially known as the Typhoon Mk II) to Specification F.10/41 by lengthening the fuselage and fitting a new wing. So many other smaller changes were incorporated, however, that it was classed as a new aircraft type. The new wing was some 127 mm (5 in) thinner at the root, with a thickness-to-chord ratio of 14.5% at the root and 10% at the tip, and was of semi-elliptical planform. To offset the loss of wing fuel tanks the fuselage was lengthened to house an additional fuel tank. In all other respects the Tempest was constructed in the same way as the Typhoon.

A whole family of Tempest fighters and fighter-bombers were proposed, and the Tempest Mk I was the designation of a prototype powered by a Napier Sabre IV, although it was actually the second prototype to fly on February 24, 1943. The engine was closely cowled, giving a smaller frontal area than the Typhoon, while the radiator and oil cooler were sunk into the inboard-wing leading edge. Production plans were eventually abandoned after difficulties with the engine, although during trials, it reached a speed of 750 km/h (466 mph) at 7500 m (24 500 ft).

Although second in type numbering, the Tempest Mk II came second in production priority, and was intended for operations in the Far East. It was powered by the Bristol Centaurus V or VI air-cooled radial engine, rated at 2520 hp, and the first prototype flew on June 28, 1943. Contracts were placed with Hawker and Gloster, but the development of the Meteor necessitated transferring the latter's order to Bristol. The Tempest II had a useful range of 2640 km (1640 miles) and was to be used for island-hopping in the Pacific. The end of the war came before the Tempest II could be deployed, and over 1000 aircraft were cancelled. In the end, final production totalled 472, of which 50 were built by Bristol.

The Tempest II was the last piston-engined fighter-bomber in RAF service and only served with one unit, 54 Squadron, in the UK from November 1945 to September 1946. Three squadrons of Tempest IIs served with the British Air Forces of Occupation in Germany from 1946 to 1948, and four squadrons were in India. In 1949, 33 Squadron took their aircraft from Germany to Hong Kong, and later moved to Malaya, seeing action against guerrillas there. Some 89 surplus aircraft were supplied to the Indian Air Force in 1947, and 24 went to Pakistan a year later, and they remained in service with both countries until 1953.

The designations Mk III and Mk IV were allocated for proposed Griffon-powered versions of the Tempest, which were never built.

The Tempest Mk V, which was the first version to fly on September 2, 1942, was powered by the Napier Sabre II series of engines, of which the IIA was replaced in turn by the IIB and then the IIC, the latter being rated at 2260 hp. It was the only version of the Tempest to be used operationally during the Second World War, and after some initial problems with propeller over-speeding had been solved, proved a most effective fighter.

The RAF's first Tempest Wing, comprising 3 and 486 Squadrons, was formed at Newchurch in April 1944, and was followed by 56 Squadron in July 1944. They initially operated over northern France in the ground-attack role, but were soon in action against FZG 76 (V-1) flying bombs. The Tempest was faster than the defending fighters, and destroyed 638 out of the 1771 V-1s claimed by the RAF between June 13 and September 5, 1944. With the 2nd Tactical Air Force on the continent, Tempests were successfully used throughout the push into Belgium, Holland and the crossing of the Rhine. They also came into contact with the Messerschmitt Me 262 jet fighter, destroying 20 in air combat. After VE-Day, the Tempest V was phased out in favour of the Mk VI or Mk II, pending the arrival of the first jet fighters.

The least known of the Tempest variants was the Mk VI, which was powered by the thoroughly refined Sabre V 24-cylinder H-type radial engine, rated at 2340 hp and driving a four-bladed Rotol propeller. This became the 'tropical' Tempest, and featured improved cooling, with the radiator enlarged and the oil cooler moved to the wing leading edge. In all, 142 Tempest VIs were built between July 1945 and June 1947.

The RAF equipped nine squadrons with the Tempest VI, of which five were distributed around the Middle East and four were in Germany. With the arrival of the Vampires in 1949, the Tempest VI was phased out of service.

After the war many Mk V and Mk VI airframes were converted for target-towing duties by the addition of an air-driven Malcolm winch under the port wing. Redesignated TT.5 and TT.6 respectively, these aircraft served with various squadrons, OCUs and armament practice stations. Some

were in service at Sylt in North Germany as late as 1953.

Throughout its operational career as a fighter-bomber, the Tempest II, V and VI carried the same basic armament of four 20-mm (0.79-in) Hispano Mk II or V guns. Their wing racks could accommodate two 454-kg (1000-lb) bombs, two 205-litre (45-Imp gal) napalm bombs, two mines, two 409-litre (90-Imp gal) drop tanks or up to eight 27-kg (60-lb) warhead 3-in (7.6-cm) rocket projectiles.

(Mk II) *Span:* 12.5 m (41 ft) *Length:* 10.49 m (34 ft 5 in) *Gross weight:* 6151 kg (13 560 lb) *Maximum speed:* 711 km/h (442 mph) at 4630 m (15 200 ft)

(Mk V) *Span:* 12.5 m (41 ft) *Length:* 10.26 m (33 ft 8 in) *Gross weight:* 6187 kg (13 640 lb) *Maximum speed:* 686 km/h (426 mph) at 5640 m (18 500 ft)

(Mk VI) *Span:* 12.5 m (41 ft) *Length:* 10.31 m (33 ft 10 in) *Gross weight:* 6232 kg (13 740 lb) *Maximum speed:* 705 km/h (438 mph) at 5430 m (17 800 ft)

Tenacious

British frigate class. In the late 1940s the Admiralty began an extensive programme of converting wartime destroyers to fast antisubmarine frigates to counter the postwar development of high-speed submarines. As originally planned these Type 15 (*Rapid* Class) conversions were fairly extensive, but in 1951 it was decided that some ships should receive the minimum of modifications for their new role: the limited conversions were designated Type 16. Although not as effective as the Type 15s, they had the advantage of being cheaper and quicker and allowed for the available finance to be extended to include more ships. The prototype for the Type 16 was the *Tumult* Class destroyer *Tenacious* which was converted at Rosyth dockyard during 1951-52. In effect the conversion involved rearmament rather than reconstruction, combined with a general refit and the addition of improved sonar, radar, direction-finding and communication equipment. Unlike the Type 15s the superstructure of *Tenacious* was not altered, and although this meant accepting restricted space for accommodation and control and operations rooms it also allowed for an improvement in the AA armament giving her limited value as a dual-purpose A/S and AA escort. The original armament was removed completely, except for the after bank of torpedo tubes which were retained for use with A/S homing torpedoes, and replaced by a twin 4-in (102-mm) DP gun mounting in B position, five single 40-mm (1.57-in) Bofors AA, mounted in the bridge wings (two), abaft the funnel (two) and on the quarterdeck (one), a twin 40-mm Bofors Mk V mount on the platform amidships and two three-barrelled Squid A/S mortars on the after superstructure.

The remainder of the *Tumult* Class destroyers, except *Troubridge* which was given the full conversion, were similarly modified during 1952-55 but four, *Teazer, Termagant, Terpsichore* and *Tumult*, were given the added sophistication of a new enclosed bridge somewhat smaller than the original. The remaining pair, *Tuscan* and *Tyrian*, were

altered as *Tenacious*, retaining their original bridges. In addition to the 'T' Class vessels one 'O' Class destroyer, *Orwell*, and two 'P' Class destroyers, *Paladin* and *Petard*, were converted to Type 16s during 1952-55, and two more 'O' Class destroyers, transferred to Pakistan in 1949-50, the *Tippu Sultan* and *Tughril* (ex-*Onslow* and *Onslaught*) were also converted in 1957-59. Most of these refits followed the pattern set by *Tenacious*, but the two Pakistani ships did not mount the two single 40-mm guns abaft the funnel and several other vessels of the class had either these or the mountings in the bridge wings removed during the late 1950s. *Paladin* was converted to a minelayer during 1957 and had all her single 40-mm guns and her torpedo tubes removed to compensate for the added weight of 30 mines and the laying gear. In 1962-66 the South African *Sunar vand der Stel* underwent a similar conversion, but with a flight deck and hangars aft for two Wasp A/S helicopters.

The conversion programme was never more than a means of providing the navy with a reasonable A/S force until such time as new-construction ships entered service, and as the Type 16s were the least satisfactory of the two types they were the first to go to the scrapyard. The 'T' Class ships were sold during 1965-66, *Paladin* in 1962, *Orwell* in 1965 and *Petard* in 1967. By 1978 the two Pakistani ships were serving as static training ships and only one of the South African ships was still in service.

('T' Class) *Displacement:* 2000 tons (standard), 2530 tons (full load) *Length:* 110.6 m (362 ft 9 in) oa *Beam:* 10.9 m (35 ft 8 in) *Draught:* 4 m (13 ft) *Machinery:* 2-shaft geared steam turbines, 40 000 shp=36.75 knots *Armament:* 2 4-in (102-mm) (1×2); 7 40-mm (1.57-in) (5×1, 1×2); 4 21-in (53-cm) torpedo tubes (1×4); 2 triple Squid A/S mortars *Crew:* 175

('O' and 'P' Class) *Displacement:* 1800 tons (standard), 2300 tons (full load) *Length:* 103.2 m (338 ft 6 in) oa *Beam:* 10.7 m (35 ft) *Draught:* 4 m (13 ft) *Machinery:* 2-shaft geared steam turbines, 40 000 shp=34 knots *Armament:* 2 4-in (1×2); 5/7 40-mm (1×2, 3/5×1); 4 21-in torpedo tubes (1×4); 2 triple Squid A/S mortars *Crew:* 170

Tenacity

British patrol craft, built 1968-73. The builders, Vosper Thornycroft, built this patrol craft as a private venture to demonstrate their ability to build light craft with significantly heavier armament and range than before. Although never mounted, the fits proposed included a twin Oerlikon 35-mm (1.38-in) power-operated mounting, an Oerlikon twin 30-mm (1.18-in), a Bofors 57-mm (2.24-in) L/70 or an OTO-Melara 76-mm (3-in) Compact, with four Contraves Sea Killer surface-to-surface missiles aft.

After some time spent as a demonstration vessel with dummy missiles aft and a mockup of a gun-mounting forward with twin broom handles, *Tenacity* was bought by the Royal Navy in January 1972 and refitted for service as a patrol craft. This involved fitting davits for Gemini inflatable boats on the forecastle, two machine-guns and a navigation radar. She now serves on fishery-protection duties n coastal waters in place of *Brave Borderer* and *Brave Swordsman*, with pendant number P.276.

Displacement: 165 tons (standard), 220 tons (full load) *Length:* 44 m (144 ft 6 in) oa *Beam:* 8.1 m (26 ft 6 in) *Draught:* 2.3 m (7 ft 8 in) *Machinery:* 3-shaft Proteus gas turbines and cruising diesels on wing shafts, 12 750 shp=40 knots *Armament:* 2 7.62-mm (0.30-in) mgs (2×1) *Crew:* 32

Tench

US submarine class. These submarines were basically an extension of the *Balao* Class, dimensions remaining the same but displacement being increased by some 50 tons. In other respects the vessels remained the same, except for slight variations in the machinery fitted.

The original design provided for a 5-in (127-mm) gun to be carried forward of the conning tower, but as in the previous *Balao* and *Gato* Classes this was subsequently moved to a position aft of the conning tower. The original design also provided for a 40-mm (1.57-in) forward and a 20-mm (0.79-in) aft on the conning tower. This too was altered, a 40-mm replacing the 20-mm while some units

No and name	launched	fate
SS.417 *Tench*	7/44	to Peru for spares 1976
SS.418 *Thornback*	7/44	Turkish *Uluc Ali Reis* 1971
SS.419 *Tigrone*	7/44	stricken 6/75
SS.420 *Tirante*	8/44	—
SS.421 *Trutta* (ex-*Tomatate*)	8/44	stricken 7/72
SS.422 *Toro*	8/44	stricken 3/65
SS.423 *Torsk*	9/44	stricken 12/71
SS.424 *Quillback* (ex-*Trembler*)	10/44	stricken 3/73
SS.425 *Trumpetfish*	5/45	stricken 10/73
SS.426 *Tusk*	7/45	Taiwanese *Hai Pao* 10/73
SS.435 *Corsair*	5/46	stricken 1963
SS.436 *Unicorn*	8/46	stricken 6/58

USS *Tigrone*, one of three *Tench* Class submarines converted to the radar picket role. The *Tench* Class conversions were given a large air-search scanner on the conning tower, a height finder abaft it and a surface-search scanner on a stub mast

US Navy

had an extra 5-in weapon added in front of the conning tower.

SS.417-424 and SS.475-490 were built by Portsmouth navy yard, SS.425 and 426 by Cramp, Philadelphia, SS.435-437 by the Electric Boat company, Groton, and SS.522-525 by Boston navy yard. The following were cancelled in 1944-45: SS.427-434, SS.438-474, SS.491-521 and SS.526-562.

Construction of SS.436 and 437 was suspended in 1946, and the incomplete SS.427 (*Turbot*) and 428 (*Ulua*) were used for test purposes. *Toro* was sunk as a sonar target during the search for the lost *Thresher* off Cape Cod in 1963. *Tigrone*, *Requin* and *Spinax* were converted to radar picket submarines from 1948. The least sophisticated of such conversions, they served as prototypes for the subsequent conversion of large numbers of *Balao* and *Gato* Class boats.

See also GUPPY.

Displacement: 1570/2428 tons (surfaced/submerged) *Length:* 95 m (311 ft 9 in) *Beam:* 8.3 m (27 ft 3 in) *Draught:* 4.6 m (15 ft 3 in) *Machinery:* 2-shaft diesels/2 electric motors, 5400 bhp/2740 hp=20.25/8.85 knots (surfaced/submerged) *Armament:* 1 5-in (127-mm); 1 20-mm (0.79-in); 1 40-mm (1.57-in); 10 21-in (53-cm) torpedo tubes (6 bow, 4 stern), 24 torpedoes *Crew:* 80

Tennessee

US armoured cruiser class, built 1902-08. In 1902 Congress authorized the construction of two armoured cruisers, followed by another pair in 1904. They were improved versions of the *Pennsylvania* Class, with the same speed but heavier armament and better armour. With 10-in (254-mm) guns they were virtually 2nd Class battleships, and resembled the contemporary British *Duke of Edinburgh* Class. *Tennessee* (CA.10) was built by William Cramp, Philadelphia and commissioned in July 1906. *Washington* (CA.11) was built by New York Shipbuilding company, Camden, NJ and commissioned in August 1906; *North Carolina* (CA.12) and *Montana* (CA.13) were both built by Newport News shipbuilding and dry dock, and were commissioned in May and July 1908.

In 1911 all four ships were refitted with cage foremasts. *Tennessee* was renamed *Memphis* in May 1916 to release her name for a new battleship, but on August 29 she was stranded by a seismic wave near Santo Domingo. In November 1916 *Washington* was renamed *Seattle*, and she and *North Carolina* were both fitted with catapults between mid-1916 and early 1917. *North Carolina* had received hers in October 1915, and on November 5, 1915, she carried out the

No and name	launched	fate
SS.437 *Walrus*	9/46	stricken 6/58
SS.475 *Argonaut*	10/44	Canadian *Rainbow* 1968
SS.476 *Runner*	10/44	stricken 12/71
SS.477 *Conger*	10/44	stricken 8/63
SS.478 *Cutlass*	11/44	Taiwanese *Hai Shih* 4/73
SS.479 *Diablo*	12/44	Pakistani *Ghazi* 1964, lost 12/71
SS.480 *Medregal*	12/44	scuttled 8/70
SS.481 *Requin*	1/45	stricken 12/71
SS.482 *Irex*	1/45	stricken 11/69
SS.483 *Sea Leopard*	3/45	Brazilian *Bahia* 3/73
SS.484 *Odax*	4/45	Brazilian *Rio de Janeiro*
SS.485 *Sirago*	5/45	stricken 6/72
SS.486 *Pomodon*	6/45	stricken 8/70
SS.487 *Remora*	7/45	Greek *Katsonis* 10/73
SS.488 *Sarda*	8/45	stricken 3/65
SS.489 *Spinax*	11/45	stricken 10/69
SS.490 *Volador*	1/46	Italian *Primo Longobardo* 1972
SS.522 *Amberjack*	12/44	Brazilian *Ceara* 10/73
SS.523 *Grampus*	12/44	Brazilian *Rio Grandedo Sul* 5/72
SS.524 *Pickerel*	12/44	Italian *Gianfranco Gazzana Priaroggia* 1972
SS.525 *Grenadier*	12/44	stricken 5/73

first shipboard launch. By 1917 the three ships had a secondary armament of only ten 3-in (76-mm) guns and four 6-pdr (57-mm), and two 3-in AA had been added.

In 1919 they were used as troop transports, and in June 1920 *North Carolina* and *Montana* were renamed *Charlotte* and *Missoula* to release their names for new ships. *Charlotte* and *Missoula* were stricken in 1930 and scrapped. *Seattle* was hulked as *IX.39* in 1931 and was not scrapped until 1946.

Displacement: 14 500 tons (normal) *Length:* 153.8 m (504 ft 6 in) oa *Beam:* 22.2 m (72 ft 10 in) *Draught:* 7.6 m (25 ft) *Machinery:* 2-shaft reciprocating steam, 26 000 ihp=22 knots *Protection:* 127-76 mm (5-3 in) belt, 229 mm (9 in) turrets and conning tower *Armament:* 4 10-in (254-mm)/40-cal Mk III (2×2); 16 6-in (152-mm)/50-cal Mk VIII (16×1); 22 3-in (76-mm) QF (22×1); 12 3-pdr (47-mm) QF (12×1); 2 1-pdr (37-mm); 6 0.30-in (7.62-mm) machine-guns; 4 21-in (53-cm) torpedo tubes (beam, submerged) *Crew:* 914

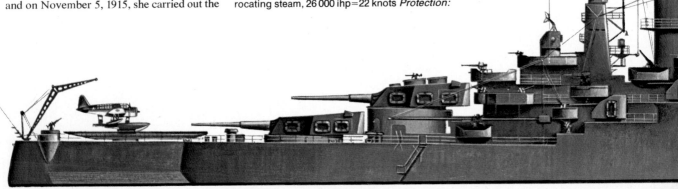

A *Tennessee* Class armoured cruiser, possibly the USS *Seattle* which was hulked in 1931

Tennessee

US battleship class. Two ships were ordered as improved versions of the *New Mexico* Class battleships. *Tennessee* (BB.43) was laid down at New York navy yard on May 14, 1917, launched on April 30, 1919 and completed on June 3, 1920; *California* (BB.44) was laid down at Mare Island navy yard on October 25, 1916, launched on November 20, 1919, and completed on October 8, 1921.

The two ships mounted all their secondary armament in the superstructure, where it was much less affected by bad weather, rather than in the hull and they had larger bridges and two funnels instead of one. Otherwise they were virtually identical to *New Mexico* (BB.40): they had the same turbo-electric main machinery and the 14-in (356-mm) main armament, and the same thickness of armour, though the layout was modified to incorporate wartime experience and the underwater protection was significantly improved. *Pennsylvania*, *New Mexico* and *Tennessee* Classes all had the same main armament and speed, and made a powerful and homogeneous fleet. The design of the *Tennessee*s had been approved before the British *Queen Elizabeth* Class fast battleships had been completed, and the four succeeding *Colorado* Class battleships (only three of which were completed) were almost identical to the *Tennessee*s except that the triple 14-in turrets were replaced by twin 16-in (406-mm) to outgun the British ships.

California's original beam was 29.6 m (97 ft 3 in), with a standard displacement of 32 600 tons, and her original armament consisted of 12 14-in in four triple turrets, 14 5-in (127-mm)/51-cal, four 3-in (76-mm) AA and two 21-in (53-cm) submerged torpedo tubes. Two 5-in guns and the submerged torpedo tubes were removed in 1923 when four more 3-in AA guns were added, and in 1929-30 the 3-in AA guns were removed and replaced by eight 5-in/25-cal AA guns. At the same time catapults were added on X turret and on the quarterdeck, and an aircraft-handling crane was fitted at the stern.

California spent most of the interwar years in the Pacific, and like *Tennessee* was caught at Pearl Harbor by the Japanese surprise attack on December 7, 1941. *California* was hit by two torpedoes early in the attack before the crew had time to close the watertight doors. She was ringed by blazing oil from the ruptured fuel tanks, and was hit later by three bombs. Power was lost almost immediately and the ship was abandoned. After three days she finally sank and settled on the bottom with only the upperworks above water. Initial salvage work at Pearl Harbor was concentrated on those battleships that had remained afloat, but *California* was eventually raised on March 25, 1942. She was patched up at Pearl Harbor, and in June

1942 sailed under her own steam to the United States, where like *Tennessee* she was completely rebuilt at the Puget Sound navy yard. Her bridge, superstructure, masts and funnels were removed and replaced with a single-funnelled structure similar to that fitted to the *South Dakota*s. Wide bulges were fitted to improve the underwater protection and they were carried up to the upper-deck level to enable a new dual-purpose secondary armament of 16 5-in guns to be mounted in twin turrets amidships. A powerful light AA armament was also fitted and the catapult on X turret was removed. The conversion was completed on January 31, 1944, and in 1944-45 she was employed in the shore-bombardment role in the Pacific. In June 1944 she was hit by a Japanese coast-defence gun at Saipan, and on January 6, 1945 was hit by a kamikaze plane off Luzon, necessitating a month's repairs at Puget Sound navy yard. *California* also took part in the Battle of Surigao Strait (part of the Battle of Leyte Gulf) on October 25, 1944.

California was placed in reserve on August 7, 1946, and was mothballed in February 1947, where she remained until finally discarded on March 1, 1959. She was broken up at Baltimore by the Boston Metals company in 1960. *Tennessee* was placed in reserve in December 1945. She remained at Philadelphia until July 1959 when she was sold for scrapping at Baltimore.

Displacement: 37 000 tons (standard) *Length:* 190.4 m (624 ft 6 in) oa *Beam:* 34.7 m (114 ft) *Draught:* 10.7 m (35 ft) *Machinery:* 4-shaft turbo-electric, 27 200 shp=21 knots *Protection:* 356-203 mm (14-8 in) belt, 457-228 mm (18-9 in) turrets, 89-64 mm (3.5-2.5 in) decks *Armament:* 12 14-in (356-mm) (4×3); 16 5-in (127-mm) (12×1); 12 5-in AA; 56 40-mm (1.57-in); 52 20-mm (0.79-in); 4 aircraft *Crew:* 2375

Tenryu

Japanese cruiser class. These two cruisers, ordered under the 1916 Programme, were the first modern light cruisers to be designed for the Japanese navy and laid the foundations for subsequent Japanese light cruiser designs. The design was based closely on a study of the British 'C' Class and remained more or less constant until Japan ceased the construction of light cruisers during the mid-1920s.

The two vessels were laid down in 1917 (*Tatsuta* in July, at Sasebo navy yard; and *Tenryu* in May, at Yokosuka navy yard) and they were the first ships in the Imperial Navy to carry a triple torpedo-tube mount. *Tatsuta*

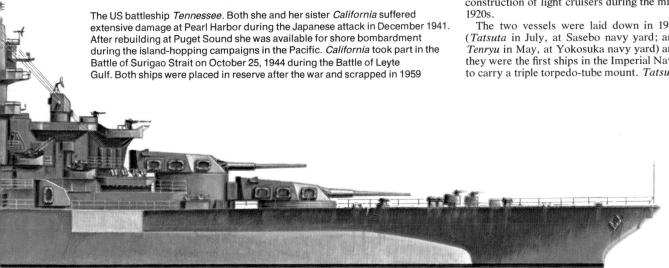

The US battleship *Tennessee*. Both she and her sister *California* suffered extensive damage at Pearl Harbor during the Japanese attack in December 1941. After rebuilding at Puget Sound she was available for shore bombardment during the island-hopping campaigns in the Pacific. *California* took part in the Battle of Surigao Strait on October 25, 1944 during the Battle of Leyte Gulf. Both ships were placed in reserve after the war and scrapped in 1959

Terne, Konsberg Våpenfabrikk

was launched in May 1918 and completed the following March; *Tenryu* was launched in March 1918 but was not completed until November the following year. A mixture of British and US machinery was fitted (Parsons turbines in *Tenryu* and Curtiss in *Tatsuta*), and the fine hull lines enabled the cruisers to achieve a speed of 33 knots. They were eminently suited for the role of flagship to destroyer squadrons. Both vessels were extensively refitted and modernized in 1927, the pole foremast being replaced by a tripod to carry more extensive command positions.

The ships were active during the early part of the Second World War until *Tenryu* was sunk by the US submarine *Albacore* on December 18, 1942. *Tatsuta* was obsolete and thereafter remained in home waters. She was not modernized, and no armament changes were effected. She was finally sunk by the US submarine *Sandlance* on March 13, 1944.

Displacement: 3230 tons *Length:* 142.6 m (468 ft) oa *Beam:* 12.3 m (40 ft 6 in) *Draught:* 4 m (13 ft) *Machinery:* 3-shaft geared turbines, 51 000 shp=33 knots *Protection:* 51 mm (2 in) main belt, 38 mm (1.5 in) deck *Armament:* 4 5.5-in (140-mm); 1 13-pdr (80-mm); 2 13-mm (0.51-in); 6 21-in (53-cm) torpedo tubes (2×3) *Crew:* 332

Tenzan Japanese name for Nakajima B6N torpedo bomber   See **B6N**

Terne, Konsberg Våpenfabrikk

Norwegian antisubmarine rocket. The Terne III system derives target position from the launch ship's sonar, the six-round launcher being aimed and elevated so that the unguided rockets will impact over the enemy submarine. The Mk 8 rocket, which has about twice the range of the earlier Mk 7, is powered by two concentric solid-propellant

A Konsberg Våpenfabrikk Terne A/S missile lifts off from a US evaluation ship

Konsberg Våpenfabrikk

rocket motors and carries a high-explosive warhead which is detonated by hydrostatic or contact fuzes. The rounds can be fired singly or in salvo, all six being launched in five seconds if desired.

Length: 1.95 m (6 ft 5 in) *Diameter:* 20 cm (8 in) *Weight:* 135 kg (298 lb) *Range:* 3 km (2 miles) estimated *Warhead:* 50-kg (110-lb) high-explosive

Terrier

US Navy surface-to-air missile. The progenitor of the Standard missile, Terrier began as an effort to develop an interim missile during the Bumblebee programme, using the rocket-powered STV as a basis. Although flight tests in 1950 were somewhat disappointing, the design was frozen in order to obtain an operational weapon; this urgency was due to the outbreak of the Korean war, which many in the United States saw as a precursor of some wider conflict. Although Terrier was given the service designation SAM-N-7 in 1951, it suffered delays. For example, the original design, adapted from an experimental device, was found to be difficult to produce in numbers, and had a poor storage life. Redesign was required, after which Terrier passed its operational evaluation in June 1955. Even then the weapon was not entirely satisfactory; and through the early 1960s the US Navy expended considerable funds in efforts to cure the problems of its Talos, Tartar, Terrier missiles.

The original impulse to make the STV into an operational missile was due to its great success in early tests. For example, in October 1949 STV-3 was able to ride a beam for 54 seconds. In April 1951, a Lot 1A Terrier detonated a smoke-puff warhead at intercept, and that September one was successfully launched from a test ship, the converted seaplane tender *Norton Sound*. Two F6F Hellcat drones were successfully destroyed by a Lot 3 Terrier at the Naval Ordnance Test Station in May 1952. By this time the urgency of the naval antiaircraft missile requirement was such that there was pressure for the immediate conversion of a cruiser to an operational Terrier ship. However, the ordnance test ship *Mississippi* was converted instead, firing its first Terrier in July 1953. Meanwhile, plans were drawn up for the conversion of two heavy cruisers, *Boston* and *Canberra*, which became the world's first operational surface-to-air missile ships when they were completed in 1955 and 1956, respectively. Each had two twin launchers aft with 144 Terriers.

There followed a series of light cruiser conversions, and then five classes of guided-missile frigates, most of them more recently redesignated missile cruisers: ten *Coontz* Class missile destroyers, nine *Leahy* Class (each with two missile launchers), nine *Belknap* Class, and the two nuclear frigates *Bainbridge* and *Truxtun*. Each carried launchers with a capacity of 40 Terriers per dual-rail launcher. The Second World War destroyer *Gyatt* served as a kind of prototype for the missile frigates; she was experimentally fitted with a launcher and a magazine for 12 missiles in 1956. However, although it had proved possible to replace one of her twin 5-in (127-mm) guns with a Terrier system, the

limitations of her system were quite evident, and missile frigates were considered the lower limit of ships suitable for Terrier. At the upper end of ship size, Terrier was installed aboard the nuclear missile cruiser *Long Beach* and also aboard the carriers *Kitty Hawk, Constellation* and *America*.

Terrier began as a short-range companion to Talos. It followed that beam-riding would suffice for guidance; there was no need for a secondary terminal-homing system. Early Terriers, therefore, were designated BW-0 (beam-riding, wing-manoeuvred). In fact it proved possible to extend both Terrier's and Talos's range as both rocket and ramjet propulsion systems improved, and the beam-riding system became less and less adequate, leading to the development of a semiactive homing missile. At the same time, development of the Terrier missile itself tended towards the use of the tail fins for guidance, the former long wings being replaced by relatively narrow fixed ones. The resultant homing weapon was designated HT. This development made launching simpler, as the missiles were generally stowed in magazines without their wings, which had to be fitted just prior to launch. A wingless weapon could be fired much more simply. Terrier HT thus resembled very closely the rapidly launched Tartar, which had a very compact launching system.

The BT-3 version, which became operational in 1956, included a two-pulse main missile engine, which extended its range. It was developed into an antiship weapon, BT-3A/-3A(N) operational in 1958; the (N) suffix indicated a nuclear weapon. By this time the semiactive Tartar programme was well under way, and technology developed for it could be applied to Terrier HT-3. Terrier was built by General Dynamics, Pomona. An advanced version of Terrier became operational in 1964; it incorporated improved propulsion and semiactive homing, and is being replaced by Standard SM-2.

Under the Department of Defense missile designation system introduced in 1962, Terrier was RIM-2. Terrier BW-0 was designated RIM-2A, BW-1 became RIM-2B, BT-3 became RIM-2C, and BT-3A/-3A(N) became RIM-2D. Terrier BT-3 was also sometimes referred to as Terrier II; HT-3 became RIM-2E. Advanced Terrier was designated RIM-2F. Since nuclear warheads are generally employed only under positive control, the Terrier nuclear-option weapon, the BT(N), is a beam-rider. It is effective against surface targets and also against formations of aircraft or missiles.

Terrier serves with the US Navy and has also been exported: it was mounted aboard the Dutch cruiser *De Zeven Provincien* (later transferred to the Peruvian navy without her missiles), the converted Italian cruiser *Giuseppe Garibaldi*, and the missile cruisers *Vittorio Veneto, Andrea Doria*, and *Caio Duilio*. In the US *Belknap* Class frigates, the nuclear frigate *Truxtun* and in the *Vittorio Veneto* it was fired from a system which could also fire the Asroc antisubmarine weapon.

Length: 8 m (26 ft 2 in) *Diameter:* 34 cm (13.5 in) *Weight:* 1360 kg (3000 lb) *Speed:* over Mach 2.5 *Range:* over 35 km (22 miles) *Warhead:* continuous-rod or nuclear

Tetrarch

British airborne light tank. The Tetrarch began life before the Second World War as one of the light tank projects proposed by Vickers. Accepted in 1938 it was not originally intended to be an air-portable tank and as a conventional light tank saw action in North Africa and Madagascar before being passed to the 6th Airborne Reconnaissance Regiment of the 6th Air Landing Brigade. Some Tetrarchs were sent to the Soviet Union and in 1942 were used in southern Russia.

The tank had three compartments—driving position, fighting compartment and engine. The driver had a car-type steering wheel and was flanked by two 102-litre (22.5-Imp gal) fuel tanks. Steering worked through a connector rod to the steering head on each suspension unit which 'warped' the tracks like the steering on the Universal carrier.

The fighting compartment housed the gunner and commander/loader with a 2-pdr QFSA gun and 7.92-mm (0.312-in) Besa machine-gun.

The engine was mounted above the gearbox and all accessories except the fans were mounted on top for easy access through two detachable inspection hatches on the hull top.

When the Tetrarch was proposed as an airborne vehicle, an entirely new glider, the Hamilcar, was built to carry it. The Tetrarch was used at the Orne landings in 1944.

Weight: 7.5 tonnes *Length:* 4.29 m (14 ft 1 in) *Width:* 2.31 m (7 ft 7 in) *Height:* 2.11 m (6 ft 11 in)

The British Tetrarch airborne light tank

Armour thickness: 14-6 mm (0.6-0.2 in) *Armament:* 2-pdr (40-mm) or 3-in (76-mm) howitzer, 7.92-mm (0.312-in) machine-gun *Powerplant:* Meadows 12-cylinder, 165 bhp at 2700 rpm *Speed:* 64 km/h (40 mph) roads *Range:* 320 km (200 miles)

Texan, North American AT-6 (T-6)/SNJ

US advanced training aircraft. The Texan (known as Harvard by the Royal Air Force) was a member of a huge family of fixed- and retractable-undercarriage monoplanes that stemmed from the NA-16 fixed-gear prototype of 1935: a family that was to total nearly 22 000 aeroplanes in all. Of these, close on 20 000 were Texans or one of its many variants.

The prototype was North American design NA-26, evolved in 1937 to a basic combat trainer requirement and being a retractable-gear, 600-hp variant of the original NA-16. Before the BC (basic combat) designations were changed to AT (advanced trainer), North American produced 177 BC-1s for the

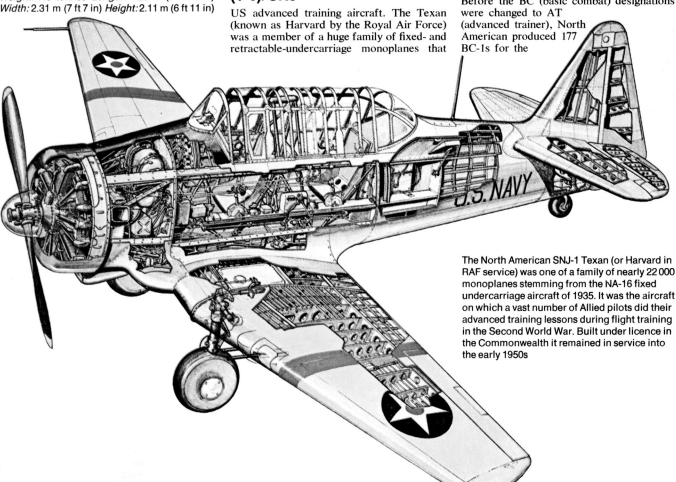

The North American SNJ-1 Texan (or Harvard in RAF service) was one of a family of nearly 22 000 monoplanes stemming from the NA-16 fixed undercarriage aircraft of 1935. It was the aircraft on which a vast number of Allied pilots did their advanced training lessons during flight training in the Second World War. Built under licence in the Commonwealth it remained in service into the early 1950s

Texas

A T-6G Texan of the USAF. Some were used for forward air-control duties in the Korean war

Army Air Corps, 16 similar SNJ-1s for the navy, 83 BC-1As and three BC-2s. The BC-1/SNJ-1s had a rounded rudder, the BC-1A/BC-2 a straight trailing edge, apart from other variations in powerplant, fuel system, propeller and wingtip shape. Production continued with 94 AT-6s and 61 SNJ-2s before the first large-scale contracts for 1847 AT-6As (600-hp Pratt & Whitney R-1340-49 Wasp radial) and 270 SNJ-3s. Four hundred AT-6B gunnery trainers followed these, and then came a switch to huge batches which were built using a greater proportion of non-strategic materials, to conserve aluminium alloy for more important combat aircraft. These realized 2970 AT-6Cs and 2400 navy SNJ-4s, and a change from 12V to 24V electrical system resulted in the similar AT-6D (3404 built) and SNJ-5 (1357). Final production models were the AT-6F (25 built for the USAAF) and SNJ-6 (931 for the navy).

Before and during the Second World War some 1800 or so variants of the NA-26 were exported, recipients including Australia (one), Brazil (81), Canada (978), China (15), the Netherlands (one), New Zealand (67), Britain (635) and Venezuela (six). Those for the RAF and RCAF were known as the Harvard I and II, and included 450 aircraft ordered by the French air force but diverted to her allies after the fall of France. In addition to these, some 2300 of those from US procurement were supplied to the United States' allies (Brazil, Britain, China and the USSR, among others) under Lend-Lease, the AT-6Cs for the RAF being known as Harvard IIAs and the AT-6D/SNJ-5s as Harvard IIIs.

Licence production also took place in Australia and Canada. The Commonwealth Aircraft corporation in Melbourne produced 755 under the name Wirraway before and during the Second World War. In Canada, Noorduyn built 210 AT-6As for the RCAF and 2400 AT-16s as Harvard IIBs for the Royal Air Force, Royal Navy and all other Commonwealth air forces.

After the war, the USAF dropped the 'A' in the AT-6 series designations in 1948, by which time it had about 2000 still in service after supplying many war-surplus Texans to other countries. Those in USAF service became T-6A, C, D and F, and a rebuilding and modernization programme started in 1949 brought 1812 of these up to a new T-6G or navy SNJ-7 standard with improved cockpit layouts, modified landing gear, increased fuel tankage, etc. Some of these were used for forward air control duties in Korea, and many others were supplied to other countries under the Mutual Defense Aid Program. A

second Canadian production programme was started in 1951, when the Canadian Car & Foundry company of Montreal produced a further 555 to T-6G standard as Harvard IVs for the RCAF (270) and the USAF (285, designated T-6J).

After more than 40 years the Texan could still be found in service with many of the world's air forces, but it will always be remembered chiefly for the great task it assumed during the Second World War, when it formed the mainstay of the great Commonwealth Air Training Plan.

(AT-6A) *Span:* 12.8 m (42 ft) *Length:* 8.84 m (29 ft) *Gross weight:* 2338 kg (5155 lb) *Maximum speed:* 338 km/h (210 mph)

(T-6G) *Span:* 12.8 m (42 ft) *Length:* 8.99 m (29 ft 6 in) *Gross weight:* 2548 kg (5617 lb) *Maximum speed:* 341 km/h (212 mph)

Texas

US battleship, built 1889-95. Following the tentative steps towards recreating a fleet with the 'reconstruction' of the Civil War monitors, the Naval Advisory Board in 1886 advised the US Navy to build two seagoing armoured ships of 6000 tons each. Because the country was now considered to be capable of providing both steel and machinery it was recommended that at least one of the ships should be built in a US navy yard.

The first ship authorized was *Texas* (the armoured cruiser *Maine* was the second), sanctioned in August 1886. It was considered that the design capability in the United States was so limited that a competition should be held, for a prize of $15 000. This was won by the British Naval Construction and Armaments company (later Vickers) of Barrow-in-Furness, who submitted a design for a small turret ship with two single 12-in (305-mm) guns sponsoned amidships. In theory this allowed fore and aft fire but in practice the superstructure and light guns were subjected to severe blast, and arcs of fire were restricted to the broadside.

The keel was not laid until 1889 to allow time to bring Norfolk navy yard up to the standard required, and because of bickering over the somewhat unorthodox design, which by then looked thoroughly dated in comparison with the latest British and French designs. The contractors were also late, and although the ship was launched on time on June 28, 1892, she did not commission until August 1895, by which time she was a distinct oddity.

The turrets were of an old-fashioned type with the rammers outside the barbettes, so that the guns could only be loaded when trained in one of two positions. The interval between each round was seven minutes, until just before the war against Spain in 1898 an enterprising gunnery officer devised a telescopic rammer. This increased the rate of fire to a round every two minutes, and as the ship was good for nearly 18 knots she was as effective as any of her US contemporaries.

Texas fought in the Battle of Santiago on July 3, 1898, and engaged Admiral Cervera's cruiser squadron without sustaining damage or casualties. She was soon reduced to second-line status and on February 18, 1911, was renamed *San Marcos*. She was used in a series of tests to establish the armour scheme for the *Nevada* Class and was finally sunk in Chesapeake Bay on October 11 that year.

Displacement: 6315 tons (normal) *Length:* 94.1 m (308 ft 9 in) oa *Beam:* 19.5 m (64 ft 1 in) *Draught:* 6.9 m (22 ft 6 in) *Machinery:* 2-shaft reciprocating steam, 8600 ihp=17.75 knots *Protection:* 305 mm (12 in) belt and turrets *Armament:* 2 12-in/35-cal Mk I (2×1); 6 6-in (152-mm)/35-cal Mk III (6×1); 12 6-pdr (57-mm) QF (12×1); 10 1-pdr (37-mm) QF (10×1); 2 0.30-in (7.62-mm) Gatling machine-guns; 4 45-cm (17.7-in) torpedo tubes (above water, bow, stern and beam) *Crew:* 392

Thames

British submarine class. The *Thames* Class was the Admiralty's final attempt to produce a group of submarines which could operate in conjunction with the main Fleet. This concept had much to recommend it in theory but always proved disastrous in practice as it was virtually impossible to coordinate safely the operations of submarines and surface ships. They were never seriously operated as fleet submarines and subsequently proved highly successful as long-range patrol vessels. The first of the class, *Thames*, was provided under the 1929 Programme, and completed in 1932; *Clyde* and *Severn* were provided under the 1931 and 1932 Programmes respectively, both being completed in 1935. All three were constructed by Vickers-Armstrongs who provided the detailed design to a basic Admiralty layout worked out during 1928-29. In order to provide the high surface speed necessary for them to accompany the fleet they were fitted with two large ten-cylinder supercharged diesels of over twice the power installed in the comtemporary patrol submarines of the 'O', 'P' and 'R' Classes. Compared with these latter vessels they were 5 knots faster and almost 400 tons heavier, but they carried a lighter torpedo armament because the machinery plant did not leave room for the usual pair of stern torpedo tubes. *Thames* was the first diesel-powered submarine to exceed 21 knots, and the speed of the class was not exceeded for several years except by a few Japanese submarines completed in the mid-1930s.

On the outbreak of war all three ships were operating with the Home Fleet; *Clyde* and *Severn* spent a short period operating in the mid-Atlantic in late 1939, but for the most part they remained with the Home Fleet until early 1941. During this period they were mainly employed in the North Sea and off

Norway against German shipping. On June 20, 1940, *Clyde* torpedoed and seriously damaged the battlecruiser *Gniesenau* off the coast of Norway, but on July 23 *Thames* was sunk by a mine in the same area. The two survivors transferred to the Mediterranean in 1941 where they enjoyed moderate success operating against Italian supply routes. Late in 1942 *Clyde* ran six supply trips to Malta carrying aviation spirit, torpedoes and ammunition and in all delivered 1200 tons of stores to the island. In 1944 they transferred to the Eastern Fleet where they remained until the end of their careers. Both were sold locally in 1946, *Clyde* being scrapped at Durban and *Severn* at Bombay.

Displacement: (Thames) 1805/2680 tons; *(Clyde and Severn)* 1850/2723 tons (surfaced/submerged) *Length:* 105.2 m (345 ft) oa *Beam:* 8.6 m (28 ft 3 in) *Draught:* 4.1 m (13 ft 6 in) *Machinery:* 2-shaft diesel/2 electric motors, 10 000 bhp/2500 shp=22.5/10 knots (surfaced/submerged) *Armament:* 1 4-in (102-mm); 6 21-in (53-cm) torpedo tubes *Crew:* 61

Theodor

German railway guns. In 1936 the German army became alarmed at the slow rate of development and production of railway guns and initiated a crash programme aimed at providing a reasonable gun strength by the end of 1939. The Krupp company, who built all German railway artillery, responded by simply taking a number of ex-naval gun barrels and adapting them to mountings based on First World War designs.

The two 24-cm (9.4-in) guns to be built under this arrangement were both known as Theodor. The first to be built used the 24-cm SK L/40 naval gun fitted with a heavy counterweight to avoid the need for balancing gear to balance the muzzle weight. The mounting was a relatively simple box of steel carried on two eight-wheel bogies, while the rear of the box allowed a slight amount of traverse across the rear bogie to allow for fine pointing of the gun; coarse pointing was done by placing the equipment on a turntable or on a curved section of track. Three of these were built and issued in 1937; they were originally called Theodor Karl, but this led to confusion with the Karl self-propelled guns and the title was shortened to Theodor.

The second equipment was Theodor Bruno which used the 24-cm SK L/35 gun barrel, a

naval weapon dating from 1910. The mounting was of the same type as before, though rather different in outline, and the gun was mounted into a rectangular cradle which carried the recoil system and acted as a counterbalance to the gun's weight. Six of these guns were built and issued in 1939. Both versions remained in service until 1945.

(Theodor Bruno) Weight: 94 tonnes *Length:* 20.7 m (67 ft 11 in) *Calibre:* 238 mm (9.37 in) *Length of gun:* 8.4 m (27 ft 7 in) *Traverse:* 1° *Elevation:* +10° to +45° *Shell weight:* 148.5 kg (327 lb) *Muzzle velocity:* 675 m/sec (2215 ft/sec) *Range:* 10 000-20 200 m (10 935-22 090 yards)

(Theodor) Weight: 95 tonnes *Length:* 18.54 m (60 ft 10 in) *Calibre:* 238 mm (9.37 in) *Length of gun:* 9.55 m (31 ft 4 in) *Traverse:* 1° *Elevation:* +10° to +45° *Shell weight:* 148.5 kg (327 lb) *Muzzle velocity:* 810 m/sec (2660 ft/sec) *Range:* 13 700-26 750 m (15 000-29 250 yards)

Thomas-Morse US aircraft   See **MB-3**

Thompson

US submachine-gun. Brigadier-General John Tagliaferro Thompson (1860-1940) was an officer of the US Ordnance Department who spent most of his service life involved in small-arms design and manufacture. In 1914 he retired, joining the Remington company as chief engineer, but was recalled to duty during the war and placed in charge of rifle production, retiring for the second time in 1918. Outside his military duties, Thompson's aim in life was to develop an automatic rifle; he rejected gas operation as being too complicated, recoil operation as being too heavy, and blowback as too weak for military calibres. He then, in 1915, discovered a locking system patented by a Commander Blish, USN, which relied on inclined faces locking under great pressure but releasing as the pressure dropped, so that a bolt would be held while chamber pressure was high but released to recoil when the bullet had left the barrel. Together with Blish, he set up the Auto-Ordnance company and hired two engineers, Eickhoff and Payne, to work on the rifle design.

After Thompson had been recalled to the army his designers continued work and discovered that the Blish lock was useless with high-powered rifle cartridges, but that it

appeared to work well with the low-powered 0.45-in (11.4-mm) Auto pistol cartridge. On being told this, Thompson was inspired to change his design to a hand-held machine-gun which he called the Trench Broom. By the time the design was perfected the war was over, but Thompson invented the name 'submachine-gun' for his weapon and began promoting it as a police weapon.

The first production model was the M1921, which set the pattern for all subsequent types. It used a rectangular receiver and a finned barrel, pistol grips for both hands and a wooden stock, and a bolt with a reduced-diameter forward section. The cocking handle was on top, slotted so that the sight line passed through it, and box or drum magazines were provided. Five calibres, 0.45-in ACP, 9-mm (0.354-in) Parabellum, 9-mm Mauser, 0.45-in Thompson-Remington (a more powerful version of the 0.45-in ACP cartridge) and 0.351-in (8.9-mm) Winchester were offered, but it is doubtful if any other than the 0.45-in versions were made. Since the Auto-Ordnance company had no production facilities, manufacture was contracted to Colt and sufficient components for 15 000 guns were made, for assembly by Auto-Ordnance.

In the following years the company's catalogues offered a variety of model numbers, but, though these were all based on the M1921 stock of parts and differed little from that model, some were single-shot only, some had longer or shorter barrels or were fitted with bayonets. But few military bodies took much interest, and Thompson's gun found most of its fame in the hands of gangsters and G-Men in the late 1920s. In 1926, after a mail truck had been robbed in New Jersey, the US Post Office acquired the services of the US Marines to guard mail shipments, and provided the marines with 250 Thompson guns. A few weeks later, when the marines were sent to Nicaragua to help the newly elected President Diaz, they took Thompsons with them, and later took them to Shanghai. In this way the gun achieved military recognition.

Thomas Ryan, the financier who had put up the money to start the Auto-Ordnance Company, died in 1928. The sales of the gun were not brisk, and Ryan's son wanted to be rid of it, so in 1930 he bought out Thompson and eventually, in 1938, sold the company to Russell Maguire. Maguire was betting on a European war boosting sales, and late in 1939 his gamble paid off when the British and

A Thompson M1928A1 with a horizontal foregrip and 20-round box magazine. By later standards it was an expensive and bulky submachine-gun

Thor

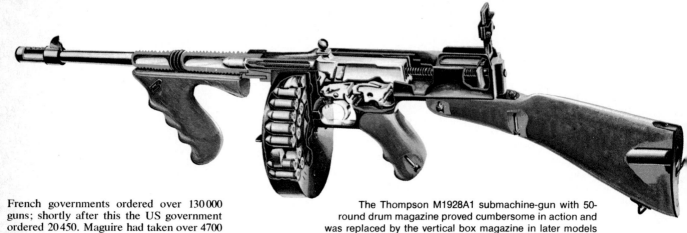

The Thompson M1928A1 submachine-gun with 50-round drum magazine proved cumbersome in action and was replaced by the vertical box magazine in later models

French governments ordered over 130000 guns; shortly after this the US government ordered 20450. Maguire had taken over 4700 of the original 15000 guns which had not been sold, and now turned to Colt to make more. But Colt's had never been happy with the 'gangster' image and refused the contract; it was taken by the Savage arms company, but orders continued to pile up and eventually Auto-Ordnance built their own factory. In June 1940 Thompson died, just as his Trench Broom was about to fulfil his dreams.

The gun being manufactured in 1940 was the M1928A1, the service version of the M1921 which had a Cutts muzzle compensator fitted. It was expensive, the contract price to the French being $250, though volume production brought the price down to $70 by 1942. But the Savage corporation engineers were convinced that the gun would work just as well and be easier and cheaper to make if the Blish breech lock was removed and the gun turned into a simple blowback. Maguire was aghast: the Thompson's greatest selling point had always been the Blish lock, and without it the Thompson wasn't the Thompson. But the Savage engineers were unrepentant, seeing it as a waste of money in a time of need, and threatened to put their own simplified version on the market to undercut Maguire. They won, and early in 1942 the Thompson M1 appeared, much the same but without the controversial lock.

Eventually 1750000 complete guns, plus sufficient spares to make another 250000, were made during the war. After the war Maguire sold the company and it has since changed hands a number of times, but is still selling the Thompson design in a long-barrelled semiautomatic version.

The Thompson submachine-gun was to be found in all theatres of war. The worst that anyone could ever say about it was that it was heavy. It became legendary for its absolute reliability, accuracy and resistance to hard conditions, and it was preferred by Allied servicemen over every other submachine-gun, the only possible exception to this being the Australian Owen.

(M1928A1) *Calibre:* 0.45 in (11.4 mm) *Ammunition:* .45 ACP *Weight:* 4.88 kg (10 lb 12 oz) *Length:* 857 mm (33.7 in) *Barrel length:* 267 mm (10.5 in) *Magazine:* 20- or 30-round box; 50- or 100-round drum *Rate of fire:* 600-725 rds/min *Muzzle velocity:* 280 m/sec (920 ft/sec)

(M1) *Calibre:* 0.45 in *Ammunition:* .45 ACP *Weight:* 4.73 kg (10 lb 7oz) *Length:* 813 mm (32 in) *Barrel length:* 267 mm (10.5 in) *Magazine:* 20- or 30-round box *Rate of fire:* 700 rds/min *Muzzle velocity:* 280 m/sec (920 ft/sec)

Thor

German auxiliary cruiser. *Thor* was built as the Oldenburg-Portugeisische Line's *Santa Cruz* in 1938, and was converted to *Hilfskreuzer 4 (Schiff 10)* in 1939-40. To the British she was known as *Raider E. Thor* sailed from Kiel in June 1940, using first a Soviet disguise and then the Yugoslav flag. On July 28 she engaged the British AMC *Alcantara* and drove her off with damage. On December 12 she met another AMC, HMS *Carnarvon Castle*, and again the raider came off best, the ex-liner being forced to break off the engagement. A third AMC, *Voltaire*, encountered *Thor* on April 4, 1941, and was not so lucky, and the raider succeeded in crippling her opponent and sinking her.

When *Thor* returned to Hamburg the same month she had spent 329 days at sea and had sunk or captured 12 ships totalling 96 547 grt. After a refit she sailed again from Kiel in November 1941 and sank a further ten ships. On November 30, 1942, she was lying in Yokohama when the German oiler *Uckermark* (formerly *Altmark*) blew up. *Thor* was also sunk in the explosion.

Tonnage: 3862 grt *Length:* 115.5 m (379 ft) wl *Beam:* 16.5 m (54 ft) *Draught:* 7 m (23 ft) *Machinery:* 1-shaft steam turbine, 6500 shp=18 knots *Armament:* 6 15-cm (5.9-in)/45-cal (6×1); 2 37-mm (1.46-in) AA (2×1); 4 20-mm (0.79-in) AA (4×1); 4 53-cm (21-in) torpedo tubes (2×2, above water) *Aircraft:* 1 Ar 196 floatplane *Crew:* 345, including 4 prize officers

Thor

Norwegian coast-defence ship, built 1871-72. *Thor* was the last of a trio of monitors built from 1866, when Norway was under a dual monarchy with Sweden. The ship was launched in 1872 from the naval dockyard at Horten and resembled the monitors building in Sweden at that time. The original armament comprised two large Armstrong rifled muzzle-loaders in a twin turret, but in 1897-98 she was rebuilt with two 12-cm (4.7-in) quick-firers and two 65-mm (2.6-in) QF guns of French manufacture. She was stricken in 1910 and scrapped.

Displacement: 2000 tons (normal) *Length:* 62.2 m (204 ft 1 in) wl *Beam:* 14.5 m (47 ft 7 in) *Draught:* 4 m (13 ft 2 in) *Machinery:* 1-shaft reciprocating steam, 600 ihp=8.25 knots *Protection:* 176 mm (6.9 in) belt, 25 mm (1 in) deck, 368 mm (14.5 in) turret *Armament:* 2 26.4-cm (10.4-in)/26-cal RML (1×2) *Crew:* 90

Thor, Douglas

US intermediate-range ballistic missile. The SM-75 Thor, which formed part of WS-315A (Weapon System No 315A), was developed concurrently with the Atlas and Titan ICBMs, the three missiles sharing many common parts such as engines and guidance systems. The United States Air Force was authorized to begin development of an IRBM with a speed of 16000 km/h (10000 mph) and a maximum range of 2780 km (1725 miles) in November 1955 to complement the 25700 km/h (16000 mph) ICBMs, and the development contract was signed with Douglas on December 27. From the outset WS-315A was regarded as a single entity, with the missile and all associated equipment being developed concurrently. This approach, and the use of items already in the pipeline for the related programmes, allowed the contractor to deliver the first Thor in October 1956, only ten months after go-ahead.

Thor was a single-stage missile constructed from etched and milled aluminium alloy and powered by a Rocketdyne LR-79-NA-7 (MB-2) rocket motor burning RP-1 (a kerosene derivative) oxidized by liquid oxygen to produce 68000 kg (150000 lb) of thrust. The main thrust chamber could be gimballed to steer the weapon, with roll control and final adjustment of the missile's trajectory being provided by two Rocketdyne LR-101-NA-7 vernier motors, each supplying 450 kg (1000 lb) of thrust. Rocketdyne delivered a research and development model of the main propulsion system to Douglas in June 1956 for test firings, and the first production model followed three months later.

The initial Thor was launched at Cape Canaveral on January 25, 1957, but exploded when only 15 cm (6 in) above the pad. The next three shots were also failures, but on September 20 the fifth missile flew successfully. Trials of rounds carrying the AC Spark Plug AChiever inertial-guidance package began in December of that year and nose-cone separation tests started two months later. The USAF had already formed its first IRBM training unit, the 672nd Strategic Missile Squadron, in January 1958; in September of that year the initial class of Thor students, most of whom were destined to become instructors on the weapon system, completed advanced crew training at Vandenberg Air

Force Base in California. Another Strategic Air Command Thor unit, the 392nd Missile Training Squadron, carried out the first firing from Vandenberg on December 16, using a complete operational launch facility.

Four months later Thor was launched for the first time by Royal Air Force personnel, although the weapon system had been delivered to the RAF the previous autumn. Britain received 80 missiles, which were allocated to four 15-round squadrons with a further five in reserve for each. The first RAF Thor unit was 77 Squadron at Feltwell, Norfolk, which had formed in a training role on September 19, 1958. The other squadrons, each with five complexes of three missiles each, were based at Driffield, Yorkshire; Hemswell, Lincolnshire; and North Luffenham, Rutland. The IRBMs were based in soft emplacements comprising a hangar-like structure protecting each missile from the weather. Before launching, the hangar would be pulled away from the round, which would then be elevated to the vertical on its transporter/launcher and pumped full of propellant. The complete process took 15 minutes, although the missiles could be held for a period at six minutes' readiness by stopping the procedure at this point.

Thor was declared operational by the RAF's Bomber Command in December 1959, making it the first US-designed IRBM to be deployed overseas. The weapon was operated under a dual-key arrangement and could not be fired without the authority of USAF personnel. Thor was also the first ballistic missile with inertial guidance, and the first to carry a full stabilized heat-sink re-entry vehicle (the General Electric Mk 2, containing a thermonuclear warhead of about 1.5 megatons yield). The deployment of fleet ballistic missiles and the build-up of ICBM forces soon made Thor redundant, especially as it was virtually unprotected from an attack; the weapon system was therefore deactivated at midnight on August 14, 1963. Thor had been used as a space booster even before it entered military service, and the rounds returned by the RAF have since also been used in this role.

Length: 19.81 m (65 ft) *Diameter:* 2.44 m (8 ft) *Weight:* 49 900 kg (110 000 lb) *Range:* 2800 km (1750 miles) *Warhead:* 1.5 megatons (approx)

Thora Allied codename for Nakajima Ki-34 Japanese transport aircraft **See Ki-34**

Thresher

US nuclear-powered submarine class, built 1959-68. Developed from the *Skipjack* Class and *Tullibee* the *Thresher* hunter-killer class was authorized in 1957. They were designed to be quieter and dive deeper than previous nuclear-powered submarines. *Thresher* was laid down in May 1959, launched bow-first on July 9, 1960, and completed in July 1960. *Gato* was the last of the class to commission on January 25, 1968.

Permit (SSN.594), *Plunger* (SSN.595, ex-*Pollack*)—built by Mare Island navy yard *Thresher* (SSN.593), *Jack* (SSN.605), *Timosa* (SSN.606)—built by Portsmouth navy yard *Barb* (SSN.596, ex-*Pollack*, ex-*Plunger*),

A Douglas Thor IRBM in service with 77 Squadron RAF at Feltwell, Norfolk in February 1960. Thors were deactivated in 1963

Dace (SSN.60), *Haddock* (SSN.621)—built by Ingalls
Pollack (SSN.603, ex-*Barb*), *Haddo* (SSN.604), *Guardfish* (SSN.612)—built by New York shipbuilding
Flasher (SSN.613), *Greenling* (SSN.614), *Gato* (SSN.615)—built by General Dynamics (Electric Boat)

On April 9, 1963, *Thresher* left harbour after an extensive refit to undergo sea trials. All went well with the first day's trials, but at 0913 the following day a garbled message was received from her while she was performing a test dive. Nothing more was heard from her, and she was later located lying in 2650 m (8400 ft) of water; her crew, which consisted of 107 officers and men, and the 17 civilian observers on board were all lost in this mysterious accident.

Jack was built to test a modified powerplant designed to reduce still further the operating noise of the submarine. This involved fitting two contrarotating turbines without reduction gearing, driving two different-sized propellers driven by coaxial shafts. *Jack* is 5.5 m (18 ft) longer than her sisters, an extra 3 m (10 ft) being required in the turbine room alone.

Flasher, Gato and *Greenling* were also modified during construction and are longer and displace more than others of the class. They are fitted with improved Subsafe rescue equipment, heavier and more robust turbines and have a taller sail. *Gato* and *Greenling* had already been launched when it was decided to incorporate these modifications, and so they were towed from the Electric Boat company's yard at Groton, Connecticut, to Quincy in Massachusetts for completion, a process which included adding an additional section to the hull.

Displacement: 3750/4300 tons (surfaced/submerged) *Length:* 84.9 m (278 ft 6 in) *Beam:* 9.7 m (31 ft 9 in) *Draught:* 7.7 m (25 ft 2 in) *Machinery:* 1 S5W pressurized water-cooled reactor, 15 000 shp=20/30 knots (surfaced/submerged) *Armament:* 4 21-in (53-cm) torpedo tubes (amidships); Sub-Harpoon and Tomahawk missiles *Crew:* 103

(Jack) Displacement: 3750/4470 tons (surfaced/submerged) *Length:* 90.4 m (296 ft 6 in) (Other specifications as above)

(Flasher group) *Displacement:* 3800/4242 tons (surfaced/submerged) *Length:* 89.1 m (292 ft 2 in) (Other specifications as above)

Thulin K

Swedish fighter aircraft. Dr Enoch Thulin, who died in 1919, did more than anyone else to help found an aviation industry in Sweden. With Oskar Ask he formed the first aircraft manufacturing company in the country in 1913. Known as AVIS, it built two 50-hp Blériot monoplanes before Thulin and others took it over completely in 1914 and renamed it AETA (AB Enoch Thulins Aeroplanfabrik). Twenty-three more Blériots were produced by AETA, 21 for Thulin's own flying school at Ljungbyhed and two for evaluation by the Swedish army aviation service, formed in 1911. The Blériots were known as the Thulin Type A, and were followed by eight Type Bs, based on a two-seat Morane-Saulnier monoplane; the Swedish navy and Danish army each received two of these. Other military orders were received for the Type D (two for the Swedish army and two for Finland, of five built); Type E (Swedish army, two); Type FA (Swedish army, eight); Types G and GA floatplanes (Swedish navy, five and two respectively); Type H three-engined floatplane (army, one); and Types L (five built) and LA (15 built), used by the Swedish and Dutch armies.

Largest output, however, was of the Type K, a single-seat monoplane fighter modelled on Blériot/Morane lines, and first produced in 1917. Eighteen were built, 15 being sold over the next two years to the Royal Netherlands Naval Air Service and two to the Swedish army; the 18th was owned privately by Thulin himself. Powerplant was a 90-hp Thulin Type A rotary engine, an improved version of the French Le Rhône 9J. Strangely, there is no record of armament being fitted, or of the Type K ever being used for fighting. On December 30, 1917, the company flew another fighter prototype, the Thulin Type N, which had a 135-hp Thulin G rotary. This led, after Thulin's death, to the similarly-powered Type NA prototype of 1921.

Span: 9 m (29 ft 6 in) *Length:* 6.6 m (21 ft 8 in) *Gross weight:* 525 kg (1157 lb) *Maximum speed:* 150 km/h (93 mph)

Thunderbird, English Electric

British surface-to-air missile. Both Thunderbird, which was the responsibility of English Electric at Luton, and the similar Bloodhound developed by the Bristol Aeroplane company were designed to meet an immediate need after the Second World War for guided weapons to counter high-flying

Thunderbolt, Republic P-47

BAC

An English Electric Thunderbird SAM. This missile equipped Royal Artillery heavy AA units

Soviet bombers. The British armed services and research establishments, led by the Royal Aircraft Establishment, specified such a surface-to-air missile development programme under the general name of Red Heathen, and in August 1949 the RAE's director submitted a report outlining the proposed propulsion, guidance and associated ground-radar systems. The report dealt with two weapons, one (Red Shoes—later Thunderbird) to be powered by four solid-propellant boosters and a liquid-propellant rocket sustainer motor and the other (Red Duster, which became Bloodhound) based on a ramjet sustainer if such a motor proved to be practicable.

In March 1949 English Electric was awarded a contract to study the problems associated with development of a SAM with an effective range of 91 500 m (100 000 yards) and able to defeat subsonic bombers flying at heights up to 18 300 m (60 000 ft). The Luton team submitted its report in March 1950, and a full development contract was awarded in August.

Trials began with a large number of LTVs (Luton test vehicles), and these were followed in July 1951 by the first flight of a missile in the D3 series. Thunderbird was originally planned to use a liquid-propellant sustainer motor burning kerosene oxidized by hydrogen peroxide, and the D3 employed this type of powerplant. Advances in solid-propellant rocket technology allowed a new sustainer motor to be developed, however, which removed the handling and safety difficulties associated with liquids. The D4 model with a solid sustainer made its first flights in 1955; in July of that year the initial guided round successfully hit a stationary target at the RAE Aberporth range, and interceptions of radio-controlled Firefly drones followed in early 1956.Trials with the W1 design, which incorporated the lessons

learnt from D3 and D4, started in late 1956. Numerous problems were encountered, especially involving fin flutter, but these were gradually solved and Thunderbird 1 entered service with the British Army in 1958, becoming fully operational in 1960.

Thunderbird was a mobile system which normally formed part of a comprehensive air-defence network. Each battery had its own surveillance and height-finding radars, and a battery command post which could control up to six firing troops. Each such troop had a launch-control post, target-tracking and target-illuminating radar, and three missile launchers. Thunderbird 1 employed a pulse-type radar for tracking and illumination, and in about 1956 the major contractors began work on an improved Thunderbird 2 which was to employ the higher-frequency Ferranti Indigo Corkscrew continuous-wave tracking/illuminating radar, a type which it shared with the Bloodhound 2 programme. The so-called Stage 1½ project which became Thunderbird 2 was required to be as much like the original weapon as possible, but in addition to using a new radar the missile itself had to have a greater range and ceiling, with improved performance against high-speed targets.

Initial firings of the uprated Thunderbird 2 missile took place from 1960 to April 1962, when the first of 50 evaluation rounds was launched by No 16 Joint Services Trials Unit. The last ten of these were to full production standard, and this phase was completed in May 1964. The British Army's system user and evaluation trials at Ty Croes lasted from then until April 1968, but the weapon had already been declared operational with the Royal Artillery's No 30 Heavy Air Defence Regiment in Germany by mid-1967.

Eight ex-British Army Thunderbird 1 launchers and 37 rounds were supplied to Saudi Arabia in 1966 as an interim weapon until the

Raytheon Hawk could be brought into service, but these are no longer operational. An air-defence contract including Thunderbird 2 was signed with Libya in April 1968 but was subsequently cancelled after a coup in September 1969, and by the mid-1970s the British Army was running down its own Thunderbird regiment because of increased costs and a shortage of manpower as the short-range Rapier and Blowpipe weapons were introduced. Thunderbird is no longer operational with any armed forces.

(Thunderbird 2) *Length:* 6.35 m (20 ft 10 in) *Span:* 1.63 m (5 ft 4 in) *Diameter:* 53 cm (1 ft 9 in) *Range:* 74 km (46 miles) approx *Warhead:* continuous-rod

Thunderbolt, Republic P-47

US Army single-seat fighter and fighter-bomber aircraft. The line of fighters begun by Alexander Kartveli with the Seversky P-35 and continued in the Republic P-43 Lancer reached its peak in the latter company's P-47 Thunderbolt of Second World War fame. As a potential successor to the P-43, Kartveli and his team proposed two alternative designs, both of which received contracts from the US Army Air Corps. One, which was allocated the USAAC designation P-44, was a direct development of the P-43, to be powered by either a Pratt & Whitney Twin Hornet or a Double Wasp radial engine. The other, to which the prototype designations XP-47 and XP-47A were given, was to be an altogether smaller and lighter design, with an Allison V-1710 V-type engine. However, in June 1940 the US Army Board met at Wright Field to evolve new standards for future fighters, taking into account the limitations of existing US fighter aircraft as revealed by the early reports of air combat over Europe. As a result it issued a new specification calling for a fighter able to exceed the expected ceilings of enemy bombers, with sufficient firepower to out-gun them, a maximum speed in the order of 644 km/h (400 mph), plus the ability to fly long-range missions as escort to US high-altitude bombers and to out-fight enemy intercepters over the target. Such a requirement was clearly beyond the capabilities of the P-44 or XP-47/47A. It could be met only by an aircraft with a high-powered and super-charged engine, which would also need armour protection, self-sealing fuel tanks, and a high degree of manoeuvrability. Very quickly, Kartveli offered a greatly redesigned (and nearly twice as heavy) development of the XP-47, with a turbo-supercharged Double Wasp engine and an eight-gun armament. This was accepted, the earlier pair of projects were cancelled, and in September 1940 Republic received a $56.5 million order for one XP-47B prototype and 773 production P-47B and P-47C fighters—the largest single order placed up to that time by the US Army for a fighter aircraft.

On May 6, 1941, less than a year after the revised specification had been drawn up, the XP-47B flew for the first time. The new fighter was not only massive, with an all-up weight of 5482 kg (12 086 lb), but was unique in having, literally, been designed around the engine turbo-supercharging system. The turbocharger itself, described at the time as 'the size of a washing machine', was mounted in

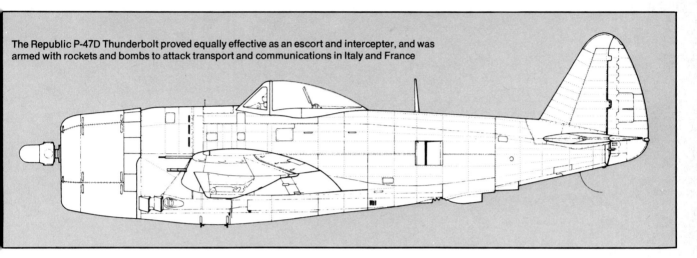

The Republic P-47D Thunderbolt proved equally effective as an escort and intercepter, and was armed with rockets and bombs to attack transport and communications in Italy and France

the rear of the fuselage, air being fed to the impeller of the turbine from a scoop under the engine, in the lower part of the oval-section engine cowling. Exhaust gases, after passing through the turbine, were vented into the atmosphere through a ventral opening, while the compressed air was routed back towards the nose, passing into the carburettor via an intercooler set inside the fuselage amidships. The engine itself was the Pratt & Whitney XR-2800-21, a huge two-row 18-cylinder air-cooled radial developing 2000 hp and driving a large-diameter, four-blade fully feathering Curtiss Electric propeller. On test, the XP-47B exhibited a maximum speed of 663 km/h (412 mph), and with its wing-mounted armament of eight 0.5-in (12.7-mm) Browning machine-guns was clearly going to be an opponent to be reckoned with. (The production Thunderbolt carried a maximum of 425 rounds of ammunition per gun, although this was usually reduced somewhat in the fighter-bomber versions, which carried bombs or rockets as well). The single-seat cockpit was, according to a contemporary report in *The Aeroplane,* "spacious and would easily accommodate two pilots of normal girth sitting side by side. Its size, and the neat arrangement of the instruments, make it seem sparsely furnished. Clearly, the designer had the last word and the junk shop untidiness of some fighters' cockpits is pleasantly absent."

Such was the size of the fighter that it eventually earned itself the nickname of Juggernaut or, more familiarly still, simply The Jug. However, the size of the aircraft caused few development problems, and the turbo-charging system worked well. But at high altitude the XP-47B proved to be susceptible to aileron 'snatch', control loads on the ailerons and rudder became excessive, and the sideways-hinged canopy could not be opened in an emergency. Eventually, cures for all of these problems were found, but the Thunderbolt's estimated date for entry into combat of May 1942 meanwhile slipped considerably, despite an accelerated flight-test programme. However, by the end of that year two USAAF Fighter Groups (the 56th and the 78th) had been equipped with the P-47B, and they arrived in Britain in January 1943 to join the US Eighth Air Force, flying their first operational sorties (on fighter sweeps and as high-altitude escorts for B-17 bombers) on April 8. With the production

version of the R-2800-21 engine the top speed of the P-47B rose to 690 km/h (429 mph), but its range on only 784 litres (172 Imp gal) of fuel was clearly inadequate for the long-range escort role. Production was therefore restricted to 171 of this model, and the P-47C (602 of which were built, from late 1942 onwards) introduced shackles for an under-fuselage 757-litre (166-Imp gal) drop tank; it also featured a modified engine mounting, which had the effect of lengthening the forward fuselage by 33 cm (13 in), thereby also improving manoeuvrability.

Main changes in the initial P-47D series were a choice between either the R-2800-21 or the 2300-hp R-2800-59 version of the Double Wasp, equipped with water injection to prolong their combat power; increased armour protection for the pilot; and reinforcement of the wing structure to allow a total external load (under wings and fuselage) of 1134 kg (2500 lb) of bombs or drop tanks to be carried. A typical load was one 454-kg (1000-lb) bomb under each wing, plus a single 227-kg (500-lb) bomb beneath the fuselage. With the extra engine power overcoming the inevitable weight increase, maximum speed of the early P-47D series rose to 697 km/h (433 mph) at 9145 m (30 000 ft), and it soon became a much-feared protector of the large B-17 and B-24 bomber formations daily attacking targets in Europe. With the increasing number of P-47s becoming available, the Thunderbolt began to enter service in other major theatres of the war: the south-west Pacific in June 1943, Europe (P-47D) in July, the Mediterranean in November, and China in April 1944. By the end of the war, it had served in virtually every theatre of operations except Alaska. Production was augmented by 354 P-47Gs built by Curtiss; these were essentially similar to the 6315 early-series P-47Ds produced by the two Republic factories at Farmingdale, New York, and Evansville, Indiana.

The latter were built in batches, with suffix batch numbers up to P-47D-22 and, like all the preceding Thunderbolts, had a characteristic hump-backed fuselage aft of the rearward-sliding framed cockpit canopy. Beginning with the P-47D-25 block, these familiar contours later underwent a notable change when the depth of the rear fuselage was cut down and a fully transparent teardrop canopy was fitted, vastly improving the all-round view from the cockpit. Despite the narrower

fuselage, space was found to increase the internal fuel tankage. The late-series P-47D became the second most numerous Thunderbolt variant, Republic production totalling 6293. Various structural and other improvements were made to several batches, including the provision for underwing launchers for up to ten unguided rocket projectiles for the ground-attack role—one in which the Thunderbolt was particularly effective. From the P-47D-27, one important modification was the introduction of a long, shallow dorsal stroke to offset the decline in longitudinal stability resulting from the loss of 'keel' area by the cutting down of the rear fuselage.

Only two other variants of the Jug were to attain production status. The first of these, of which 130 were completed, was the P-47M, a sprint version of the D evolved for use in Europe against the FZG 76 (V-1) flying bombs and the German jet- and rocket-powered intercepters. Since it was required for interception only, the P-47M omitted the underwing weapon racks, and, powered by a 2800-hp R-2800-57 Double Wasp, it was the fastest production model of the aircraft with a top speed of 761 km/h (473 mph). Final model was the P-47N, which at a gross weight of 9616 kg (21 200 lb) was also the heaviest Thunderbolt built. New, square-tipped wings of 0.56 m (1 ft 10 in) greater span were introduced, strengthened for additional load-carrying; with the same engine as the P-47M, speed was only marginally lower. Republic built 1816 P-47Ns, primarily intended as escorts for B-29 Superfortress formations in the Pacific where their 4792-litre (1054-Imp gal) maximum fuel capacity gave them a combat radius in the order of 1610 km (1000 miles). With full internal fuel and four underwing drop tanks, a P-47M could remain airborne for up to nine hours.

Overall production of the Thunderbolt exceeded that of any other fighter acquired by the USAAF, reaching a grand total of 15 683 (including the prototype) before production ended in 1945. By comparison with some other wartime types of US aircraft, relatively few from this huge total were supplied to Allied forces. Those that were included 240 early-series and 590 late-series P-47Ds to the Royal Air Force, by whom they were designated Thunderbolt I and II and used mainly in South-East Asia. Some 103 early-series and 100 late-series P-47Ds were supplied as Lend-Lease aid to the Soviet

Thunderchief, Republic F-105

Union, and 446 P-47Ds were employed by the Free French forces.

Thunderbolts of all models are credited with dropping 119 748 tonnes of bombs, firing more than 135 million rounds of 0.5-in ammunition, 60 000 rocket projectiles, and releasing several thousand gallons of napalm. About 10 000 of all the Thunderbolts built served outside the continental US, and over half of those were lost in combat despite a considerable capacity for absorbing battle damage, though their loss rate per sorties was only 0.7%. In Europe alone they are claimed to have destroyed, between D-Day (June 6, 1944) and VE-Day (May 8, 1945) no fewer than 86 000 railway coaches, 68 000 motor vehicles, 9000 locomotives, and 6000 armoured vehicles, apart from their successes against the Luftwaffe.

As might be expected from its suitability as a mount for large, powerful engines, and its innate high speed, the Thunderbolt was used in a number of experimental programmes. Among testbeds were two XP-47Hs, converted from early-series P-47Ds for trials with the 2500-hp Chrysler XIV-2220-1 inverted-V engine, with which a level speed of 789 km/h (490 mph) was achieved. Even faster was the single XP-47J, a more extensively modified P-47D having a lighter-weight airframe, two of the eight guns deleted, and a 2100-hp R-2800-61 Double Wasp in a new, close-fitting cowling with a separate ventral intake for the supercharger. In August 1944 the XP-47J achieved a level speed of 811 km/h (504 mph), the fastest speed achieved

by a piston-engined aircraft up to that time. Other experimental Thunderbolts included the XP-47E, a converted P-47B fitted with a pressurized cockpit as part of a research programme for a high-altitude escort version; the XP-47F, another converted P-47B which tested a laminar-flow wing section in 1943; the XP-47K, an early-series P-47D which flight-tested the teardrop cockpit hood for the later-series Ds and subsequent models; and the XP-47L, another early-series P-47D which was modified to test a new and larger internal fuel tank. In addition to these, three other P-47Ds were redesignated as YP-47Ms when modified to serve as prototypes for the P-47M production version.

The ending of the Second World War brought the cancellation of 5934 additional P-47Ns then on order, and, inevitably, there existed a huge surplus of P-47s far beyond the needs of the postwar US Air Force. Large numbers consequently became available to other countries, notably under the US government's Rio Pact of 1947 under which defence assistance was supplied to Latin American nations. Among those to receive and operate Thunderbolts (mostly of the late P-47D model) after 1945 were Bolivia, Brazil, Chile, China, Colombia, Dominica, Ecuador, France, Guatemala, Honduras, Iran, Italy, Mexico, Nicaragua, Peru, Turkey, Venezuela and Yugoslavia. Some of these aircraft, especially those with the various Central and South American air forces, remained in service until the mid-1960s.

(P-47B) *Span:* 12.42 m (40 ft 9 in) *Length:* 10.67 m (35 ft) *Gross weight:* 6058 kg (13 356 lb) *Maximum speed:* 690 km/h (429 mph)

(P-47C) *Span:* 12.42 m (40 ft 9 in) *Length:* 11 m (36 ft 1 in) *Gross weight:* 6770 kg (14 925 lb) *Maximum speed:* 697 km/h (433 mph)

(P-47D-25) *Span:* 12.42 m (40 ft 9 in) *Length:* 11 m (36 ft 1 in) *Gross weight:* 8800 kg (19 400 lb) *Maximum speed:* 689 km/h (428 mph)

(P-47M) *Span:* 12.42 m (40 ft 9 in) *Length:* 11.07 m (36 ft 4 in) *Gross weight:* 7031 kg (15 500 lb) *Maximum speed:* 761 km/h (473 mph)

(P-47N) *Span:* 12.98 m (42 ft 7 in) *Length:* 11 m (36 ft 1 in) *Gross weight:* 9616 kg (21 200 lb) *Maximum speed:* 752 km/h (467 mph)

Thunderbolt II, Fairchild US close-support attack aircraft   See **A-10**

Thunderchief, Republic F-105

US supersonic long-range tactical fighter-bomber. This single-seat design began developing in 1951 as a private venture, and was intended as the eventual replacement for the F-84F Thunderstreak. It was the last design to emanate from the Republic Aviation corporation, before it became a division of the Fairchild Hiller corporation in mid-1965. Several layouts, all designated AP-63 by the company, were considered for this most powerful aircraft, which was intended to carry nuclear weapons, with a speed of Mach 1.5 and capable of carrying an extensive range of both air-to-surface and air-to-air missiles.

Tentative orders were received from the USAF during 1952-53, but due to delays in production at Republic's factory and the USAF's own changes in operational equipment required, the order was gradually reduced to 15 aircraft by February 1954, with the delivery of the first aircraft due in the spring of 1955. These were eventually completed as two YF-105As, three RF-105Bs (later given the 'special test' designation JF-105B) and ten F-105Bs. The first YF-105A flew initially on October 22, 1955, powered by a Pratt & Whitney J57-P-25 engine, whilst awaiting delivery of the intended 7257-kg (16 000-lb) st Pratt & Whitney J75 powerplant. These 15 aircraft were also fitted with a more sophisticated fire-control system and in-flight refuelling equipment. The second

The Republic F-105D Thunderchief first flew in June 1959 and became one of the standard ground attack and tactical bombers in Vietnam. Over North Vietnam some F-105s carried ECM equipment for use against SAMs and enemy fighters and these were designated Combat Martins. The Thunderchief was withdrawn from South-East Asia in 1970

YF-105A (also with J57 engine) flew for the first time on January 28, 1956, but no others of this model were produced.

The first J75-powered F-105B made its maiden flight on May 26, 1956, but was damaged on landing. This, together with other delays (and, again, USAF requirement changes), slowed down the test programme considerably. However, in March 1956 an order had been issued by the USAF for 65 F-105Bs and 17 RF-105s; the latter were cancelled in July 1956, and the five F-105Cs (two-seat variant), also ordered around the same time, met a similar fate in 1957. The first production F-105B was delivered to the USAF on May 27, 1958; this incorporated an inertial navigation system, an area-ruled fuselage and swept-forward air intakes. Production continued to be slow, and it was mid-1959 before Tactical Air Command (TAC) had a full squadron of Thunderchiefs. These were powered by J75-P-5 engines and could carry 3630 kg (8000 lb) of bombs internally and a further 1814 kg (4000 lb) of stores externally. At the time they were the heaviest single-seaters ever to have served with the USAF; three TAC squadrons were equipped with them. Armament comprised an M61 Vulcan 20-mm (0.79-in) multibarrel cannon, fitted into the forward fuselage.

Modifications called for by the USAF in November 1957 led to the development of the major service version, the all-weather F-105D. A second version, the two-seat F-105E, was also ordered into development at the same time, but was cancelled about a year later. The D model was equipped with the Doppler AN/APN-131 all-weather navigation system, new instrument display panels and a General Electric FC-5 automatic flight-control system. Other differences included an air-data computer, a toss-bombing computer and NASARR search/ranging radar. It was powered by the uprated 11 113-kg (24 500-lb) st J75-P-19W afterburning turbojet and had the same 20-mm armament as the B model. The entire weapon load of 5444 kg (12 000 lb) could be carried externally if necessary, and there was external provision for four air-to-air Sidewinder or air-to-surface Bullpup missiles. First flight of the F-105D was made on June 9, 1959, and deliveries to TAC squadrons commenced in early 1961. At the end of that year all those in service were grounded when a fuselage frame failed a routine fatigue test in the laboratory. This fault was corrected and the production total reached

610 aircraft before the end of the run in mid-1964. Most of these saw intensive combat service in the Vietnam war and phasing-out did not begin until the late 1960s. During 1970 about 30 Thunderchiefs were adapted to carry the T-Stick II bombing system and had a deep dorsal saddle-type spine fairing, running from the cockpit to the tail fin, making them easy to distinguish from other models.

The last 143 D variants off the production line were two-seaters for operational training duties, designated F-105F. They had a higher tail fin and rudder and a 0.79 m (2 ft 7 in) longer fuselage to accommodate the second (tandem) cockpit. Otherwise they were similar to the F-105D. A few serving in Vietnam were fitted with radio-jamming devices and were called Combat Martins. In 1968 the aircraft were modified to carry the Standard ARM missile. The last machines off the production line were converted to F-105G standard, although they were built as F models. These 'Wild Weasel' G variants accounted for approximately one-third of the F-105F total. They were fitted with a fuselage pod containing jamming equipment, antiradiation missiles and a new combat/event recorder. The type was withdrawn from service in Vietnam in 1970, but Thunderchief B and D models continued to equip four wings of the Air National Guard in the US. Production ended in 1964, by which time the total of all Thunderchiefs (including prototypes) had reached 833 aircraft.

(F-105D) *Span:* 10.64 m (34 ft 11 in) *Length:* 20.42 m (67 ft) *Gross weight:* 23 840 kg (52 550 lb) *Maximum speed:* 2237 km/h (1390 mph)

Thunderflash, Republic RF-84F

US Air Force photo-reconnaissance aircraft. As its name and designation imply, the Thunderflash was a photo-reconnaissance variant of the F-84F Thunderstreak fighter-bomber. It followed the same overall basic configuration as its stablemate, except in one major respect. In a single-engined aircraft the nose is the logical location for the camera bay, but in the case of the F-84F this was occupied by the air intake for the J65 jet engine. Since the Thunderflash was required to carry a battery of six cameras in the nose, it was therefore necessary to design an alternative engine-intake system: this took the form of twin ducts, one in the wing root on each side, the wing chord being extended forward at this point to encompass the new structure. Boundary-layer fences were added on the outer wings. An armament of four 0.5-in (12.7-mm) machine-guns was retained, and

the underwing attachment points were used to carry magnesium flare cartridges for night photography, and/or drop tanks for extended-range missions.

Development of the Thunderflash began in 1951, Republic first testing the new intake configuration on one of the YF-84F Thunderstreak prototypes and later (February 1952) on a YRF-84F which also had the intended arrangement of camera ports in a newly contoured nose. Deliveries of production Thunderflashes began in March 1954. The type served with units of both Strategic Air Command and Tactical Air Command. Production of the RF-84F, which ended in January 1958, totalled 715, of which 386 were supplied by the US government to the air forces of Belgium, Taiwan, Denmark, France, West Germany, Greece, Italy, the Netherlands, Norway and Turkey. None remained in service by the late 1970s.

One of the most interesting applications of the RF-84F was in the US Air Force programme known as FICON (Fighter conveyor). This concept originally entailed the use of a fighter as a parasite aircraft, to be carried on operations by the huge B-36 intercontinental bomber as a means of extending the fighter's range. Experiments were conducted with both the Thunderstreak and the Thunderflash, but it was only the latter which was actually chosen for service. A trapeze was attached under the B-36 mother aircraft, which the RF-84F pilot had to engage with a hook on his own aircraft's nose; the RF-84F's vertical tail went up inside the B-36's open bomb bay, its horizontal tail being given anhedral so as not to foul the edges of the bay. One strategic reconnaissance squadron (the 91st) was equipped in 1955 with the FICON Thunderflash, 25 of which were modified to this standard and redesignated GRF-84F (later RF-84K).

(RF-84F) *Span:* 10.24 m (33 ft 7 in) *Length:* 14.53 m (47 ft 8 in) *Gross weight:* 12 156 kg (26 800 lb) *Maximum speed:* 1093 km/h (679 mph)

Thunderjet, Republic F-84

US Air Force fighter-bomber aircraft. In service for more than 20 years, and a major combat workhorse of the Korean war of 1950-53, the Thunderjet served steadily and reliably with more than a dozen air forces all over the world. Conceived in 1944 as a straight-winged, subsonic jet successor to Republic's famous wartime P-47 Thunderbolt, its design and construction were orthodox though it was an entirely new aircraft. It was designed around one of the first US axial-flow turbojet engines, the General Electric TG-180, which in its production form was built by Allison Motors as the J35.

Republic received a contract in early 1945 for three XP-84 prototypes and 400 production aircraft, the former being powered by the 1700-kg (3750-lb) st J35-GE-7 turbojet. The first XP-84 made its maiden flight on February 28, 1946, and in September of that year the second aircraft set up a new US national speed record of 983 km/h (611 mph). The next 15 aircraft were YP-84As, for service trials, and differed in having a more powerful 1814-kg (4000-lb) st J35-A-15 engine. Other modifications included an armament of six 0.5-in (12.7-mm) M2

Thunderstreak, Republic F-84F

USAF

A Republic F-84 Thunderjet of the 49th Fighter Bomber Wing in Korea takes off using JATO (jet assisted takeoff) equipment in June 1952

machine-guns, four mounted above the nose and one in each wing; and provision for wing-tip-mounted auxiliary fuel tanks.

For the initial production model, the P-84B (F-84B from 1948), the USAF specified the Allison J35-A-15C engine (of the same rating as the -15), an ejection seat for the pilot, and M3 machine-guns instead of the slower-firing M2s. In addition, from the 86th example onwards, the F-84B was equipped with underwing rocket launchers. A total of 226 of this model were built, deliveries (to the 14th Fighter Group) beginning in the summer of 1947. The 191 F-84Cs which followed differed little from the B model, except for a new electrical system and more reliable J35-A-13C engines.

The first version to serve in Korea was the F-84D. This was a more powerful model, fitted with a 2268-kg (5000-lb) st J35-A-17D engine, and featuring also thicker wing skins and other detail structural changes. By the end of 1950 the F-84D was in service in Korea with the USAF's 27th Fighter Escort Wing, its initial function being that of an escort fighter for the B-29 Superfortress bomber. Later, however, it found its ideal role as a ground-attack aircraft using bombs, rockets and napalm, and Thunderjets are remembered especially for two spectacular attacks on the irrigation dams at Toksan and Chusan in May 1953.

Only 154 F-84Ds were built, but an increased production tempo resulting from the Korean war led to 843 of the next model, the F-84E, being manufactured. Incorporating recommendations made as a result of operational experience, the F-84E had a 30 cm (12 in) longer fuselage, roomier cockpit, underwing wet-points for two 871-litre (192-Imp gal) drop tanks, improved combat tip-tanks, and a radar gunsight. Typical underwing ordnance loads could include pods of 5-in (12.7-cm) HVAR rockets, 2.75-in (7-cm) rockets, bombs of up to 454 kg (1000 lb), or napalm. One hundred of the F-84Es built were for distribution to the United States' European allies in NATO, and some of these were passed on in second-hand deals to third countries.

While the F-84F designation was allocated to a swept-wing development that became the Thunderstreak, the USAF's Tactical Air Command was placing considerable emphasis upon a version able to carry a 544-kg (1200-lb) tactical nuclear weapon. Development of such a version began as early as 1950, and emerged in the following year as the F-84G. It became the major Thunderjet version for, apart from its nuclear capability (it was the USAF's first single-seat aircraft able to carry a nuclear weapon), the F-84G had the important additional facility of being able to refuel in flight. Indeed, the F-84E and G Thunderjets played a large part in the evolution of USAF flight-refuelling techniques during the late 1940s and early 1950s; on September 22, 1950, the technique was used by an EF-84E (one of two of this model) to make the first non-stop crossing of the Atlantic by a jet aircraft. The powerplant of the F-84G was a 2540-kg (5600-lb) st J35-A-29 turbojet engine; it could carry an external load of 1814 kg (4000 lb) of conventional ordnance; and it was fitted with an autopilot. Deliveries to TAC began in 1951, and production eventually reached 3025, bringing the overall Thunderjet total to 4457 by July 1953, including the three prototypes. Under the US Mutual Security Program, 1936 F-84Gs were allocated to various NATO air forces. Many other air forces bought them second-hand, but none are thought to remain in use.

(F-84E) *Span:* 11.1 m (36 ft 5 in) *Length:* 11.73 m (38 ft 6 in) *Gross weight:* 10190 kg (22 465 lb) *Maximum speed:* 987 km/h (613 mph)

(F-84G) *Span:* 11.1 m (36 ft 5 in) *Length:* 11.61 m (38 ft 1 in) *Gross weight:* 10670 kg (23 525 lb) *Maximum speed:* 1000 km/h (622 mph)

Thunderstreak, Republic F-84F

US Air Force fighter-bomber aircraft. In late 1949, convinced that the basic F-84 Thunderjet fighter was ultimately capable of transonic performance, Republic Aviation planned a company-funded development programme to evolve a swept-wing variant. Republic took the 409th production F-84E to modify as a prototype, giving it a new wing with 40° of sweepback at the quarter-chord line (and more area), and a similarly swept tail unit. It was planned to retain the Allison J35 as the basic powerplant, the new prototype being given a J35-A-25 of 2359 kg (5200 lb) thrust. With this it made its maiden flight on June 3, 1950, later exhibiting a sea-level maximum speed of 1115 km/h (693 mph). Originally, it had been given the new fighter designation YF-96A, but in August 1950 this was revoked, and it was renumbered YF-84F in the basic F-84 series.

Official interest in the swept-wing version, at first lukewarm, increased with the outbreak of the Korean war in June 1950, and in the following month the USAF awarded Republic a letter contract for a production model, stipulating that the somewhat low-powered J35 engine should be replaced by the Wright J65, a licence-built version of the Armstrong Siddeley Sapphire. Two more YF-84Fs with this powerplant were completed in 1951, the second having a solid nose and wing-root intakes as planned for the RF-84F Thunderflash photo-reconnaissance variant. The production F-84F was delayed by engine-supply and airframe manufacturing difficulties so that deliveries, planned to start in the autumn of 1951, did not actually begin until the end of the following year. As a result the new straight-winged F-84G Thunderjet was put into mass production instead, and it became the most numerous model to be used in Korea.

First flight of a production F-84F, now named Thunderstreak, was made on November 22, 1952, and the standard powerplant for this aircraft, apart from a small early batch, was the 3275-kg (7220-lb) st J65-W-3. Armament remained similar to the straight-winged models, with four 0.5-in (12.7-mm) M3 machine-guns in the upper front fuselage and another in each wing root. There were no tip-tanks on the swept wing, but the inboard pair of underwing points ould each carry either a 1705-litre (375-Imp gal) drop tank or a 907-kg (2000-lb) bomb. With all four underwing pylons occupied by weapons, a maximum external bomb and/or rocket load of 2722 kg (6000 lb) was possible. As this load could include a tactical nuclear weapon, the Thunderstreak was equipped with LABS (low-altitude bombing system) gear so that this weapon could be delivered without endangering the launch aircraft.

A total of 2711 Thunderstreaks were built by two main production sources: Republic at Farmingdale, New York, built 2112, and another 599 were contributed by General Motors at Kansas City, the last F-84F being delivered in August 1957. Among other modifications compared with the straight-winged F-84 models were an upward-opening instead of rearward-sliding cockpit canopy; twin under-fuselage perforated airbrakes instead of a single unperforated brake; leading-edge wing slats; and power-assisted flying controls. Further improvements appeared in successive production batches of the F-84F, these including an all-moving horizontal tail instead of the original fixed tailplane with elevators. Like the late-model Thunderjets, the Thunderstreak was equipped for in-flight refuelling, although its self-contained fuel capacity (including drop tanks) of 6655 litres (1764 Imp gal) gave it the very respectable ferry range of 3724 km (2314 miles). Normal combat radius was about 1370 km (850 miles).

Of the total built, 1410 Thunderstreaks were allocated to the US Air Force, with whom it equipped 12 wings in mid-1955. Initially, six of these served under Strategic Air Command, but later all 12 operated under Tactical Air Command, until replaced by the supersonic F-100 Super Sabre. The Thunderstreak was recalled briefly to first-line service in 1961, then giving way to F-4C Phantoms and reverting to use by the Air National Guard. The other 1301 Thunderstreaks were allocated under the Mutual Defense Assistance Program to various European NATO air forces: Belgium (two wings), France (five escadres), Germany (five Geschwadern), Greece (six squadrons), Italy (three air brigades), the Netherlands (six squadrons) and Turkey (six squadrons). Those of the French Armée de l'Air became the only Thunderstreaks to be used in combat when they were deployed in the Middle East during the 1956 Suez invasion, attacking Egyptian airfields from bases in Israel and Cyprus.

Span: 10.24 m (33 ft 7 in) *Length:* 13.21 m (43 ft 4 in) *Gross weight:* 11 442 kg (25 226 lb) *Maximum speed:* 1059 km/h (658 mph)

Tiger

British battlecruiser. *Tiger*, of the 1911-12 Programme, was a modified version of the immediately preceding British battlecruiser *Queen Mary*. However, the alterations made to the original design were such as to make *Tiger* a substantial improvement on the previous ship both in military qualities and appearance. This largely resulted from the adoption of two features already applied to the battleship designs of the 1911-12 Programme (the *Iron Duke* Class), namely the substitution of a secondary battery of 6-in (152-mm) guns for 4-in (102-mm) and the fitting of two extra submerged torpedo tubes in an after torpedo room. The 6-in guns, besides providing greatly improved defence against destroyers, effectively increased the height of the side armour by one deck as the battery was protected by 152-mm and 127-mm (5-in) armour which was extended from the A turret to abaft Q turret, between the main side armour and the forecastle deck. The provision of an after torpedo room necessitated a rearrangement of the internal layout and resulted in the most marked modifications of the design, as the midship turret was moved to a position between the after boiler room and the engine room and was thus abaft all three funnels instead of between the 2nd and 3rd funnel. Besides giving the turret a clear arc of fire across the stern the resultant well-balanced layout of three equally sized and spaced funnels amidships, combined with a single mast forward and a main armament disposed fore and aft, gave her an elegant appearance which sharply contrasted with the ungainly profile of *Queen Mary*. In other respects the ship's structural arrangements and protection followed that of her predecessor except that she carried an additional strip of 76-mm (3-in) armour below water, along the lower edge of the side armour, as protection against shells going under the belt. To compensate for the added weight of the 6-in guns and their armour the beam was increased by 0.45 m (1 ft 6 in), and the ship was some 1500 tons heavier than her predecessor. The original design provided for a speed of 28 knots with 85 000 shp but at an early stage the machinery design was modified to allow an overload power for short periods up to 108 000 shp for a speed of 30 knots. On trials she made 29 knots with 104 635 shp, but these were run in shallow water and better results were obtained in service. She was often credited with greatly exaggerated speeds, as much as 35 knots being quoted, but this was pure propaganda and it is unlikely she exceeded her designed

speed by more than a fraction of a knot.

Tiger was laid down at John Brown's yard in Clydebank on June 20, 1912, launched on December 15, 1913, and completed in October 1914. After trials she joined the Battlecruiser Squadron of the Grand Fleet with which she operated throughout the First World War. She saw action at the Battles of Dogger Bank, in January 1915, and Jutland, in May 1916, and was damaged on both occasions, being hit by three shells in the former and 21 in the latter action. Apart from the casualties involved the damage received was not serious, although that received at Jutland was extensive and involved one month under repair. After Jutland 25-mm (1-in) protective plating was added on the decks around magazines and on the turret roofs; searchlight towers and an aircraft flying-off platform on Q turret were fitted during 1917-18, and the bridgework and foretop were enlarged. At the end of the war a topmast was added to the derrick post forward of the 3rd funnel. Wartime additions added about 400 tons to the ship's displacement.

Tiger served with the Battlecruiser Squadron of the Atlantic Fleet from 1919 until May 1922 when she began an extensive refit to make her suitable for service as a seagoing gunnery-training ship. Alterations and additions included fitting four single 4-in AA guns and an experimental AA control system, replacing her derrick post with a full mainmast and converting her boilers from coal and oil firing to oil firing only. On completion of the refit in February 1924 her standard displacement was 28 880 tons and her full load displacement 33 220 tons. She served as a training vessel until 1929 when she rejoined the Battlecruiser Squadron. She was paid off in 1931 and sold for scrap in the following year.

Displacement: 28 500 tons (load), 33 260 tons (full load) *Length:* 214.6 m (704 ft) oa *Beam:* 27.6 m (90 ft 6 in) *Draught:* 9.8 m (32 ft) *Machinery:* 4-shaft direct-drive turbines, 108 000 shp=30 knots *Protection:* 229-152 mm (9-6 in) sides, 229-203 mm (9-8 in) barbettes, 229-89 mm (9-3.5 in) turrets, 76-25 mm (3-1 in) decks *Armament:* 8 13.5-in (343-mm) (4×2); 12 6-in (152-mm) (12×1); 2 3-in (76-mm) AA (2×1); 4 21-in (53-cm) torpedo tubes (submerged) *Crew:* 1110

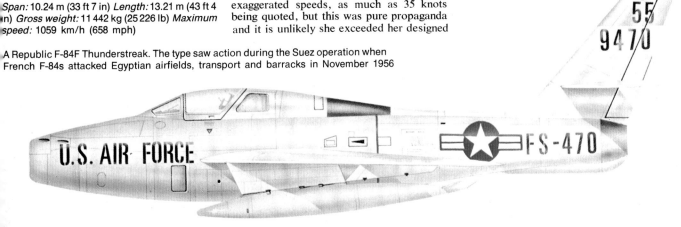

A Republic F-84F Thunderstreak. The type saw action during the Suez operation when French F-84s attacked Egyptian airfields, transport and barracks in November 1956

Tiger

HMS *Tiger*. Refitted in the late 1960s she was nicknamed 'Liger' since equipment from HMS *Lion* was used by Devonport dockyard in the refi

Tiger

British cruiser class. The three ships of the *Tiger* Class, *Tiger* (built by John Brown), *Blake* (built by Fairfield) and *Lion* (built by Scotts), were originally authorized in 1941 as *Minotaur* (modified *Fiji*) Class cruisers. *Tiger* was laid down in 1941 and her two sisters in the following year, but their construction was not pressed and by the end of the war only *Lion,* launched in September 1944, had entered the water. *Tiger* and *Blake* were progressed sufficiently to allow their launch at the end of 1945 in order to clear their building slips, and all three were subsequently laid up until sufficient funds became available for their completion. In the meantime the opportunity was taken to completely redesign the ships as fully as possible to incorporate the lessons of the war together with the latest advances in armament, fire control, radar, etc. Postwar austerity seriously hampered the development of this latter equipment which, combined with the general run-down in design facilities and available finance, delayed the completion of the design until well into the 1950s; it was not until 1955 that work on the three ships was recommenced. *Tiger* was finally completed in 1959, *Lion* in 1960 (by Swan Hunter) and the *Blake* in 1961, by which time their value had considerably diminished. In place of the original armament of three triple 6-in (152-mm) and five twin 4-in (102-mm) mountings they carried two twin 6-in, one in A position and one in X, and three twin 3-in (76-mm), one in B position and one on each side amidships. The design of these guns originated from the latter years of the war and although they would have been very advanced weapons in the late 1940s, when they should have appeared, they were nearing obsolescence by the early 1960s. Both the 6-in and 3-in were fully automatic dual-purpose weapons with a rate of fire of 20 rds/min and 80 rds/min respectively, requiring very large magazines. Each mounting was provided with its own fully stabilized radar-controlled director, two being fitted on the bridge, two abreast the funnels and one aft. Other variations from original design included slightly more powerful machinery which compensated for an 800-ton increase in weight, a completely new superstructure with a large fully enclosed bridge, lattice masts and funnel caps and the provision of defences against nuclear and biological attack. At the

time of their completion they were criticized for their comparatively small armament, but their volume of fire was such that another 6-in turret would only have served to empty the magazines more quickly. In any case the whole design was very space- and weight-critical, and such an addition would not have been possible without accepting a serious loss in efficiency.

Their primary roles were originally envisaged as providing defence against aircraft and surface vessels for convoys and aircraft carriers, and shore support for amphibious landings. But they were not ships of the missile age and it was clear that their value in the former role would rapidly diminish unless they were re-equipped, although for the latter they were among the few modern vessels in the fleet big enough to provide adequate command facilities. Within a few years of their completion it was therefore decided to convert all three ships to command/helicopter cruisers. Apart from the usual modernization of electronic equipment, this involved replacing the after turret and superstructure with a large hangar and raised flight deck to accommodate four A/S helicopters. In addition, the beam 3-in mountings were replaced by two quadruple Seacat missile launchers and, to provide the steadiest possible flight deck, stabilizers were also fitted. The resultant ships, although still dated, can provide command, A/S and AA facilities either at sea or off a beachhead while their helicopters can also be employed to carry troops or stores ashore in support of amphibious landings. The conversion of *Blake* was carried out during 1965-68 and that of *Tiger* during 1969-72. *Lion* was to have followed, but her refit was cancelled and she has been scrapped.

Displacement: 9630 tons (standard), 11 700 tons (full load) *Length:* 169.3 m (555 ft 6 in) oa *Beam:* 19.5 m (64 ft) *Draught:* 6.2 m (20 ft 6 in) *Machinery:* 4-shaft geared steam turbines, 80 000 shp=31.5 knots *Protection:* 89 mm (3.5 in) side, 51-32 mm (2-1.25 in) decks, 76-38 mm (3-1.5 in) turrets *Armament:* 4 6-in (152-mm) (2×2); 6 3-in (76-mm) (3×2) *Crew:* 716

Tiger I

German tank. Judged by the standards of the late 1970s the Tiger I was a crude tank. With its vertical armour and sharp angles it had many shock traps, it was slow, maximum cross country speed being only 20 km/h (12

mph) and the turret traversed slowly by hand (720 turns for 360°) and rather erratically under hydraulic power. For rail or road transport special preparations were necessary due to the 3.15 m (10 ft 4 in) width of the tank—this went up to 3.73 m (12 ft 3 in) when the battle tracks were fitted for cross-country driving.

Despite these deficiencies the Tiger enjoyed a reputation with Allied tank crews which became legendary. Its most notable feat in the West was the single-handed attack by Oberstürmfuhrer Michel Wittmann on June 13, 1944, who destroyed 25 vehicles of the British 7th Armoured Division and stopped the advance on Caen. Like the T-34 and Panther, the Tiger had its day and in the years 1942-44 its thick armour and powerful 8.8-cm (3.46-in) KwK 36 were universally feared.

Work on a heavy tank which began before the war produced designs, one of which was built as the cumbersome NbFz Neubaufahrzeug or New Construction Vehicle of 1934. The Henschel engineers introduced interleaved road wheels for the VK. (*Vollkettenkraftfahrzeug*) 3001 (H) fully tracked experimental vehicle which was deployed as an SP gun in the USSR in 1942. While this work was in progress an order was placed for a VK. 3601, a 36-ton tank. This was followed in May 1941 by an order for a VK.4501, a 45-ton tank with an 8.8-cm gun. With the order came the stipulation that a prototype was to be ready for a demonstration on Hitler's birthday on April 20, 1942.

On the day Henschel and Porsche both produced models and after the trials the Henschel tank was accepted. It incorporated the best features of the VK.3001 (H) and the VK.3601(H) and in August 1942 received the designation Panzerkampfwagen VI Tiger Ausf H; two years later this designation was changed to Ausf E. Between August 1942 and August 1944 some 1350 Tigers were built.

The Tiger I was initially fitted with triple overlapping and interleaved rubber-tired steel disc wheels. In later models this was changed to steel-tired internally sprung wheels. This configuration gave good weight distribution and a notably smooth and stable ride for a tank weighing 56 tons. This was achieved by eight independently sprung torsion-bar axles supporting the wheels on each side. There were two types of track, a 724-mm (28.5-in) combat track and a 521-mm (20.5-in) track for transportation. The outer wheels were removed when the tank was nning on its narrow track and near the front e crew had a back-breaking job of fitting e wheels and new track. The disc wheels ere fine in dry, firm conditions, but in the ud and snow of the USSR they could get ogged and become jammed.

The steering was developed from the Brit- h Merritt-Brown system, a clutch and brake pe but with a gearbox with eight forward tios.

The Tiger I could wade to a depth of 1.22 m ft), though the first 495 vehicles were uipped for total submersion to a depth of 96 m (13 ft) with a snorkel and rubber aling rings for hatches, the turret ring and n apertures. The Tiger could stay under ater for 2½ hours when it had been prepared, d a bilge pump could be used to pump out y water that penetrated the sealing rings.

The hull layout was in four compartments, e forward pair housing the driver and hull achine-gunner/radio operator, the central hting compartment and the engine to the ar. The substantial breech of the 8.8-cm n divided the fighting compartment in two, hile the engine was behind a large bulkhead. he ammunition was stowed in bins on either de of the turret and under the floor decking ith additional rounds by the driver. A total 92 rounds of mixed HE and APCBC could e carried.

The gunner had a TZF 9b binocular tele- cope, while the later models of the Tiger ceived a Panther-type cupola for the com- ander with six episcopes.

Variants of the Tiger I included the 38-cm 5-in) Raketenwerfer 61 auf Sturmmörser iger. The Pz Bef Wg Tiger Ausf E, a ommander's version, was a gun tank less its oaxial machine-gun and ammunition with 26 ounds of 8.8-cm ammunition stowed. The ace saved was filled with two extra radio ts, one for ground-air co-operation and a ar divisional link. The crew were cross- ained as radio operators and gunners, load- rs or hull machine-gunners. A field conver- on to an ARV was also found.

iger I [H]) *Weight:* 56 tons *Length:* 6.3 m (20 8 in) *Width:* 3.73 m (12 ft 3 in) *Height:* 2.87 m (9 5 in) *Armour thickness:* 110-26 mm (4.3-1.02) *Armament:* 1 8.8-cm (3.46-in) KwK 36; 2 7.92- m (0.312-in) machine-guns *Powerplant:* aybach V-12 cylinder water-cooled gasoline, 0 bhp at 3000 rpm *Speed:* 37 km/h (23 mph) ad *Range:* 117 km (73 miles) road *Crew:* 5

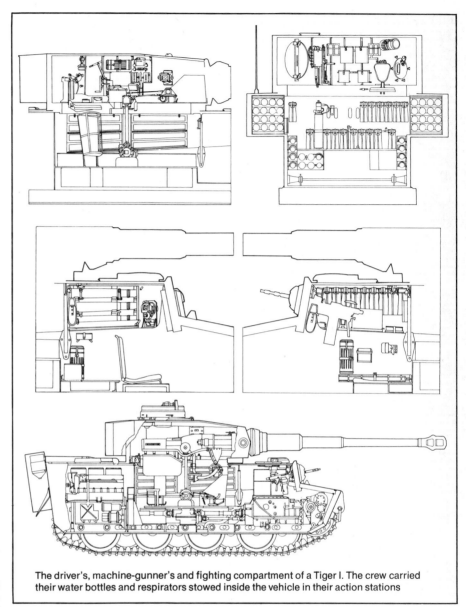

The driver's, machine-gunner's and fighting compartment of a Tiger I. The crew carried their water bottles and respirators stowed inside the vehicle in their action stations

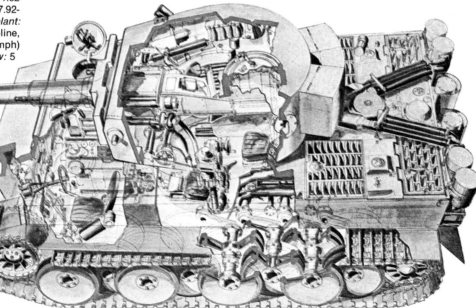

he PzKpfw VI Tiger was heavily rmoured and mounted an 8-cm (3.46-in) gun which was ore than capable of estroying Allied tanks and very ffective against Soviet armour. igers were always welcome hen they appeared in the front ne with German forces and ecause of this and the near nvulnerability of their vehicles e morale of Tiger crews was ormally very good

Tiger, Grumman F11F

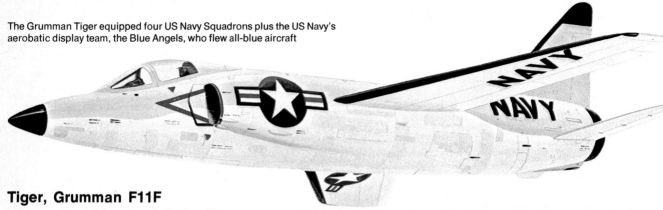

The Grumman Tiger equipped four US Navy Squadrons plus the US Navy's aerobatic display team, the Blue Angels, who flew all-blue aircraft

Tiger, Grumman F11F

US carrier-based fighter aircraft. Designed in the early 1950s, the Tiger was ordered by the US Navy in April 1953 under the designation F9F-9, implying that it was a further development of the straight-winged Panther and swept-wing Cougar. But any connection between those two fighters and the Tiger was a tenuous one, and the new design had an area-ruled fuselage and an afterburning engine in a bid for a substantial supersonic performance. The first prototype flew on July 30, 1954, originally with a non-reheat Wright J65-W-7 turbojet, flights with an afterburner fitted beginning six months later with the second prototype. The production designation was regularized as F11F-1 in April 1955, and these were built in two batches, 157 aircraft in the second batch having longer noses than the first 42 to accommodate a radar scanner. Armament consisted of four 20-mm (0.79-in) cannon in the underside of the forward fuselage, and two/four Sidewinder infrared homing AAMs on underwing launchers.

First Tiger deliveries were made in March 1957, to Squadron VA-156, and the type eventually equipped four Pacific and two Atlantic Fleet squadrons, plus the US Navy's Blue Angels aerobatic display team, though the Tiger proved a disappointing performer. There were recurrent problems with the 4763-kg (10 500-lb) st J65-W-18 engine, with which the fighter could only reach Mach 1.35; and the intended nose radar was never installed, limiting its use to that of a clear-weather day fighter only. It began to be transferred to training units in 1959, less than a year after production ended, though the Blue Angels kept their Tigers until 1969. After 1962 the designation was changed to F11A.

In an attempt to overcome the engine problems, two more Tigers were built, these being designated F11F-1F and powered by a General Electric J79-GE-3A reheat engine that made a Mach 2 performance possible. This Super Tiger version was evaluated by Japan, but was eventually rejected in favour of the Lockheed F-102 Starfighter.

Span: 9.63 m (31 ft 7 in) *Length:* 14.3 m (46 ft 11 in) *Gross weight:* 10 052 kg (22 160 lb) *Maximum speed:* 1432 km/h (890 mph)

Tiger II, Northrop Improved F-5E version of US tactical fighter   See **F-5**

Tigercat, Short

British surface-to-air missile. Tigercat uses the same missile as the naval Seacat system, from which it was developed. Between

Sporting suitable insignia Grumman F11F-1 Tigers of the US Navy Sqdn VF-21 in flight in 1958 Despite its clean and attractive lines the Tiger proved a disappointing aircraft in service

October 1955 and June 1957 Shorts fired a number of GLTV test vehicles to prove that command-link guidance was viable for Seacat, and both the British Army and Royal Air Force Regiment (which, like the Royal Navy, were seeking to replace their Bofors 40-mm [1.57-in] guns) studied this early work. The manufacturer submitted proposals for a land-based system in early 1958, but it became evident that such a weapon could not meet the army's requirement for a short-range surface-to-air missile to defend a complete area rather than individual points. The RAF Regiment's need to protect an airfield was, however, much more compatible with the RN's concept of point defence. Both the army and RAF Regiment were nevertheless attracted by the weapon's simplicity, and its need for fewer men than a comparable gun, and the RAF were also greatly impressed by its air-portability.

The army pressed ahead with its area-defence requirement, which crystallized in 1959 with the issue of design-study contracts which eventually led to the BAC PT428 project being adopted. When this was cancelled in 1961 it was replaced by the General Dynamics Mauler, and when this in turn was abandoned, Shorts again proposed Tigercat to the RAF Regiment and offered to contribute to development costs. A contract to supply Tigercat to the RAF Regiment was let

in November 1966, the service fired its first rounds a year later and all equipment had been delivered by March 1968.

Firing trials carried out by the West German army in 1965, with Tigercat mounted on a combined 40-mm gun/missile launcher controlled by a Contraves Fledermaus fire director, did not lead to an order. In mid-1966, however, the Imperial Iranian Air Force placed the first export contract for the system, which has since been followed by orders from countries such as India, Jordan, Qatar and Argentina.

A Tigercat fire unit comprises a three-round lightweight launcher which is towed by a Land Rover or similar vehicle, a trailer-mounted controller's station towed by another vehicle, missiles and other equipment carried in the vehicles, and five men. Tigercat is normally steered manually by the operator, who sights his target through a pair of binoculars and issues commands using a joystick. A radar tracker such as the Marconi ST850 can be added to the system for operation at night or in bad weather. By the end of 1978 Tigercat had been replaced by Rapier surface-to-air missiles in the RAF Regiment, but remained in service overseas.

Length: 1.47 m (4 ft 10 in) *Span:* 66 cm (2 ft 2 in) *Diameter:* 19 cm (7.5 in) *Weight:* 68 kg (150 lb) *Range:* 5 km (3 miles) *Warhead:* continuous-rod

The Grumman Tigercat was unusually large for a carrier-borne aircraft. It had a heavy cannon and machine-gun armament and could carry bombs or napalm in a close-support role, or a torpedo or drop tank

Tigercat, Grumman F7F

US Navy carrier-based fighter-bomber. This big single-seater, Grumman's largest piston-engined shipborne fighter, was ordered in June 1941 to operate from the *Midway* Class aircraft carriers. The first of two XF7F-1 prototypes made its initial flight on November 3, 1943; 500 were ordered as close-support aircraft for marine corps squadrons, though only 34 were delivered to the original F7F-1 standard, beginning with squadron VMF-911 in April 1944. There followed a prototype and (from November 1944) 65 production F7F-2N two-seat night fighters; 189 F7F-3 single-seaters from March 1945, with twin 2100-hp R-2800-34W Double Wasp radials (instead of the -22Ws in the F7F-1); and, in 1946, two more two-seat night-fighter models, the F7F-3N (60 built) and F7F-4N (13 built).

Armament varied, from four 20-mm (0.79-in) wing and four 0.5-in (12.7-mm) nose guns in the F7F-1 and -3, to four wing guns only in the night fighters. The close-support models could carry up to 454 kg (1000 lb) of bombs under each wing, or a torpedo or drop tank under the fuselage. A 44-cm (17.5-in) longer nose, with radar, and an enlarged vertical tail, characterized the F7F-3N and -4N; the latter was, in the end, the only model fitted with deck arrester gear, since most Tigercats operated from shore bases.

The Tigercat saw no operational service before VJ-Day. Postwar, it served chiefly in the Pacific, Japan and China before giving way to jet-driven replacements, the last being F7F-3N/4Ns with VJ-62. Some aircraft were modified to F7F-3E or photo-reconnaissance F7F-3P standard.

(F7F-3) Span: 15.7 m (51 ft 6 in) *Length:* 13.82 m (45 ft 4 in) *Gross weight:* 11 666 kg (25 720 lb) *Maximum speed:* 700 km/h (435 mph)

Tigerfish

British torpedo. The Tigerfish or Mk 24 torpedo, formerly codenamed Ongar, is a submarine-launched acoustic homing torpedo developed by the Marconi Space and Development Systems company for the Royal Navy. Like the earlier Grog, or Mk 23, it is wire-guided during the initial phase of its run, the wire being paid out from both the submarine and from a dispenser in the torpedo's tail, thus enabling the submarine to have freedom of movement during the guidance run while at the same time reducing the likelihood of a break in the wire. The torpedo carries its own miniature fire-control system which receives information from the parent submarine's own fire-control system throughout the guidance phase. Once the acoustic homing of the torpedo takes over, the information given from this is passed to the torpedo's fire-control computer which controls the final approach to the target.

A practice version is available with positive buoyancy at the end of the run for recovery, rechargeable batteries, and a package of analysis instrumentation. The normal warhead carries a proximity/impact fuze. The Tigerfish is thought to have a range of 11 000 m (12 000 yards), which is an improvement on the Mk 23. The Mod 0 is being replaced by the Mod 1.

Tiny Tim, CIT

US air-to-surface rocket. The incongruously named Tiny Tim—it was an extremely large and powerful weapon—was developed by the California Institute of Technology during the last stages of the Second World War specifically for use against Japanese pillboxes, bunkers and large ships. Early difficulties were encountered with launching the weapon, and on its first airborne firing the rocket destroyed its launch aircraft and killed the crew. Experiments with retractable launchers and wing-mounted zero-length rails were abandoned in late 1944 in favour of an arrangement using standard bomb racks, the rocket dropping free before its motor ignited. Four blocks of solid propellant, each weighing 18 kg (40 lb), burnt simultaneously and exhausted through 24 nozzles, producing a total of 13 600 kg (30 000 lb) thrust for one second. Several squadrons of US Navy Grumman F6F Hellcats armed with Tiny Tim were deployed aboard carriers in the Pacific from early 1945, and the weapon proved extremely effective. Tiny Tim also served in Korea, arming the AD Skyraider and other types.

Length: 3.12 m (10 ft 3 in) *Diameter:* 29.8 cm (11.7 in) *Weight:* 582 kg (1284 lb) *Speed:* 275 m/sec (900 ft/sec) *Warhead:* 270 kg (590 lb), including 68 kg (150 lb) of TNT

A British Mk 24 Tigerfish torpedo being tested before leaving the Marconi factory in 1970

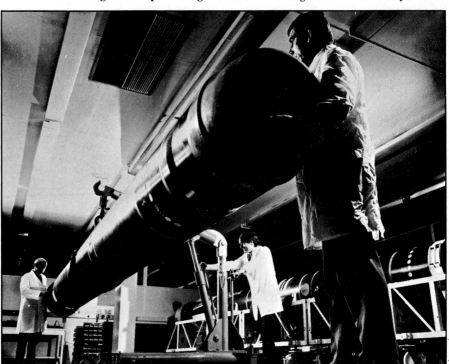

Marconi

Tirpitz

Foto Drüppel

The German battleship *Tirpitz* with her guns elevated to port. She was attacked by the Fleet Air Arm, Royal Navy and RAF and finally capsized by RAF Lancasters in Tromsö Fjord

Tirpitz

German battleship. Identical in most respects to her sister-ship *Bismarck*, the career of *Tirpitz* was, to all intents and purposes, as long and unadventurous as her sister's was brief and glorious. But this would ignore the practical achievements of the two ships, one of which stimulated a ten-day convulsion in the Royal Navy in Home and Atlantic Waters. It ended in the exchange of one old and unmodernized battlecruiser for a brand-new battlecruiser, while the other forced the Royal Navy to keep two battleships, a carrier and supporting fleet units in waters where they were not otherwise needed for a period of nearly three years, simply by occupying threatening positions in Norwegian fjords.

Tirpitz was laid down at the Wilhelms-haven Marinewerft in October 1936, launched on April 1, 1937, and completed for sea trials on February 25, 1941. She differed from her sister-ship in minor ways, such as her aircraft hangar and crane arrangements and the addition of two quadruple torpedo-tube mountings for use against merchant ships. Trials and work-up in the Baltic, with defect rectification at Kiel, occupied seven months and not until September 20, 1941, was she declared to be operational.

She was almost immediately despatched on her first mission—an uneventful cruise off the Aland Islands, at the mouth of the Gulf of Finland, between September 26-29, to guard against a possible break-out by the Soviet fleet from Leningrad. Thereafter, *Tirpitz* remained in the Baltic, exercising, until January 12, 1942, when she left Kiel to proceed to Trondheim via the Kiel Canal. Like her sister ship, she was never to return to Germany.

Tirpitz' prime role was to disrupt Allied sea communications with north Russia, by direct action or by the threat of interception of the convoys bound for Murmansk and Archangel. Her only full sortie for this purpose began on March 6, 1942, when she left Trondheim to intercept the Murmansk-bound convoy PQ 12. Sighted and reported by British submarines shortly after leaving her base, the German battleship and her three screening destroyers failed to find the con-

voy, which had been diverted by the Admiralty away from its planned route. Tracked intermittently by means of decoded radio signals, *Tirpitz* was attacked and only narrowly missed by aircraft from the carrier *Victorious*, off Narvik on March 9.

Tirpitz achieved her major success against the convoys in early July 1942, simply by moving from Trondheim to Altenfjord, in the far north of Norway, where her presence close to the route of convoy PQ 17 led to the Admiralty's order to scatter the merchant ships on July 4. *Tirpitz* did not sail until July 5 and was reported three times and attacked once by a Soviet submarine during a sortie which lasted less than 12 hours: she had no direct part in the sinking of the 24 Allied ships lost from the convoy.

Although she never again stirred to attack a convoy, the threat of her intervention obliged the Royal Navy to maintain at least two capital ships and a fleet carrier in Home Waters, to protect the convoys and to guard against a foray into the North Atlantic. In October 1942, an attempt to attack her at Trondheim using human torpedoes (Chariots) came to nothing with the accidental loss of the weapons within 8 km (5 miles) of *Tirpitz'* berth, where she was at that time refitting.

Tirpitz became operational once again at the end of January 1943 and in March she was moved to Altenfjord which became her permanent base for the next 19 months. Here she was joined by *Scharnhorst* and the pocket-battleship *Lützow*: great events were afoot elsewhere during the spring and summer of 1943 and the Home Fleet 'heavies' were detached to the Mediterranean, so that the sailing of the Soviet convoys was suspended until November 1943, leaving the powerful German squadron with no targets. At last, in early September, *Tirpitz* and *Scharnhorst* were found employment, although the bombardment of almost-defenceless Spitzbergen was hardly a worthy task for these fine ships. They were at sea from September 6-9, and this fifth offensive sortie was to be *Tirpitz'* last, for on September 22, two British midget submarines laid explosive charges which caused extensive shock damage to the main machinery and gunnery systems.

Repairs were undertaken in situ—remarkable engineering achievement—but a she was getting underway to begin trials o April 3, 1944, she was attacked by 40 Hom Fleet Barracuda dive-bombers and exten sively damaged. Further attacks in July an August, by which time she had been repaire again, inflicted only minor damage.

The Royal Air Force had made unsucces ful attacks on *Tirpitz* at Kiel in 1941 and a Trondheim in March and April 1942, but no until the autumn of 1944 did Bomber Com mand have the right combination of aircraf (Avro Lancaster), weapon (5443-kg [12 00(lb] Tallboy bomb) and stabilized automati bomb sight to make a raid at such a distance profitable undertaking. On September 15, 2 Lancasters took off from a Soviet airfield an scored one direct hit with a 12 000-pdr whic hit right forward and caused extensive dam age over the 36-m (118-ft) section abaft th bows.

Repairs to such severe damage wer impossible in Norway and on October 15 an 16, *Tirpitz* proceeded under her own steam t an anchorage near Tromsö, where she was t form part of the fixed defences, as a floatin battery. Tromsö was within range of bomber based in northern Scotland and she wa attacked by 32 Lancasters on October 29, thi attack achieving only one near-miss. The en came on November 12, 1944: 29 Lancaster obtained three hits and a very near mis between B and C turrets, opening the mid ships port side from the keel to the waterlin and causing *Tirpitz* to capsize 11 minute after the first bomb had been released. Ove 1000 of her crew were lost with her.

Displacement: 41 700 tons (standard), 53 50 tons (full load) *Length:* 250.5 m (821 ft 10 in) o *Beam:* 36 m (118 ft 1 in) *Draught:* 11 m (36 1 in) *Machinery:* 3-shaft geared turbine 163 000 shp=31.1 knots *Armament:* 8 38-cm (1 in) (4×2); 12 15-cm (5.9-in) (6×2); 16 10.5-cr (4.1-in) AA (8×2); 16 3.7-cm (1.46-in) AA (16×1 16 2-cm (0.8-in) AA (16×1); 64 2-cm AA (16×4 (added 1942-43); 8 53.3-cm (21-in) torped tubes; 4 aircraft *Crew:* 1905

Titan, Martin

US intercontinental ballistic missile. Tita was originally planned as a back-up to th Convair Atlas to ensure that unforesee difficulties would not prevent the Unite States Air Force from deploying at least on type of ICBM. In the mid-1950s missil designers had little experience of separatin stages at altitude and igniting the second stage engines, so Atlas used a conservativ 'one-and-a-half-stage' approach: the propel lant tankage remained fixed, but two of th three main engines were jettisoned during th flight, together with some structure, thereb avoiding the problem of starting a larg liquid-propellant rocket motor at hig altitude. Titan, however, was a more ad vanced two-stage vehicle and was thus inhe ently more efficient. Separate teams of cor tractors were assigned to the two ICBMs which were both developed as part o Weapon System 107A; Atlas was designate WS 107A-1, while Titan was WS 107A-2. Th latter missile was larger than its predecesso but was lighter, being built from alloy rathe than stainless steel.

Titan, for which Martin was awarded the development contract in October 1955, benefited from work done both on Atlas and on the Douglas Thor intermediate-range weapon. The first version, Titan 1 (also designated SM-68, for Strategic Missile No 8; or HGM-25A), was designed to be stored in hardened silos but launched from the surface. The type's first flight was made by missile A3, which travelled 640 km (400 miles) down the Atlantic test range from Cape Canaveral in February 1959. The next three missiles were also successes, and the third of these was the first in which the two stages separated. Two more rounds blew up on the pad, but in February 1960 missile B7A—the first to have a powered second stage, with radio-inertial guidance being used to control both stages—successfully flew 4000 km (2500 miles).

Titan was originally planned to carry an all-inertial guidance system developed by American Bosch-Arma, which weighed only 159 kg (350 lb), but in 1958 this had been transferred to the Atlas programme and Titan had in turn been allocated the Bell Telephone Laboratories radio-inertial guidance previously intended for Atlas. The Titan 1 research-and-development phase involved 47 firings from Cape Canaveral, of which 34 were successful, nine partially successful and four failed. The last of these took place in January 1962, and three months later the first Titan unit, the 724th Strategic Missile Squadron, was declared operational at Lowry Air Force Base, Colorado. Each squadron, of which a total of six were deployed at five bases, had nine operational silos with a round in each, plus one spare missile. The nine Titans were spread among three complexes, each with three missile silos, two silos housing the radio-command aerials, a launch-control centre and ancillary services.

Both stages of Titan 1 were powered by rocket engines burning RP-1 (kerosene) oxidized by liquid oxygen; the latter has to be kept at very low temperatures to maintain its liquid state, so Titan 1 had to be supplied with its oxidant immediately before launching and was raised to the surface on a lift during the final stages of countdown. The first stage contained two Aerojet-General LR87-AJ-1 engines, each producing 68 180 kg (150 300 lb) of thrust at sea level; no vernier motors were fitted to the first stage, the main-engine thrust chambers being gimballed to provide control in the yaw, pitch and roll axes. The missile was unguided until ten seconds after its second stage separated, control up to this point being provided by an on-board programmer which locked out radio signals from the ground station. Immediately after launch the programmer commanded the missile to roll onto its target bearing; the roll rate was constant for all missions and always ended at the same time after lift-off, the start of the roll sequence being varied according to the angle through which the Titan had to be turned. Some 20 seconds after leaving the pad the round began to pitch over towards its target, this process continuing until separation of the first and second stages at a speed of 8500 km/h (5700 mph) about two minutes into the flight.

Following shut-down of the first-stage engines, the second stage was separated by four explosive bolts and, after a preset coast-

A US Air Force Titan II ICBM. It has a thermonuclear warhead of at least 10 megatons and a range of 10 100 km (6300 miles)

ing period, the gas generator supplying the turbopump for the second-stage main propulsion engine was started and its exhaust pumped through nozzles to give a clean separation. The Aerojet-General LR91-AJ-1 engine, developing 36 290 kg (80 000 lb) of thrust at altitude, was then ignited and the missile came under the control of the ground-based Western Electric/Remington Rand radio guidance system. This used a single General Electric tracking radar which followed the round in flight; a ground-based computer calculated the commands needed to bring the missile back onto its desired trajectory, and these were transmitted over a radio link. The disadvantages of this system were that it could theoretically be jammed and it precluded salvo launches.

The second stage was steered in pitch and yaw by gimballing the main-engine thrust chamber, with roll control provided by vectoring the vernier nozzles through which the turbopump gas generator exhaust passed out of the missile. When the Titan approached its desired final velocity (about Mach 26) the main second-stage motor was shut down and the exact speed was set up by means of these verniers; the 3640-kg (8000-lb) re-entry vehicle then separated and the spent second stage was retarded by feeding the turbopump exhaust through forward-facing nozzles.

The original re-entry vehicle designed by Avco for Titan 1 was of the heat-sink type made of stainless steel coated with nickel, but in 1959 the company's Research and Advanced Development Division was awarded a contract to develop an ablative nose cone. This design, the Mk 4, was coated with quartz ceramic reinforced with a metal honeycomb structure and contained a heavy thermonuclear warhead with a yield of some eight megatons.

By 1957 the Titan programme had become an important project in its own right rather than merely a back-up for Atlas, and as testing progressed it became obvious that many improvements could be planned without having to worry any further about the feasibility of a two-stage ICBM. Martin accordingly received the go-ahead for the SM-68B Titan 2 (also designated LGM-25C) in June 1960. The new weapon had several major advantages over its predecessor. A combination of non-refrigerated propellants with a specific impulse virtually as good as those used in Titan 1 (262 seconds, compared with 280 seconds) was found, thus allowing the missile to be kept fuelled for long periods and hence reducing reaction time from at least ten minutes to about 60 seconds. These propellants—fuel comprising a half-and-half mixture of anhydrous hydrazine and unsymmetrical dimethyl hydrazine, with nitrogen tetroxide as the oxidant—also had the advantage that they were hypergolic, igniting on contact and thus removing the need for an ignition system. The ability to launch the weapon from the silo bottom rather than first raising it to the surface further contributed to a fast reaction and reduced vulnerability, and improvements to the motors used in both stages—coupled with larger fuel capacity—allowed the maximum range to be increased and the payload to be raised by half. An all-inertial guidance system was at last fitted, and check-out procedures were simplified.

The AC Spark Plug guidance system was tested on seven Titan 1s of the M series, the first of which was launched in July 1961, and two months earlier another Titan 1 had been fired from the bottom of a silo at Vandenberg AFB to ensure that such a launch method was possible. The first Titan 2 flew 8000 km (5000 miles) in March 1962, and the research and development phase was completed with the 33rd mission in April 1964; of these, 24 were successful, eight partially successful and only one a complete failure.

The 570th Strategic Missile Squadron, the first of six nine-missile units to operate Titan 2, had already been deployed at Davis-Monthan AFB in Arizona from June 1963 and was soon joined by the other squadrons. Titan 2, which has remained in service throughout the 1970s, is powered by a pair of first-stage Aerojet-General LR87-AJ-5 rocket motors, each producing 97 540 kg (215 000 lb) of thrust and with gimballed thrust chambers for steering. The single second-stage motor is an Aerojet-General LR91-AJ-5 generating 45 370 kg (100 000 lb) of thrust. Titan 2 carries a General Electric Mk 6 re-entry vehicle containing a thermonuclear warhead with a yield of some ten megatons, together with penetration aids to improve its chances of defeating antiballistic missiles.

(Titan 1) *Length:* 29.9 m (98 ft) *Diameter:* 3.05 m (10 ft) *Weight:* 100 000 kg (220 460 lb) *Range:* 10 100 km (6300 miles) *Warhead:* 8 megatons thermonuclear (approx) in Avco Mk 4 re-entry vehicle

(Titan 2) *Length:* 31.4 m (103 ft) *Diameter:* 3.05 m (10 ft) *Weight:* 136 000 kg (300 000 lb) *Range:* more than 10 100 km (6300 miles) *Warhead:* at least 10 megatons thermonuclear in General Electric Mk 6 re-entry vehicle

TNHP

Czech light tank. The TNHP tank was developed by the Ceskomoravska Kolben-Danek company for entry in a Czech army trial of 1937. It was the culmination of a series of light tank designs which had begun in about 1931. The TNHP entered Czech service in 1938 as the LT-38 and 150 were ordered to be built; the order was delayed and first deliveries began in March 1939. After the German occupation CKD became the Bohmische-Mahrische Maschinenfabrik AG and the new company was instructed to complete the order for supply to the German army as the PzKpfw 38(t) Ausf A.

The tank was an extremely good design, using a modified form of Christie suspension with four large road wheels at each side. The hull was of riveted and bolted construction and the two-man turret carried a 37-mm (1.46-in) gun with a coaxial 7.92-mm (0.312-in) machine-gun; a further 7.92-mm machine-gun was mounted in the hull front plate alongside the driver.

Experience with the Ausf A version showed that the tank was reliable, robust and easy to maintain, and the German army ordered a further 325 in late 1939. These had minor changes to suit German operation, and were known by the Germans as the Ausf B, C and D models.

In November 1940, after experience in France, it was decided to improve the armour protection, and the frontal armour was doubled while turret and side armour was thickened. Vision arrangements for the driver and hull gunner were improved and various other small changes made, and the resulting vehicles were known as the Ausf E and F models; 525 were produced before production ended in October 1941.

The final version was the Ausf G model, of which 90 were made during 1941. The armour was again improved and the hull redesigned to facilitate manufacture by welding instead of riveting. By this time, however, the TNHP design was out of date, and production for tank purposes ceased in June; thereafter the chassis were manufactured for incorporation into a variety of self-propelled gun designs, notably the Marder series.

A variation of the TNHP was the TNH-SV, which was an export version ordered by the Swedish army in 1939. Upon the German occupation, these tanks continued to be buil for the Swedish order but in early 1940 production was diverted to the German army the tank being known as the PzKpfw 38(t) Ausf S; 321 were produced up to June 1942 while the Swedes were granted a licence to build their own, which they called the Striv m/41.

(Ausf G) *Weight:* 9.7 tonnes *Length:* 4.6 m (15 f 1 in) *Width:* 2.14 m (7 ft) *Height:* 2.4 m (7 ft 10 in *Armour thickness:* 50-8 mm (2-0.3 in) *Arma ment:* 1 37-mm (1.46-in); 2 7.92-mm (0.312-in machine-guns *Powerplant:* Praga 6-cylinde gasoline, 150 bhp at 2600 rpm *Speed:* 42 km/l (26 mph) *Range:* 250 km (155 miles) *Crew:* 4

Tojo Allied codename for Nakajima Ki-44 Japanese fighter aircraft See **Ki-44**

Tokagypt

Hungarian semiautomatic pistol. Developed by Femaru es Szerszamgepgyar NV of Budapest in 1958, the Tokagypt in essence is the Soviet Tokarev pistol redesigned to chamber the 9-mm (0.354-in) Parabellum cartridge. Other additions include a safety catch and a one-piece wrap-around plastic butt grip. It was designed to meet an order from the Egyptian government, but after receiving the pistols the Egyptian army decided against them and they were given to the civil police instead. After the first few batches had been delivered the contract was abruptly terminated. There is no technical reason for this, as the pistols are a sound design and well made, so there may well have been political considerations behind the decision. The balance of the production was released to the commercial market and many were subsequently sold in West Germany under the trade name Firebird.

The Czech TNHP as it appeared in German service as the PzKpfw 38(t). It was a very welcome addition to the German armoured forces in 1940 and superior to their light tanks

Calibre: 9 mm (0.354 in) *Ammunition:* 9-mm Parabellum *Weight:* 910 g (2 lb) *Length:* 195 mm (7.7 in) *Barrel length:* 115 mm (4.5 in) *Magazine:* 7-round detachable box *Muzzle velocity:* 350 m/sec (1150 ft/sec)

Tokai Japanese name for Kyushu Q1W maritime patrol aircraft   See **Q1W**

Tokarev

Soviet semiautomatic pistol. This pistol was designed by Feodor Tokarev during the late 1920s and the first version was approved for service as the TT-30 in 1930; the initials stood for Tokarev and Tula, the arsenal in which it was made. Basically it was a Browning design, using the usual swinging-link method of locking the barrel to the slide, but to simplify production and maintenance some small design changes were made. The hammer and lockwork were built into a removable module, making initial assembly and subsequent repair much quicker; the magazine was formed without lips, control of ammunition feed being done by 'lips' formed in the pistol frame; and no safety catch was used, the only safety measure being a half-cock notch on the hammer. The pistol was chambered for the Soviet 7.62-mm (0.30-in) auto-pistol cartridge, a very slight modification to the 7.63-mm Mauser round.

In 1933, however, the design was changed. In the original model the locking ribs were machined on the barrel top, as in the original Browning designs. In order to speed up production, this was changed to two circumferential ribs passing completely round the barrel. The effect was the same, but it meant that the ribs could be cut on the lathe which finish-turned the barrel and did not require a separate milling operation. This model became the TT-33 and completely replaced the TT-30 pattern. It is believed that mass production did not commence until about 1940, but thereafter it was widely used by Soviet forces until the mid-1950s, when it began to be replaced by the Makarov and Stetchkin pistols. A great number were exported to communist countries and copies were also made: in China it was the Model 51; the Polish army had theirs made at Radom arsenal and supplied these to the East German and Czech armies for several years. It has also been made in Yugoslavia as the M57. The only differences between these various models lies in the inscriptions and in the design and spacing of the finger-grip section of the slide.

Two variant models are said to exist but are not known in the West. The TT-R-3 is said to be a training pistol chambered for the 0.22-in (5.6-mm) cartridge, while the TT-R-4 is of 7.62-mm calibre but has an extended barrel and special sights for use as a target pistol.

Calibre: 7.62 mm (0.30 in) *Ammunition:* 7.62-mm Soviet auto pistol *Weight:* 835 g (1 lb 13 oz) *Length:* 195 mm (7.7 in) *Barrel length:* 115 mm (4.5 in) *Magazine:* 8-round detachable box *Muzzle velocity:* 420 m/sec (1380 ft/sec)

Tomahawk, Curtiss RAF name for Curtiss P-40 US fighter aircraft   See **Hawk Model 81**

The Hungarian Tokagypt semiautomatic pistol shows a number of features common to the Soviet Tokarev but fires a 9-mm (0.354-in) Parabellum round from a 7-round magazine

I V Hogg

The Soviet Tokarev was widely used from 1940 to the mid-1950s. It fired a powerful 7.62-mm (0.30-in) round derived from the Mauser round. It was produced in a number of Eastern Bloc countries after the war

I V Hogg

Novosti

A Soviet officer armed with a Tokarev pistol urges his troops into the attack in summer 1941

Tomahawk, General Dynamics

Tomahawk, General Dynamics

US cruise missile. Tomahawk is being developed in several versions to meet United States Navy and USAF requirements for both tactical and strategic cruise missiles for launch from surface ships, submarines, bomber and attack aircraft and ground vehicles. General Dynamics began cruise missile studies in September 1972, and in January 1974 the company was selected to build a number of prototype YBGM-109s to compete with the Vought YBGM-110 in the US Navy's SLCM (sea-launched cruise missile) contest. The GD design was chosen in early 1976 and the first test flight took place in March of that year.

Tomahawk exists in both tactical (antiship) and strategic (land-attack) versions. The AGM-109 TALCM (Tomahawk air-launched cruise missile) was due to take part in a fly-off against the Boeing AGM-86B ALCM-B from the spring of 1979 with the aim of selecting a strategic weapon to arm the USAF Strategic Air Command's B-52G/H Stratofortress bombers. All versions of Tomahawk are powered by a Williams Research F107-WR-100 turbofan producing 272 kg (600 lb) of thrust, although those launched from the surface or submarines additionally carry an Atlantic Research solid-propellant booster which generates 3200 kg (7000 lb) of thrust for six-seven seconds. The strategic variants carry more fuel for the sustainer engine to increase their range.

Cruise missiles have been around since the Second World War V-1s, but one of the major advances which has made possible the new generation of weapons in this class has been the development of small, self-contained yet highly accurate guidance systems. Both Tomahawk and ALCM use the McDonnell Douglas AN/DPW-23 TERCOM (terrain contour matching) system, which is basically a programme for the Litton LC-4516C guidance computer. The missile flies under the continuous control of the Litton inertial-navigation system, but this drifts by up to 900 m (3000 ft) per hour and thus needs updating if the Tomahawk is to achieve the desired accuracy. While the weapon is over the sea it relies entirely on inertial guidance, but once it makes landfall TERCOM comes into operation. A Honeywell APN-194 radio altimeter, which is effective at heights between 15-600 m (50-2000 ft), builds up a profile of the terrain over which the missile is flying. This is then compared with a stored map of the desired flightpath and, once a match is found, the computer can update the inertial navigator. Up to 20 such maps can be stored in the computer's memory, allowing the Tomahawk to zigzag to its target or make a feint off to one side without becoming lost.

The final stages of an attack are carried out with the aid of the SMAC (scene-matching area correlator), which compares the view from the missile with stored images of the target area. In the early models this is done by using film, but stored digital data are expected to replace this mechanically driven arrangement.

Land-attack Tomahawks will carry a W80 thermonuclear warhead with a yield of 200 kilotons, which they will be able to deliver with an accuracy of some 30 m (100 ft) after a flight of any distance; since the guidance is

A Tomahawk SLCM (sea-launched cruise missile) fired by the nuclear submarine USS *Hawkbill*

periodically updated, accuracy does not vary with range.

Tomahawk is also planned to arm nuclear attack submarines and surface ships in the strategic role, the missile being fired from the submarine's normal torpedo tubes or from a two-round launcher on surface vessels. Numerous faults have been discovered during testing, however, and in October 1978 it was announced that both the sea-launched and ground-launched variants of Tomahawk would remain in the research and development stage for the time being rather than entering full production.

The GLCM version is wanted by the USAF's Tactical Air Command to take over some of the nuclear and conventional tasks which are now carried out by manned aircraft, particularly in Europe. The missile would be fired from a four-round launcher mounted on transporter/erector vehicles, four of which would comprise a flight. GLCM could carry a variety of warheads such as the W80 fitted to the land-attack variant, the W70-3 enhanced-radiation type (the 'neutron bomb') or antirunway submunitions. A Tomahawk test round dropped 12 bomblets on a runway during the first trial of such a delivery method, in May 1978, and an operational version could carry up to 80

submunitions. Other proposed payloads for GLCM include jammers, television cameras, infrared sensors and other reconnaissance packages.

The shorter-range antiship variant, which can be launched from surface vessels, submarines or tactical aircraft, carries a modified version of the guidance set used in Harpoon (in place of TERCOM/SMAC) and is fitted with a conventional warhead; this could be the 445-kg (980-lb) type from Bullpup, or a new warhead being developed by the US Naval Weapons Center. The Harpoon-type guidance is augmented by PIDD (passive identification/detection and direction) terminal homer which can identify the desired target from other ships by means of its radar emissions.

Tomahawk's future remains in doubt as long as it suffers from teething problems and competition from ALCM-B in the air-launched role, but the weapon is almost certain to be deployed in at least one application.

Length: 6.4 m (21 ft) *Span:* 2.54 m (8 ft 4 in) *Diameter:* 53 cm (1 ft 9 in) *Weight:* 1440 kg (3175 lb) *Range:* over 2400 km (1500 miles) *Speed:* Mach 0.7 *Warhead:* 200-kiloton W80 thermonuclear

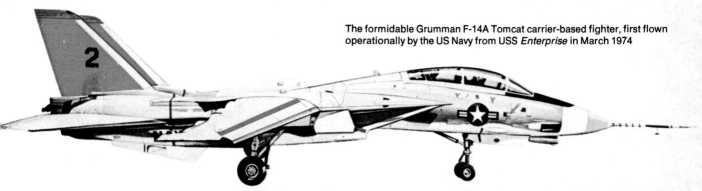

The formidable Grumman F-14A Tomcat carrier-based fighter, first flown operationally by the US Navy from USS *Enterprise* in March 1974

Tomcat, Grumman F-14A

US carrier-based multirole fighter. It was intended in the early 1960s that the F-111B, a variant of the US Air Force's swing-wing F-111A tactical fighter, should be developed to fulfil a carrier-based fleet defence fighter role with the US Navy. During the early development career of the F-111, the naval version persistently proved to be overweight for its chosen role, and after several reprieves the entire F-111B programme was finally cancelled in the summer of 1968. In its place the US Navy decided to go ahead with a replacement Grumman fighter, already in an advanced stage of design, following a competition in which four other designs were considered. The choice of the Grumman F-14 was made in January 1969, and four months later the company had completed a detailed mock-up for US Navy examination. Twelve development aircraft were ordered, and the first of these made its initial flight on December 21, 1970. The programme received a serious blow nine days later when, on only its second flight, the hydraulic systems failed and the aircraft crashed during a landing approach, though the crew ejected safely. After this setback, however, the development programme proceeded smoothly, the second F-14 flying for the first time on May 24, 1971, and the Tomcat became without doubt one of the world's most sophisticated and formidable combat aircraft.

Of variable-geometry ('swing-wing') configuration, with twin vertical tails and powered by a pair of 9344-kg (20 600-lb) st Pratt & Whitney TF30-P-412 afterburning turbofan engines, the Tomcat is unique among VG aircraft in having, in addition to its variable-sweep wings, a smaller, movable foreplane or 'glove vane' sheathed inside the leading-edge roots of the fixed inboard portion of the wings, or 'glove box'. The main outer wings have 20° of sweepback when fully spread, and 68° when swept back; the glove vanes can be extended forward into the airstream as the main wings pivot backwards, to regulate changes in the centre of pressure and prevent pitching. The use of variable-sweep wings enables the Tomcat to adapt its flying configuration to the differing aerodynamic and performance requirements of carrier takeoffs and landings, aerial dog-fighting, and low-level attack missions against surface targets. In a dog-fight, variation of wing sweep can be controlled automatically, providing the aircraft with superb manoeuvrability and enabling the pilot to concentrate on the primary task of shooting down his opponent. Other control surfaces include full-span wing flaps, spoilers and leading-edge slats, and all-

moving horizontal tail surfaces; much of the airframe is made of boron-epoxy or other composites, or titanium. The crew of two sit on tandem-mounted zero-zero ejection seats under an upward-opening bubble canopy.

For close-quarters fighting, the Tomcat (which is an excellent weapon-launching platform) has a built-in M61-A1 multibarrel 20-mm (0.79-in) rotary cannon with 675 rounds under the cockpit on the port side. It can employ this in conjunction with 'snap-shoot' air-to-air missiles such as the AIM-7 Sparrow or the latest-model AIM-9 Sidewinders, the latter being carried on launchers under the glove box on each side. What has made the Tomcat unique, however, is its capability to detect and attack airborne targets while they are still 160 km (100 miles) away. This capability is provided by the powerful Hughes AWG-9 radar mounted in the Tomcat's nose, together with its primary armament of up to six Hughes Phoenix air-to-air missiles. Four of these can be carried on pallets which fit into the semirecessed Sparrow positions under the fuselage, and a further one under each wing glove box, together with two underwing Sidewinders. With a range of more than 200 km (124 miles), the Phoenix is the world's longest-range AAM, and the Tomcat is the only combat aircraft in service to carry it. As already mentioned, the F-14 can be used also in a low-level attack role, the interception missiles then being replaced by up to 6577 kg (14 500 lb) of externally mounted weapons.

Deliveries of the initial F-14A model to the

US Navy began in October 1972, the first two squadrons being VF-1 and VF-2. The first operational sortie, by a VF-2 Tomcat, was flown from the USS *Enterprise* in March 1974, and subsequent acceptance into regular Fleet use was both enthusiastic and uncomplicated until 1976, when engine, structural and other problems came to a head. These have in the main been resolved, one improvement being an increase in reheat thrust to 9480 kg (20 900 lb). Up to early 1979 the US Navy had accepted about 320 of the F-14A model (of an anticipated total of 390), and these now equip more than a dozen navy and marine corps squadrons. On the debit side, excessive escalation of the cost per aircraft has meant the curtailment of two proposed follow-on versions. Only two prototypes have been flown of the F-14B (the first of them on September 12, 1973), these being existing F-14As re-engined with 12 741-kg (28 090-lb) thrust Pratt & Whitney F401-P-400 afterburning turbofans. The F-14C, with these engines plus new avionics and weapons, is unlikely to materialize at all. Meanwhile, Grumman has delivered 80 export F-14As to the Imperial Iranian Air Force, and in 1978-79 the US Naval Air Training Center at Patuxent River, Maryland, was developing a tactical air reconnaissance pod system (TARPS) for the F-14A.

(F-14A) Span: 19.54 m (64 ft 1 in) spread, 11.65 m (38 ft 3 in) swept *Length:* 18.9 m (62 ft) *Gross weight:* 33 724 kg (74 348 lb) *Maximum speed:* Mach 2.34 (2517 km/h [1564 mph])

Grumman

An F-14A from VF-32 Sqn US Navy touches down on a carrier during shipborne landing trials

Tomodzuru

Tomodzuru

Japanese torpedo boat class. With destroyer construction limited under the terms of the 1930 London Naval Treaty, Japan set out to design a new class of torpedo boats which were to take over much of the routine patrol and antisubmarine duties previously carried out by destroyers. The vessels were to be equipped with a heavy armament enabling them under certain circumstances to take on fleet escort duties in place of destroyers, and the requirement stipulated that this should be mounted on the smallest possible hull.

The armament was to consist of two twin 21-in (53-cm) torpedo-tube mountings with protective shields sited amidships, and three 5-in (127-mm) DP guns sited in a twin enclosed mount aft and a single enclosed mount on the forecastle. The displacement was to be not more than 535 tons.

As with many other Japanese designs prepared under naval treaty limitations they attempted too much, and the armament was more than the hull could withstand. On trials the ships were found to displace 696 tons instead of the designed 605 tons, and the stability was found to be suspect. To overcome the problem the ships were fitted with bulges, and the new trials took place at a total displacement of 726 tons. Four ships ordered under the 1931 Programme were completed to this design. A further 16 to the same design had been planned, under the 1934 Programme, but before any of them were ordered *Tomodzuru* capsized in a gale on March 12, 1934. Fortunately she did not sink, and the vessel was towed back to port keel uppermost for extensive repairs and alterations. The accident, widely reported in the international press, immediately caused grave concern to the Japanese who realized that many of their warship designs prepared under the treaty limitations were probably suspect, and feared that a similar fate could befall other vessels. By attempting to follow the letter of the treaties and not build over the displacement limits, while at the same time mounting the heaviest possible armament, they had built ships which were excessively top-heavy.

The lesson was, however, well learnt and the suspect vessels were all extensively rebuilt before the war. The second batch of 16 *Tomodzuru* Class vessels was suspended and the design recast (as the *Ootori* Class), while the four existing *Tomodzuru* Class were rebuilt. The 5-in guns were removed and two single 4.7-in (120-mm) mounts put in their place, while the after bank of torpedo tubes was removed and an extra 4.7-in gun sited in its place. In the original design a complete set of reload torpedoes was carried for the two twin mounts, but as rebuilt only the two torpedoes in the tubes were carried.

Name	completed
Chidori	11/33
Hatsukari	7/34
Manadzuru	11/34
Tomodzuru	2/34

A further reduction in topweight was achieved by reducing the height of the bridge by one deck. The bulges, which had seriously affected the performance, were removed, and extra ballast and a keel added to help lower the centre of gravity and improve stability. With the alterations the vessels re-entered service with a displacement of 775 tons and a maximum speed of 28 knots.

The four ships were extensively employed on escort duties during the Second World War and their A/S capability considerably improved. This was achieved by removing the after 4.7-in mount and the minesweeping gear and adding 48 depth charges. Light AA was also improved, up to 10 25-mm (1-in) twin and single mountings being added.

Three of the class were lost during the war. *Chidori* was sunk by the US submarine *Tilefish* on December 22, 1944, and *Manadzuru* and *Tomodzuru* by naval aircraft on March 1 and March 24, 1945, respectively. *Hatsukari* was surrendered at Hong Kong in August 1945 and subsequently scrapped.

(As designed) *Displacement:* 535 tons (standard) *Length:* 82 m (269 ft) oa *Beam:* 7.4 m (24 ft 3 in) *Draught:* 2 m (6 ft 7 in) (excluding bulges) *Machinery:* 2-shaft geared steam turbines, 11 000 shp=30 knots *Armament:* 3 5-in (127-mm); 1 40-mm (0.79-in); 4 21-in (53-cm) torpedo tubes, 8 torpedoes *Crew:* 113

(As rebuilt) *Displacement:* 600 tons (standard) *Length* and *Beam:* as above *Draught:* 2.7 m (8ft 10 in) *Machinery:* as above *Armament:* 3 4.7-in (120-mm); 1 machine-gun; 2 21-in (53-cm) torpedo tubes, 2 torpedoes *Crew:* as above

Tone

Japanese cruiser. *Tone* was laid down at Sasebo navy yard on November 27, 1905, and was quite distinctive from previous Japanese protected cruisers. She had a much greater freeboard and was designed with a pronounced clipper bow to improve her seakeeping qualities. Although quite different in appearance, the design owed much to the earlier *Otowa*. She was, however, some 9.1 m (30 ft) longer than the *Otowa* and this extra length was put to good use by mounting 16 boilers of the Miyabara type and more powerful Mitsubishi-type engines to give a better speed. An extra gun was mounted on each broadside. The armament was sited similarly to that in *Otowa*, but some time after completion the second 4.7-in (120-mm) mounting on each broadside was removed and subsequently two 3-in (76-mm) AA guns were added.

The design proved most successful, but owing to a government refusal to sanction funds a planned sister ship was never built. *Tone* was launched on October 24, 1907, and completed on May 15, 1910. She was removed from the operational fleet in April 1931 and sunk as a target in April 1933.

Displacement: 3760 tons (standard) *Length:* 113.8 m (373 ft 4 in) wl *Beam:* 14.5 m (47 ft 7 in) *Draught:* 5.1 m (16 ft 9 in) *Machinery:* 2-shaft vertical triple-expansion, 15 000 ihp=23 knots *Protection:* 76-51 mm (3-2 in) deck, 102 mm (4 in) conning tower *Armament:* 2 6-in (152-mm) (2×1); 12 4.7-in (120-mm); 3 21-in (53-cm) torpedo tubes (above water) *Crew:* 401

Tone

Japanese cruiser class. These two vessels, ordered under the 2nd Reinforcement programme of 1934, were planned as to be of an improved *Mogami* design. However, it was felt that to mount five triple turrets, as in *Mogami,* was perhaps a little extravagant and doubts had been expressed concerning stability, and it was therefore decided to mount only four triple 6.1-in (155-mm) turrets.

The Staff requirement specified that the design should provide a powerfully armed cruiser to be employed in a scouting role for the main fleet. The designers therefore decided to mount all the main armament forward of the bridge, leaving clear space aft which could be used as a seaplane operating area. Five seaplane scouts could be carried instead of the usual two or three, and two catapults were positioned on either beam just aft of the mainmast; with alternate takeoffs a continuous launching sequence could be achieved.

Following the completion of *Mogami* certain improvements in the design were found to be necessary, and these were incorporated in the new ships before launching. The designed standard tonnage of 8500 tons was exceeded even though electric welding techniques (which had been considerably improved since *Mogami* was built) were extensively used. *Tone* was laid down in December 1934, but work on *Chikuma* did not start until the following October and she was therefore able to benefit from further improvements in construction techniques and design changes stemming from experience with *Mogami*.

To overcome the stability problems experienced in *Mogami, Tone* had side armour built into the hull internally (rather than in the form of bulges as in *Mogami*) and inclined at an angle of 20° to the vertical. The armour plates were used as construction members to give added strength to the vessels. The internal armour belt tapered as it extended below the waterline.

The preoccupation of Japanese designers with the possibility of accidental torpedo explosions in the tubes on surface ships led them to site the mounts well away from the bridge area and high up on the superstructure where any blast would cause minimal damage. The tubes in the *Tone* Class were therefore mounted fore and aft of the catapults on the upper deck, and one reload torpedo was carried for each of the 12 tubes. Japanese ships had been renowned for their rather spartan accommodation, but this was considerably improved in these two ships.

The two cruisers were still under construction at the Nagasaki works of the Mitsubishi company when the naval treaties expired, and it was therefore decided to provide the ships with a much more powerful armament. The siting of four turrets was retained but 8-in (203-mm) guns in twin turrets were mounted instead of the triple 6.1-in provided for in the original design. This also led to a considerable increase in displacement, and when finally completed the standard displacement was 11 215 tons.

Tone was completed in November 1938, just 12 months after she was launched; *Chikuma* was launched in March 1938 and was completed in May 1939. The vessels saw continuous service during the war, and during 1943 the AA was increased to 20 25-mm (1-in) and after June 1944 to a total of 56 25-mm.

Both ships were present at the last great sea battle off Leyte Gulf in October 1944 and during the action *Chikuma* was torpedoed by US naval aircraft and so severely damaged that she had to be scuttled by the Japanese destroyer *Nowaki* on October 25. *Tone* suffered relatively minor damage during the action but was later damaged in air raids on Kure harbour and finally sank there from accumulated bomb damage on July 24, 1945.

Displacement: 11 215 tons (standard) *Length:* 201.6 m (661 ft 6 in) oa *Beam:* 18.4 m (60 ft 6 in) *Draught:* 6.2 m (20 ft 6 in) *Machinery:* 4-shaft geared steam turbines, 152 200 shp=35 knots *Protection:* 100 mm (4 in) main belt, 64 mm (2.5 in) deck, 76 mm (3 in) turrets *Armament:* 8 8-in (203-mm); 8 5-in (127-mm); 12 25-mm (1-in); 4 13-mm (0.51-in); 12 24-in (61-cm) torpedo tubes (4×3); 5 seaplanes *Crew:* 850

Tony Allied codename for Kawasaki Ki-61 Japanese fighter aircraft   See **Ki-61**

Tornado Swiss APC   See **Mowag**

Tornado, North American B-45

US Air Force tactical bomber. Of the four contenders to become the first US series-built jet bomber the distinction fell upon the B-45 Tornado, although the contemporary B-47 Stratojet was to prove the more significant of the two designs selected for production. The Tornado, of which three XB-45 prototypes were ordered in 1945, was of more orthodox straight-winged configuration, as were the unsuccessful Convair XB-46 and Martin XB-48. All four initially chose the Allison J35 turbojet engine for propulsion, but both the selected bombers were eventually powered instead by the General Electric J47.

A three-seat, all-metal shoulder-wing monoplane, the XB-45 was powered by four J35-A-11 turbojets, each of 1814 kg (4000 lb) static thrust, podded in pairs in long nacelles attached directly to the under-surface of the wings. The high speed of about 805 km/h (500 mph) expected of the aircraft was thought sufficient to enable it to operate without much interference from intercepting fighters, and consequently the defensive armament was confined to a tail installation of two 0.5-in (12.7-mm) Browning machine-guns, radar-directed and fired by the copilot. Normal internal bombload was 3629 kg (8000 lb), but provision was made to carry a single bomb of up to 9979 kg (22 000 lb) if required. By the time that the first XB-45 made its initial flight on March 17, 1947, the air force had placed a contract for 96 production B-45As which differed little from the prototypes. The main points of difference were the provision of a gunner's cockpit in the tail to man the two rear guns, since the gun-laying radar had not been developed in time to be installed; the substitution, before delivery, of four 2359-kg (5200-lb) st General Electric J47-GE-9 turbojets for the prototypes' J35s; and an increase in the basic bombload to 4536 kg (10 000 lb). Deliveries of the B-45A began in 1948, the bomber entering service in November of that

A North American RB-45C Tornado reconnaissance bomber with 12 cameras and extra fuel

(vertical credit:) Rockwell International

year with the 47th Bombardment Group of the USAF and moving with it to Britain in 1952 as part of the US Air Forces Europe.

The intended B-45B, with new radar and fire-control systems, was not built, but North American produced ten examples of the B-45C in 1949, this tactical support version flying for the first time on May 3 that year. The B-45C was powered by 2359-kg (5200-lb) thrust J47-GE-13 or -15 engines, and was fitted with a 4542-litre (999-Imp gal) auxiliary fuel tank on each wingtip, increasing the overall span to 29.26 m (96 ft); maximum speed was maintained at 932 km/h (579 mph), despite a higher gross weight of 51 234 kg (112 952 lb), and the airframe and cockpit canopy were strengthened for low-altitude work. Sixty B-45Cs were ordered, but 50 were then cancelled and the funds allocated instead to the Convair B-36 strategic bomber. However, North American did complete 33 reconnaissance-bomber counterparts of the C model, designated RB-45C; these carried 12 cameras, and the bomb bay was occupied by photoflash bombs and additional fuel tankage. The first RB-45C was flown in April 1950; deliveries began two months later, and were completed in October 1951.

Tornados had been withdrawn from first-line service by mid-1958, but 14 B-45As were converted to TB-45A target tugs, several others became DB-45A or C missile directors, and some were used as engine testbeds.

(B-45A) *Span:* 27.13 m (89 ft) *Length:* 22.96 m (75 ft 4 in) *Gross weight:* 43 344 kg (95 558 lb) *Maximum speed:* 933 km/h (580 mph) at gross weight of 27 624 kg (60 900 lb)

Tornado, Panavia

European multirole combat aircraft. By far the most important military aircraft outside the US and USSR, this programme has had to endure prolonged sniping from the media and from commercial competitors who have foolishly represented it as 'expensive' or 'complicated' or in some other way undesirable. In fact it has been more carefully planned than any other aircraft in history to meet the precise, numerically spelt-out requirements of four modern and capable operators: the Royal Air Force (Britain), Luftwaffe and Marineflieger (West Germany) and Aeronautica Militare Italiano (Italy). It meets all requirements, and exceeds most. It also happens to be smaller than any other aircraft offering remotely similar capability; and it offers total capability unmatched by any aircraft, though figures for reliability and maintenance burden are not readily available at the moment.

Panavia was formed on March 26, 1969, by BAC (now BAe) of Britain, MBB of West Germany and Aeritalia of Italy, to work with the customer organization NAMMO (NATO MRCA Management and Production Organization), MRCA standing for multirole combat aircraft. To produce the engine Turbo-Union was formed by Rolls-Royce (Britain), MTU (Federal Germany) and Fiat Aviazione (Italy). Project definition was complete in July 1970, structural design was complete in August 1972, the first prototype flew in Germany on August 14, 1974, and by late 1978 the basic flight-development programme was almost complete, with more than 3000 hours flown by prototypes 01-09 and pre-series aircraft 11-16 (No 10 is static test).

In some ways the Tornado can be considered an F-111 of a later generation suffering from none of the earlier machine's faults and very much smaller in dimensions (though not in capability). The pilot and navigator (pupil in the trainer variant) sit in tandem Martin-Baker zero/zero seats and have outstanding all-round view. Large lateral ducts with modulated inlets feed the two RB.199-34R-04

Torpedoes

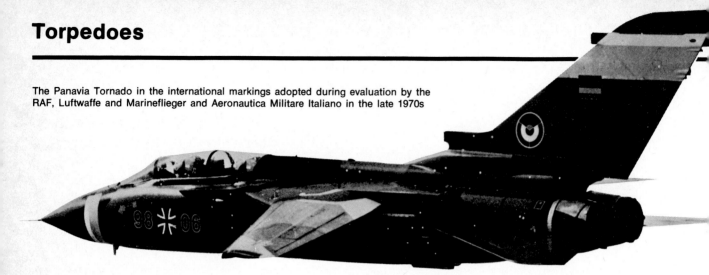

The Panavia Tornado in the international markings adopted during evaluation by the RAF, Luftwaffe and Marineflieger and Aeronautica Militare Italiano in the late 1970s

three-shaft afterburning turbofans, each rated at 7257 kg (16 000 lb) with full augmentation. The variable-profile nozzles incorporate thrust reversers, backing up antiskid brakes for very short landings. Short takeoff is achieved by the spread wing sweep of 25° combined with powerful high-lift devices including powered slats and double-slotted flaps over the entire span. Quad-actuator electrically signalled controls drive tailerons, rudder and spoilers (the latter not used at maximum sweep of 68°). Fuel is carried in Uniroyal fuselage cells and 'wet' swing-wings and fin, with provision for a detachable/retractable flight-refuelling probe on the right side of the nose, 'buddy' refuelling packs and drop tanks up to 1500 litres (330 Imp gal) each under the outer wings.

Normal weapon load is two internal 27-mm (1.06-in) Mauser cannon in the lower fuselage plus up to 8165 kg (18 000 lb) of stores on three twin hardpoints in tandem under the fuselage, two tandem inboard wing pylons and two single outboard pylons. The range of stores is believed to exceed that for any other known combat aircraft, and includes every tactical weapon of the three nations including Kormoran, Aspide 1A, P3T (air-breathing Martel) and all forthcoming laser-guided weapons. Inbuilt electronics surpass those of any known tactical aircraft, the list being too long to reproduce but including Texas Instruments Radpac multimode radar, Ferranti digital inertia navigation and nose laser, Decca 72 Doppler, Litef central computer and very advanced head-up display and cockpit display systems. There are comprehensive defensive electronics including transponders, warning radar and passive ECM. Additional active and passive pods have been carried externally.

Numerous Chiefs of Staff (including Lt-Gen Tom Stafford, USAF Deputy CoS) have flown Tornados and make far more than merely polite comments. On February 3, 1978, Aircraft 12 was delivered to the Aeroplane & Armament Experimental Establishment at Boscombe Down, since joined by others delivered to national test centres, and the emphasis in late 1978 was on completing preparation of the aircrew and ground trades manuals and setting up the three-nation Operational Conversion Unit at RAF Cottesmore and the Anglo-German weapons training unit at Honington. Total production for the basic interdictor/strike (IDS) Tornado for the three nations is 644: 220 for the RAF (designation Tornado GR.1) to replace the Vulcan and Buccaneer from 1981 in 9, 12, 15, 16, 35, 44, 50, 101 and 617 Squadrons; later also replac-

ing Buccaneers in the maritime-strike role; 212 for the Luftwaffe, replacing the F-104G in Jabo 31-34 plus a training unit; 112 for the Marineflieger, replacing the F-104G in MFG 1 and 2; and 100 for the AMI, of which 54 will replace the F-104G and G 91R in 20°, 102°, 154° and 186° Gruppi and 12 will be trainers. Two production orders, for 40 and 110 aircraft, were to be met in 1979-80.

In addition, the RAF is to receive 165 of a maximum-compatability air-defence variant (ADV), designated Tornado F.2, to cover a vast ocean area from Iceland to the Baltic and replace two squadrons of Lightnings and seven of Phantoms. Main features of the F.2 include a fuselage stretch of 1.22 m (4 ft) to give 909 litres (200 Imp gal) extra fuel and allow four Sky Flash missiles to be carried in tandem pairs; only one gun; a new Marconi/Ferranti Foxhunter radar of very high performance, especially in presence of heavy and advanced ECM; uprated engines; drop tanks on inboard wing stations and AIM-9L Sidewinders on inboard outer-wing stations; and fixed inboard wing strakes instead of constant-sweep gloves with Krüger flaps. Commonality with the RAF Tornado GR.1 is approximately 80%. Extensive planning and flight testing of the F.2 systems had been completed by late 1978, and three ADV prototypes were included in the first production batch of 40 aircraft. The first was to fly in early 1979. Before being permitted to buy this version the RAF was required to examine all possible alternatives. Only the F-14 came near the requirement, but was much costlier; the F-15 was closer in price but could not meet the requirement.

Span: (fully spread) 13.9 m (45 ft 7 in); (fully swept) 8.6 m (28 ft 3 in) *Length:* (IDS) 16.7 m (54 ft 9 in), (ADV) 18 m (59 ft) *Gross weight:* (IDS) 26 490 kg (58 400 lb) *Maximum speed:* (clean) over Mach 2 at height (2125 km/h [1320 mph])

Torpedoes

Self-propelled underwater antiship device. The torpedo takes its name from the electric ray known as the torpedo fish, which stuns its prey. The name was first applied by the American David Bushnell to his keg mine in 1776, and for another 100 years was used indiscriminately for mobile, moored and even towed antiship devices. It later became identified with the automotive or 'fish' torpedo, of which only the Whitehead design survived in the twentieth century.

Contrary to popular belief it was the Royal Navy's enthusiasm which got the Whitehead

torpedo off to a flying start in 1869, only a year after Whitehead had perfected an idea he had got from a retired Austrian, Captain Luppis. In the autumn of 1869 Royal Navy officers visited Fiume and inspected Whitehead's works, and as a result the following year the inventor went to England with two models, a 16-in (40-cm) and a 14-in (36-cm). Over 100 firings were carried out in September-October 1870 from a submerged launching tube built into the bows of the old sloop *Oberon*, and finally an old coal hulk was sunk by the 16-in torpedo. In 1870 the Admiralty ordered a production batch of torpedoes, and a year later bought the manufacturing rights for £15 000 to allow production to start at the Royal Laboratories at Woolwich. The torpedo was taken up subsequently by the French, the Germans and the Chinese, and then by all navies.

The first big advance was the heater system, with fuel sprayed into the air vessel and ignited. This produced much more energy, and therefore higher speed and longer range. The 'dry' heater was followed by the 'wet' heater, in which the combustion chamber was cooled by water. The steam thus generated added considerably to the energy, and the term 'steam-driven' was often applied to these torpedoes. Turbines were used in US torpedoes, whereas the British relied on reciprocating engines until the introduction of electric batteries.

Starting in 1920 the British developed a method of enriching the compressed air with oxygen, but it was not popular because of the risk associated with handling liquid oxygen. It was left to the Japanese to perfect a pure-oxygen torpedo, the Type 93 Long Lance, which was without equal in its day. The British abandoned enriched air and developed a very efficient Brotherhood Burner Cycle engine in its place. This was far more efficient than any other conventional torpedo engine, and even at the end of the Second World War the British Mark 8 was only beaten by the German hydrogen peroxide Steinwal on propulsive efficiency.

Hydrogen peroxide proved to be the most promising oxidant, and the electric batteries available in the Second World War were far too heavy to boost running speed. After the war batteries of various types were used in antisubmarine torpedoes, but many modern torpedoes use Otto fuel; high test peroxide (HTP) is still widely used.

US Whitehead torpedoes were driven by cold compressed-air reciprocating engines. The Bliss-Leavitt designs were turbine-driven using hot gases from combustion of

ROYAL NAVY TORPEDOES

Calibre and mark (in/cm)	weight (kg/lb)	warhead (kg/lb)	range m/yards(knots)	notes
14/36	—	8/18	548/600(7)	prototype tested in 1870; 4.3 m (14 ft) long with dynamite warhead
14/36 Mk V	299/660	26/58	548/600(24)	made at Woolwich from 1886, wet guncotton warhead
16/40	—	30/67	548/600(7)	prototype tested in 1870; 4.3 m (14 ft) long with wet guncotton warhead
18/46 Mk I	560/1236	90/198	732/800(30)	actual calibre 17.7-in (45-cm); designed in 1890 and produced by Whitehead at Weymouth. Remained standard RN torpedo until 1918. A Royal Gun Factory version was designated Mk II
18/46 Mk VII	704/1553	91/200	5029/5500(30) 2743/3000(41)	RGF 1908 model for submarines. Warhead increased to 145 kg (320 lb) in 1917. Still in service in the Second World War; one fired in action
18/46 Mk XII	702/1548	176/388	1371/1500(40)	1926 Whitehead Weymouth model for air-dropping, 693 fired in action. Also made by Morris Motors (13 fired) and Royal Naval Torpedo Factory, Greenock (395 fired)
21/53 Mk I	—	—	3200/3500(5)	RGF 1908 model
21/53 Mk II	1267/2794	102/225	9144/10 000(29)	Weymouth model, sold extensively abroad and also made by RNTF; later known as Vickers Weymouth type
21/53 Mk IV	1447/3190	233/515	4572/5000(40)	1917 RNTF model also made at Weymouth; 516 fired in action in Second World War
21/53 Mk VII	1862/4106	336/742	14 630/16 000(33) 13 716/15 000(35) 18 288/20 000(30)	introduced in 1928. World's first oxygen-enriched torpedo using 57% oxygen-air mixture; all converted to air by 1939, 9 fired in action. 8.4 m (25 ft 6 in) long
21/53 Mk VIII	1521/3353	340/750	6400/7000(40) 4572/5000(44.5)	standard Second World War torpedo made by RNTF (1692 fired), Morris (507 fired), Whitehead (1394 fired) and Bliss, US (139 fired). Some still in service in late 1970s
21/53 Mk IX	1692/3731	340/750	12 800/14 000(35) 9144/10 000(40)	for cruisers and destroyers; 109 fired in action
24.5/62.5 Mk I	2398/5287	336/742	13 716/15 000(35) 18 288/20 000(30)	enriched air model for battleships *Nelson* and *Rodney*

US TORPEDOES

Calibre and mark (in/cm)	warhead (kg/lb)	range m/yards(knots)	notes
18/46 Mk 1	—	732/800(30)	Whitehead Mk I; Mks 2 and 3 of 1892 had slight improvements
21/53 Mk 3	—	3660/4000(27)	1904 Bliss-Leavitt design. World's first turbine torpedo; used for battleships
18/46 Mk 4	—	—	1910 submarine torpedo
18/46 Mk 5	—	—	Whitehead type, built by NTS
18/46 Mk 6	—	1830/2000(35)	1910 Bliss-Leavitt type used in destroyers

Torpedoes

18/46 Mk 7	—	7315/8000(27)	introduced 1912 and used throughout First World War
21/53 Mk 8	—	—	1913 design for destroyers
21/53 Mk 9	—	6860/7500(27)	replaced Mk 3 from 1913
21/53 Mk 10	225/497 TNT	3200/3500(36)	used by 'S' Class submarines throughout Second World War
21/53 Mk 11	—	13 700/15 000(27) 5490/6000(46)	submarine torpedo in interwar years
21/53 Mk 12	—	13 700/15 000(27) 6400/7000(42)	contemporary of Mk 11 used in *Farragut* Class destroyers
22.5/57 Mk 13	272/600 TPX	5030/5500(33.5)	standard Second World War aircraft torpedo also used in MTBs
21/53 Mk 14	272/600 TPX	8230/9000(31.5) 4110/4500(46)	standard Second World War submarine torpedo; single-speed (31.5-knot) version designated Mk 23
21/53 Mk 15	363/800 TNT	13 700/15 000(26.5)	standard Second World War destroyer torpedo
21/53 Mk 16	431/950 TPX	10 060/11 000(46)	experimental Second World War peroxide torpedo to replace Mk 14; some in postwar service
21/53 Mk 17	431/950 TPX	16 460/18 000(46)	similar to Mk 16, intended for destroyers but not used
21/53 Mk 18	272/600 TPX	3660/4000(29)	electric torpedo for submarines based on German type; large numbers used. Development of Mk 19 antiship version discontinued. Wake following version designated Mk 29
21/53 Mk 20	454/1000	7320/8000(40)	electric torpedo for submarines using primary (sea-water) battery; not used
22.5/57 Mk 21	272/600 TPX	5030/5500(33.5)	air-dropped homer incorporated into postwar Petrel missile
21/53 Mk 22	272/600 TPX	4110/4500(45)	electric homer for submarines using body of Mk 14; two built
22.5/57 Mk 25	272/600 TPX	5490/6000(40)	for high-speed air-dropping
21/53 Mk 26	431/950 TPX	7320/8000(40)	experimental antiship torpedo with primary battery
19/48 Mk 27	43-61/95-135 TPX	7320/8000(12)	submarine-launched A/S homer based on air-launched Fido; widely used postwar
21/53 Mk 28	272/600 TPX	4570/5000(20)	interim submarine-launched antiship homer used during Second World War; experimental improved version designated Mk 29
21/53 Mk 31	227/500	3660/4000(29) 12 800/14 000(20)	two-speed version of Mk 18, cancelled in favour of Mk 28
19/48 Mk 32	—	—	small surface-launched low-speed medium range A/S torpedo; some in use in late 1970s

Mk 33	—	—	homer; abandoned 1946
19/48 Mk 34	—	—	air-dropped homer; modified as Mk 39
21/53 Mk 35	115-122/255-270	13 700/15 000(30)	first-generation deep-diving long-range homer, used mostly in submarines
21/53 Mk 36	—	6860/7500(55-60)	projected submarine-launched high-speed wakeless antiship torpedo
19/48 Mk 37	150/330	—	electric high-performance A/S torpedo, in use 1978; Mod 1, 2 are wire-guided
21/53 Mk 38	—	9140/10 000	projected postwar submarine-launched antiship electric homer
19/48 Mk 39	59/130	11 900/13 000	wire-guided A/S and antiship based on Mk 34
21/53 Mk 41	122/270	12 800/14 000(28.6)	projected electric air-launched A/S torpedo
19/48 Mk 43	—	—	small-charge ship or air-dropped active-acoustic A/S electric homer
10/25 Mk 43 Mod 3	—	—	based on Mk 43; first US small-diameter A/S torpedo
12.75/32 Mk 44	34/75	5030/5500(30)	electric A/S homer
19/48 Mk 45	nuclear	—	Astor wire-guided long-range torpedo
12.75/32 Mk 46	41/90	11 000/12 000(40)	introduced 1964 to succeed Mk 44
21/53 Mk 48	—	—	submarine-launched long-range high-speed antiship and A/S

ethanol; the Mk 7 introduced the wet heater.

Early Whitehead torpedoes were built under licence. Mks 1-3 were built by the Naval Torpedo Station, Newport RI. Bliss built its own Mks 3, 4, 6 and 7, but subsequent models were built at NTS. The poor performance of the Mk 14 led to the closing of the NTS, and since 1945 torpedoes have been privately built by Westinghouse, General Electric, Philco and Clevite and at the Naval Ordnance Plant, Forest Park, Illinois.

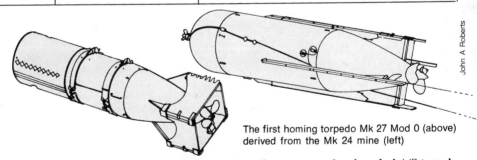

John A Roberts

The first homing torpedo Mk 27 Mod 0 (above) derived from the Mk 24 mine (left)

The Mk 32 torpedo tube. This US-designed weapon built under licence in Britain is a low-speed, medium-range, surface launched A/S torpedo

C & S Taylor

Torpedoes

FRENCH TORPEDOES

Calibre and model (in/cm)	weight (kg/lb)	warhead (kg/lb)	range m/yards(knots)	notes
14/36 M1887	318/701	42/93	400/437(27)	
15/38 M1887	423/933	42/93	600/656(27)	
17.7/45 M1892	530/1168	75/165	800/875(27.5)	
17.7/45 M1904	627/1382	72/159	600/656(36.5) 1000/1093(32.5) 1500/1640(27)	
17.7/45 M1906	648/1429	87/191	as M1904	
17.7/45 M1909R	683/1505	87/191	1000/1093(38) 2000/2186(34) 3000/3281(29)	heater type
21.7/55 M1923DT	2105/4641	415/915	10 000/10 940(39) 14 000/15 310(35)	used in destroyers
21.7/55 M1924V	1497/3300	308/680	6950/7600(35)	used in submarines
15.7/40 M1926V	674/1486	142/313	400/437(44)	air-turbine motor
21.7/55 1929D	—	—	20 000/21 900(29) 14 000/15 300(35)	for cruisers
15.7/40 DAR	—	—	3000/3282(35)	used for Latecore seaplanes and MTBs
21.7/55 L3	910/2006	200/441	5500/6015(25)	electrically driven acoustic A/S homer
21/53 L4	540/1190	—	—	air-dropped; also used as payload of Malafon missile system
21/53 L5 Mod 1	1000/2205	—	—	for surface ships
21/53 L5 Mod 3	1300/2866	—	—	

The French bought exclusively from Whitehead for many years and by 1881 they had acquired 113 36-cm (14-in) torpedoes and 105 of the 38-cm (15-in) type. From 1909 they made their own arrangement with Schwartzkopf. The 55-cm (21.7-in) Z14 was a submarine-launched electric torpedo based on the German Zaunkönig. It was replaced by the 55-cm E14, which was developed into the lengthened and improved E15.

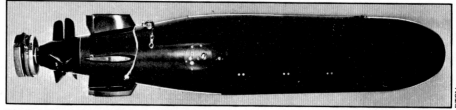

The L4 has a 200-kg (440-lb) warhead which is percussion-detonated against the submarine

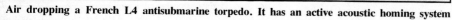

Air dropping a French L4 antisubmarine torpedo. It has an active acoustic homing system

GERMAN TORPEDOES

Calibre and mark (in/cm)	warhead (kg/lb)	range m/yards(knots)	notes
14/36 C35/91	40.5/89	500/547(27)	bronze Schwartzkopf type
17.7/45 C45/91	88-193/194-425	1000/1093(27) 1600/1750(27)	bronze and steel variants
17.7/45 C/03	148/325	3000/3280(26) 5000/5468(27)	first heater torpedoes
17.7/45 C/06	122/269	3600/3940(27) 5900/6450(27)	
19.5/50 G/6	160-164/353-361	5000/5470(27) 8400/9190(27)	
19.5/50 G/7	195/430	9800/10 717(27)	
23.4/60 H/8	210-250/463-551	14 000/15 3 10(27)	introduced in *Baden* Class battleships, *Derfflinger* battlecruisers, *Königsberg* Class light cruisers and *S.113* Class destroyers

SWEDISH TORPEDOES

Calibre and model (in/cm)	weight (kg/lb)	warhead (kg/lb)	range m/yards(knots)	notes
14/36 '76	—	—	400/437(22)	first model bought from Whitehead in 1875
14/36 '91	327/721	49.5/109	400/437(26)	Schwartzkopf model
14/36 '03	334/736	41.6/91.7	600/656(28)	Whitehead model
15/38 '76	—	26/57	400/437(19)	25 bought from Whitehead; development with contrarotating propellers designated M'83
15/38 '89	388/855	64.5/142.2	400/437(26)	Schwartzkopf model
15/38 '93	397/875	47.8/105.4	800/874(23)	Whitehead model
17.7/45 '93	440/970	74.5/164.2	800/874(24)	Whitehead model
17.7/45 '06	618/1362	77.7/171.3	—	Schwartzkopf variant
17.7/45 '12	647/1426	—	2000/2187 (36)	first Karlskrona-made torpedo

The Swedish FFV TP42 wire-guided torpedo can be air-dropped or ship- or submarine-launched

A large number of German 53-cm (21-in) torpedoes are known by name. These include the T1 (G7a); T2 and T3 (G7e); T3b (Marder); T3d (Dackel); T3e (Kreutzotter); T4 (Falke); T5, T11 and G7as12 (Zaunkönig); G7 (Steinbarsch); T8 (Schildbutt); T10 (Spinne); G7es14 (Geier); G7es48 (Lerche); G7ut30 (Schildbutt and Steinwal). The T12 was a G5e type with a 280-kg (617-lb) warhead. The T13 was a K-Butt G7ut type. The T14 was a G7a type used for Seehund midget submarines.

Additional Swedish torpedoes include the 40-cm (15.7-in) Tp41 active homer for surface ships and submarines, with battery drive. It was replaced by the 250-kg (550-lb) Tp42 which could be dropped from helicopters; the Tp42 is 2.62 m (8 ft 7 in) long (including the 18-cm [7-in] wire spool). The 53-cm (21-in) wire-guided Tp61 type with HTP drive has been developed from the British Fancy Mk 12. It is a long-range type with a speed believed to be approximately 60 knots, and is one of the world's most potent torpedoes.

Torpedoes

ITALIAN TORPEDOES

Calibre and mark (in/cm)	warhead (kg/lb)	range m/yards(knots)	notes
14/36 A37	37/82	600/660(22)	original 1877 model
17.7/45 B90	90/198	400/440(30)	introduced 1889
17.7/45 A95	95/209	800/875(34)	introduced 1906
17.7/45 A100	100/220	800/875(34)	introduced 1912
21/53 W270	270/595	4000/4375(48)	Fiume model; also made as SI 270 model by Siturfico Italiano, Naples
21/53 W250	250/551	4000/4375(50)	Whitehead *Veloce* model
17.7/45 A110	110/243	2000/2187(44)	Whitehead *Silurotto* model for MAS boats
17.7/45 W200	200/441	3000/3281(44)	Whitehead model for *Cagni* Class submarines

Launching an A184 torpedo from the stern of the Italian guided-missile destroyer *Audace*. An AB 212 A/S helicopter is on the flight deck

In addition to those for which data are given, the following torpedoes have been in RN service:

14-in Mk III Batch of 50 bought from Schwartzkopf in 1895
14-in Mk IV Built by Whitehead, Fiume; 200 bought
14-in Mk X Royal Gun Factory 1897 design used originally in 2nd Class torpedo boats from dropping gear; in 1915 used by Short 184 seaplanes
18-in Mk III Development of Mk I with Elswick heater; reached 39 knots in 1904 demonstration
18-in Mk V Used in submarines
18-in Mk VI Used in submarines; development of Mk II with heater engine
18-in Mk VIII Produced by RNTF from 1910 and used in submarines. From 1939 used from aircraft as stopgap though obsolescent; two fired in action. Brought back into service as Mk XI; 22 fired in action
18-in Mk XV Made by RNTF (440 fired), Weymouth (97 fired) and Morris Motors (54 fired)
18-in Mk XVII Used as basis for Bowler
21-in Mk V Made by RNTF and Weymouth; 198 fired in action in Second World War
21-in Mk VI Obsolete by 1939

Factory checks on an Italian Whitehead A244 torpedo; this is an improved US Mk 44 Mod 2

21-in Mk X Made by Weymouth; 61 fired in action
21-in Mk XI Electric torpedo developed from German G7e. Low-priority studies at RNTF from 1940; production-development by British Thomson-Houston from May 1943. Eventually made at rate of 25 per month; deployed in Mediterranean and Pacific but never fired in action
21-in Mk 12 Fancy
21-in Mk 20 Bidder
21-in Mk 21 Pentane
21-in Mk 22 Cable-set version; abandoned in

favour of wire-guided version Mk 23 (Grog)
21-in Mk 24 Tigerfish
18-in Mk 30 Dealer
10-in Mk 43 US pattern antisubmarine; 50 bought to replace Mk 30 Mod 1 for RAF Coastal Command in 1950s; still in service 1979
12.75-in Mk 44 US pattern A/S acoustic homer with electric battery drive; used in STWS-1, ships and helicopters
12.75-in Mk 46 US pattern improved Mk 44 with Otto fuel; bought in limited numbers with Mk 44

Torpedo Boats

Small, light torpedo-carrying craft. The first torpedo boat was HMS *Vesuvius*, launched in 1874 and used for experiments with the first Whitehead torpedoes. In 1877 HMS *Lightning* (later known as *Torpedo Boat No 1*) was launched as the first seagoing torpedo boat, followed shortly afterwards by the French *Torpilleur No 1*. The vogue for torpedo boats spread to all navies but the principal builders were in Great Britain (Thornycroft and Yarrow), France (Normand) and Germany (Schichau). Other firms came into the business later and took a bigger share of the market, but these four firms remained leaders in hull- and machinery-design.

The Royal Navy built 117 1st Class torpedo boats during 1877-1904, by which time the size approached that of the first destroyers of 1893. Between 1906 and 1909 a further series of 'coastal destroyers' was launched. They were intended to have 'insect' names, but when they proved frail they were numbered TB.1-36. Thereafter the old torpedo boats in that series which still survived were given an 'O' prefix to indicate obsolescence. In all, 70 old torpedo boats still existed in August 1914, including two originally built for individual states in Australia. At that time there also existed a series of 2nd Class torpedo boats with wooden hulls, but they were not seagoing.

As an antidote to the overwhelming preponderance of the Royal Navy, the French navy built 370 *torpilleurs numérotés* between 1876 and 1903, of which about 100 were still in existence in August 1914.

Although the Germans built some experimental torpedo craft in the mid-1870s, their first seagoing or 1st Class torpedo boats were launched in 1884. The practice was adopted of using an initial letter for the builder: thus W.1 was built by AG Weser, V.1 by Vulkan, S.1 by Schichau. Later the system was revised, with a single numerical series and distinguishing letters including G (Germania), B (Blohm und Voss) and H (Howaldt). There were also some large torpedo boats called *Divisionsboote*, D.1-10 built in 1886-98, which foreshadowed the destroyer. The numerical series ran up to G.197 in 1911, at which point it started again with V.1, while the old boats were all given T-numbers. The last torpedo boats (the German navy retained the term in preference to *Zerstörer* except for the very largest boats) in this second series were the incomplete H.186-202 of 1918.

In 1937 a new series of German seagoing light destroyers was started numbered T.1-21. They displaced about 850 tons and had a single funnel. T.22-51 were about 1500 tons (standard) and resembled destroyers, with three 10.5-cm (4.1-in) guns and six torpedo tubes. Only T.22-36 were completed, of which two served in the French navy as *l'Alsacien* and *le Lorain* and one in the Soviet navy as *Primierny*.

Tortoise

British heavy self-propelled assault gun. Late in 1942 the British Army requested a new design of antitank gun to give a 25% better performance than the 17-pdr. After some debate, a gun based on the 3.7-in (94-mm) AA gun was proposed. Since it was expected to give its best performance with a 16.8-kg (37-lb) shot it was provisionally called the 37-pdr EX1, and a self-propelled version, the EX2, was proposed. When the gun was tested in June 1944 it was found that the 16.8-kg shot was no good and a 14.5-kg (32-lb) shot was most effective: the gun was consequently renamed the 32-pdr.

Meanwhile design work had begun on the self-propelled version which came to be called the Tortoise, more officially the A-39. The result was a massive vehicle with almost 23 cm (9 in) of armour and with the gun in a ball mounting in the front of the hull, very similar to the German Ferdinand. A Besa machine-gun was mounted in the lower hull front, with two more in a cupola on the hull roof. The gun could traverse 20° each side of centre, and had 10° of elevation. A crew of seven manned the vehicle.

Tortoise had a low priority, and it was not until 1946 that the first prototype was ready for trials. But by that time the need which led to its construction had gone; the war had ended and the future direction of tank design did not appear to have any role for such a weapon. Five others were in course of construction and were completed in 1947; the six were used for a number of trials, but in 1948 they were declared obsolete and four tour were scrapped; the remaining two have been preserved at the Tank Museum, Bovingdon.

It is still not clear what Tortoise was

intended to be. It is obvious from contemporary documents that what the General Staff wanted when they asked for a self-propelled 32-pdr gun was not an 80-ton mobile fortress, and had the gun been put into a lighter vehicle it may well have been successful. It is often referred to as a 'heavy assault tank', but with the limited traverse of its gun it was ill-suited to this role. Moreover, the fate of the German Ferdinand, a similar design, should have been sufficient to deter the designers. A further point is that it was beyond the capacity of the current tank transporters, too big for railway transport and too heavy for most bridges. The best that can be said is that it was an interesting technical exercise and did not divert much effort from the mainstream of the war.

Weight: 79 tonnes *Length:* 7.24 m (23 ft 9 in) *Width:* 3.91 m (12 ft 10 in) *Height:* 3.05 m (10 ft) *Armour thickness:* 225-35 mm (8.9-1.4 in) *Armament:* 1 32-pdr gun firing 14.5-kg (32-lb) shot at 880 m/sec (2887 ft/sec); 3 7.92-mm (0.312-in) machine-guns *Powerplant:* Rolls-Royce Meteor 12-cylinder gasoline, 600 bhp *Speed:* 19 km/h (12 mph) *Range:* not known

---

Toryu Japanese name for Kawasaki Ki-45 multirole aircraft See **Ki-45**

---

la Tour d'Auvergne

French minelaying cruiser, built 1928-31. Launched as *Pluton* at Lorient arsenal on April 10, 1929, she resembled *Jeanne d'Arc* in being modelled on existing cruisers, but with her fighting qualities sacrificed for mine capacity. In this case the model was the *Suffren* Class heavy cruisers, which she resembled. She was given a light armament of four single 138.6-mm (5.46-in) Model 1927, and could stow 290 mines on an open mine deck extending as far as the forward funnel. The hull was unarmoured and the funnels were widely spaced.

With the expansion of the navy before the Second World War a second training ship was needed to support *Jeanne d'Arc*, and la Tour d'Auvergne was refitted in 1939 and renamed *Pluton*. However, on September 18, 1939, she was sunk by an internal explosion

The British heavy self-propelled gun, aptly named Tortoise, mounted a 32-pdr gun with limited traverse. Its massive armour would have been little protection due to its low speed of 19 km/h (12 mph) increasing its vulnerability

Tourville

at Casablanca, when one of her mines exploded accidentally.

Displacement: 4773 tonnes (standard), 6500 tonnes (full load) *Length:* 152.5 m (500 ft 4 in) oa *Beam:* 15.6 m (51 ft 2 in) *Draught:* 6.1 m (20 ft) max *Machinery:* 2-shaft geared steam turbines, 57 000 shp=30 knots *Armament:* 4 138.6-mm (5.46-in) Model 1922 (4×1); 4 75-mm (2.95-in) AA (4×1); 2 37-mm (1.46-in) AA (2×1); 12 13.2-mm (0.52-in) machine-guns (4×3); 290 mines *Crew:* 424

Tourville

French antisubmarine escort class, built 1970-76. Three Type C67A corvettes were authorized in 1970, but in 1971 they were rerated as frigates (Type F67) and finally appeared with D numbers like destroyers. *Tourville* (D.610), *Duguay Trouin* (D.611) and *De Grasse* (D.612) were all built by DCAN Lorient.

The design is a diminutive of *Suffren*, with a double helicopter hangar aft in place of antiaircraft missiles. They have a big bow sonar and a variable-depth version of the same set, the Thomson-CSF DUBV-23/43. The antisubmarine weapons are a single Malafon launcher and 13 missiles amidships, and two launchers for L5 torpedoes in the after superstructure. Since 1976 they have been armed with six MM-38 Exocet surface-to-surface missiles and the after 100-mm (3.9-in) gun has been removed. In 1978 *Duguay Trouin* was fitted with the Crotale close-range AA missile system in the position above the hangar formerly occupied by the third 100-mm gun.

In appearance they resemble the *Suffren* Class, with two 100-mm Model '68 DP guns forward, a prominent mack amidships and the characteristic 'droop snout' of modern French warships. They are fitted with SENIT 3 action data automation and have DRBV 26, DRBV 51 and DRBC 32D radars for surveillance and weapon control. Two WG13 Lynx helicopters are carried.

Displacement: 4580 tonnes (standard), 5800 tonnes (full load) *Length:* 152.8 m (501 ft 4 in) *Beam:* 15.3 m (50 ft 2 in) *Draught:* 5.7 m (18 ft 8 in) *Machinery:* 2-shaft geared steam turbines, 54 400 shp=31 knots *Armament:* 3 100-mm (3.9-in) Model '68 DP (3×1); 6 MM-38 Exocet SSMs; 1 Malafon A/S missile launcher; 2 torpedo tubes for A/S torpedoes; 2 Lynx helicopters *Crew:* 283

Tow, Hughes

US antitank missile. The BGM-71A Tow (tube-launched, optically sighted, wire-guided) missile was developed to replace the US Army's M40A-1 106-mm (4.17-in) recoilless rifle and its Entac and SS.11 antitank missiles of French origin. Design work on what was then known as HAW (heavy antitank weapon) started in 1962 and Hughes was selected as prime contractor by the US Army Missile Command. Test firings began in 1965, with the company receiving its first three-year production contract in November 1968. The US Army has deployed the weapon since November 1970 and some two dozen other countries had ordered Tow by the end of 1978, at which time the 200 000th round had been completed and production was

The French antisubmarine escort *Tourville* in a choppy sea. She is one of three ships authorized in 1970 as frigates but uprated to destroyers when they were commissioned

running at about 3000 missiles a month. Tow can be fired from an infantry-operated tripod launcher, which may also be attached to a wide range of vehicles such as the M151 Jeep, M274 Mechanical Mule and M113A1 armoured personnel carrier. The US Army is receiving some 1976 M901 ITVs (improved Tow vehicles), a version of the M113 with an armoured two-round launcher, and the missile is planned for the IFV (infantry fighting vehicle).

Firings from helicopters began in October 1966, using a UH-1B as the launch platform, and two of these aircraft equipped with the XM26 Tow system went into action at Kontum in Vietnam during May 1972, destroying 62 targets between them and proving the value of modern helicopter-launched missiles. The weapon was also planned to arm the Lockheed Cheyenne attack helicopter, but this project was cancelled, and firings from the AH-1 HueyCobra with the improved XM65 fire-control system began in February 1973. By 1984 the US Army will have nearly 1000 Tow-armed helicopters, and the system has been fitted on the Westland/Aérospatiale Lynx (ordered by the British Army) and Hughes 500M-D Defender.

· Tow is supplied as a round of ammunition which is inserted in its launcher, all electrical connections being made automatically. For infantry use the launcher and associated equipment are broken down into seven sub-assemblies, none of which weighs more than 24 kg (53 lb). The gunner tracks his target in the ×13-magnification optical sight and presses the firing trigger; the missile batteries are activated and the gyros run up in less than

1.5 seconds, at which time the Hercules K41 launch motor ignites. This solid-propellant rocket accelerates the missile to 67 m/sec (220 ft/sec) and burns out before the round has left its launcher, thereby preventing the operator from being harmed by hot exhaust gases. Once the Tow has flown some 12 m (40 ft) the solid-propellant sustainer motor ignites and further increases the speed to just above Mach 1.

A goniometer aligned with the gunner's sight detects radiation from a modulated infrared lamp at the rear of the missile; the off-boresight angle is measured and a small computer in the launcher generates steering corrections for transmission down trailing wires to the round, where they operate four small pistons connected to the tail surfaces. The operator thus has only to keep his cross-hairs on the target for the Tow to hit it. A Texas Instruments TAS-4 night sight can be used for engagements after dark or in poor weather. A stabilized sight assembly is used in Tow-armed helicopters, either in a chin turret or projecting through the roof, but the method of guidance remains unchanged.

Length: 1.17 m (3 ft 10 in) *Span:* 34 cm (13.4 in) *Diameter:* 15 cm (6 in) *Weight:* 20.9 kg (46 lb) *Range:* 3750 m (4100 yards) *Speed:* Mach 1.05 *Warhead:* 3.9-kg (8 lb 10-oz) hollow-charge

---

TowCobra, Bell AH-1Q Tow antitank missile carrying conversion of AH-1G HueyCobra gunship See **HueyCobra**

Toyo Japanese aircraft See **Defender**

▲ US Navy Grumman S-2 Tracker which, in an updating programme, has received Jezebel and Julie acoustic search and ranging equipment

Tracker, Grumman S-2

US Navy antisubmarine, early-warning and transport aircraft. Prior to the arrival of the Grumman Tracker, the US Navy's carrier-based air search and strike against submarines had involved the use of a pair of aircraft: a 'hunter' equipped with detection and tracking gear to locate the target, working in collaboration with a 'killer' aircraft carrying the necessary weapons to mount an antisubmarine strike. Initially the dual roles were carried out respectively by AF-2W and AF-2S versions of another Grumman type, the Model 70 Guardian, which began to enter service in October 1950.

Already, however, plans were under way to combine the hunter and killer roles in a single aircraft, and on June 30, 1950, Grumman was awarded a development contract for its twin-engined Model 89, the two prototypes being designated XS2F-1 and given the name Sentinel. The main requirements were for a reasonable cruising speed, and the ability to operate from carriers with a substantial payload of ASW equipment and weapons over ranges in the order of 1600 km (1000 miles). The XS2F-1 flew for the first time on December 4, 1952, and appeared as a shoulder-wing monoplane with a deep, roomy fuselage; it was powered by a pair of 1525-hp Wright R-1820-82WA Cyclone nine-cylinder radial engines in long nacelles. Sonobuoy compartments were built into the rear of the nacelles, an internal fuselage bay accommodated a maximum weapon load of 2182 kg (4810 lb), including two torpedoes, and there were six underwing hardpoints for additional weapons or other stores. A pod fairing under the starboard wing housed a 70-million-candlepower searchlight and there was an APS-38 search radar in a retractable ventral dustbin radome aft of the bomb bay. In the rear fuselage there was a retractable ASQ-10 magnetic anomaly detector (MAD) boom, just above the deck arrester hook.

The aircraft was renamed Tracker prior to its entry into US Navy service. In addition to the prototypes, Grumman produced 1184 Trackers, in four basic models: 755 S2F-1s; 77 S2F-2s; 100 S2F-3s; and 252 S2F-3Ss. From 1962, these were redesignated S-2A, C, D and E respectively. A further 43 CS2F-1s and 57 CS2F-2s, manufactured by de Havilland, Canada, were essentially similar to their US counterparts. First deliveries, of the S2F-1, were made in February 1954 to Squadron VS-26, and Trackers eventually equipped about 20 US Navy squadrons. Others were exported or supplied under the Military Assistance Program to allied states, including Argentina, Australia, Brazil, France, Italy, Japan, the Netherlands, Taiwan, Thailand, Turkey and Uruguay.

To update the initial S2F-1 (S-2A), many USN Trackers were equipped with Jezebel and Julie acoustic search and echo-ranging equipment, being redesignated S2F-1S (later S-2B). Others, when replaced by later antisubmarine variants, were modified into S2F-1T (TS-2A) ASW crew trainers or US-2A target tugs. Later still, in further updating programmes, most S2F-1S (S-2B) Trackers became S2F-1S1s (S-2Fs), and a utility US-2B conversion also appeared. The production S2F-2 (S-2C) differed in having an offset and protruding weapons bay housing improved homing torpedoes, and increased tail surface area. From these followed some conversions to the camera-carrying S2F-2P (RS-2C) or utility S2F-2U (US-2C). The S2F-3 (S-2D), first flown on May 21, 1959, featured a 0.46 m (1 ft 6 in) longer fuselage and a 0.89 m (2 ft 11 in) increase in wing span, the former intended chiefly to provide more spacious accommodation for the four-man crew. Tail area was again increased, extra fuel tankage installed, the nacelle compartments were each enlarged to hold 16 sonobuoys instead of eight, and wingtip ECM pods were added. The S2F-3S (S-2E) was based on the S-2D, but with Jezebel/Julie gear and a tactical navigation system added. Production ended in 1968. Fifty S-2Es were redesignated S-2F after the addition of AQA-7 sonobuoy processing gear. Performance of the S-2E includes a patrol endurance of about nine hours and a range of 1850 km (1150 miles).

In January 1955 Grumman flew the first TF-1, an interim COD (carrier-on-board-delivery) support transport derivative of the Tracker with a nine-passenger fuselage cabin. Known as the Trader, and redesignated C-1A in 1962, this entered service in 1957 as an interim type with three flight logistics support and transport squadrons of the USN, pending deliveries of the C-2 Greyhound. A total of 87 were built, including four TF-1Q (EC-1A) aircraft for ECM.

The WF-1 airborne early-warning variant appeared in 1954. Two prototypes were followed by the WF-2 (later E-1B) Tracer, based on the Trader airframe but much transformed by the addition of a huge dorsal saucer housing for its APS-82 search-radar scanner, and an entirely new tail unit of three fins and two rudders. Eighty-nine Tracers were built, deliveries beginning in February 1958 to USN Squadrons VAW-11 and VAW-12. The Tracer, too, was an interim type, replaced gradually by the E-2 Hawkeye from the mid-1960s, but the Tracker continued to serve with several air forces in the late 1970s.

(S-2A) *Span:* 21.23 m (69 ft 8 in) *Length:* 12.88 m (42 ft 3 in) *Gross weight:* 11 929 kg (26 300 lb) *Maximum speed:* 462 km/h (287 mph)

(S-2E) *Span:* 22.12 m (72 ft 7 in) *Length:* 13.26 m (43 ft 6 in) *Gross weight:* 13 222 kg (29 150 lb) *Maximum speed:* 426 km/h (265 mph)

(E-1B) *Span:* 22.12 m (72 ft 7 in) *Length:* 13.82 m (45 ft 4 in) *Gross weight:* 12 232 kg (26 966 lb) *Cruising speed:* 338 km/h (210 mph)

Tradewind, Convair R3Y

US Navy long-range transport flying boat. The Tradewind's R (for transport) navy designation conceals the fact that this large and elegant flying boat was designed as an ocean patrol aircraft, its prototype designation having been XP5Y-1 at the time of its first flight on April 18, 1950. It was the navy's only attempt at a turboprop-engined flying boat, the two prototypes each being powered by four 5500-ehp Allison XT40-A-4 engines (each one a 'double' T38 turboprop), driving six-blade contrarotating propellers. The XP5Y-1 was a handsome aircraft, having a long and beautifully streamlined hull with an excellent 10:1 length-to-beam ratio, shoulder-mounted thin-section wings (for low drag), and a large, upswept vertical tail. Provision existed for five pairs of 20-mm (0.79-in) guns, a 3629-kg (8000-lb) bombload, nose-mounted radar, an armoured flight deck, and an 11-man crew. But the XP5Y-1 appeared when the flying boat era was almost over, and the 11 production aircraft built were completed for use as transports.

Five of these, designated R3Y-1, were generally similar to the prototype, except for the omission of armament and a corresponding reduction in the number of crew; the first R3Y-1 made its initial flight on February 25, 1954. The remaining six aircraft, with 5850-

Tre Kronor

ehp T40-A-10 turboprops, were designated R3Y-2, and somewhat spoilt the Tradewind's original elegant lines by having an elevated flight deck and a thimble radome in a shorter and more bulbous nose, the whole of which opened upwards for loading and unloading vehicles or troops directly onto landing beaches via an extendable ramp. The first R3Y-2 was flown on October 22, 1954, and in later years this version of the Tradewind was adapted as a four-point hose-refuelling tanker for US Navy aircraft. As a transport, its 26.8 m (88 ft) long cargo hold could accommodate four 155-mm (6.1-in) howitzers, three 2.5-ton trucks, six Jeeps, or two half-tracks. Alternatively, seats could be installed for up to 103 passengers or, in an aeromedical role, 92 stretchers and 12 medical attendants could be carried. Cruising speed was 483 km/h (300 mph), and range about 7240 km (4500 miles).

(R3Y-2) *Span:* 44.42 m (145 ft 9 in) *Length:* 42.57 m (139 ft 8 in) *Gross weight:* 72 575 kg (160 000 lb) *Maximum speed:* 621 km/h (386 mph)

Tre Kronor

Swedish cruiser class, built 1943-47. In 1940 four ships were planned, light cruisers with nine 15-cm (5.9-in) guns, two to be laid down in 1940 and two more in 1943, for completion in 1943-45. The layout was unusual, with one triple turret forward and two aft.

The outbreak of the Second World War caused the deferment of the programme and allowed improvements to be incorporated. The sketch design published in 1940 showed a single tall capped funnel with paired AA guns on the centreline forward and abaft the superstructure. In 1942 a new design was drawn up to make use of the gun mountings available from the Dutch *Eendracht* and *De Zeven Provincien*, with a triple turret forward, two twins aft and two raked funnels. The final design was powerful, well-balanced, with twin 40-mm (1.57-in) AA amidships and 25-mm (1-in) mountings forward and aft.

Contracts were signed in February 1943 for two ships, *Tre Kronor* from Götaverken, Göteborg and *Gota Lejon* from Eriksberg Mekaniska Verkstad, also of Göteborg. The ships were launched on December 16, 1944 and November 17, 1945 respectively, and both were completed late in 1947. The radar

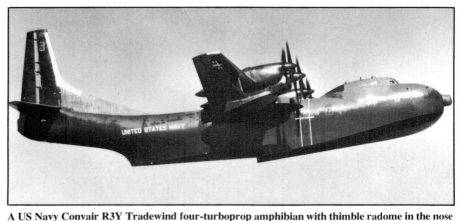

A US Navy Convair R3Y Tradewind four-turboprop amphibian with thimble radome in the nose

and communications were of British pattern, with Type 275 gunnery radar and Type 277 height-finder and Type 293 target indication.

In 1951-52 both ships were modernized, with enlarged bridgework and seven single 40-mm Bofors AA guns in place of the nine 25-mm mountings. In 1958 further modernization followed, with a Dutch HSA LW 03 air-warning radar on the foremast and four 57-mm (2.24-in) AA guns amidships.

Tre Kronor was paid off for scrapping in January 1964, and in July 1971 *Gota Lejon* was sold to Chile. She recommissioned as *Almirante Latorre* in September that year, and was still in commission in 1979

Displacement: 8200 tons (standard), 9200 tons (full load) *Length:* 182 m (597 ft) oa *Beam:* 16.5 m (54 ft 1 in) *Draught:* 6.6 m (21 ft 8 in) *Machinery:* 2-shaft geared steam turbines, 100 000 shp=33 knots *Protection:* 125-75 mm (4.9-2.95 in) belt *Armament:* (As built) 7 15-cm (5.9-in)/53-cal (1×3, 2×2); 20 40-mm (1.57-in) Bofors AA (10×2); 9 25-mm (1-in) AA; 6 53-cm (21-in) torpedo tubes (2×3); (As modernized) 7 15-cm/53-cal; 4 57-mm (2.24-in) AA (4×1); 11 40-mm AA (11×1); 6 53-cm TT *Crew:* 455

Trento

Italian heavy cruiser class, built 1925-29. In keeping with a long-standing tradition the first 203-mm (8-in) gunned cruisers built to the 10 000-ton limit of the Washington Treaty were as fast if not faster than any foreign contemporaries. This was achieved at the cost of extremely thin armour, and even then the ships were 500 tons over the limit. The design nevertheless had several advanced features. The layout of guns was logical, with two twin mountings at either end of the citadel. The flush deck had high freeboard for weatherliness, and the staggering of boilers and turbines (the 'unit' system) which reduced the risk of the ship losing motive power from a single torpedo hit. A hangar was provided under the forecastle, with a fixed catapult ahead of the forward gun turret.

The Model 1924 203-mm/50-cal was an Ansaldo-Schneider design with 48° elevation, ranging to 28 000 m (30 600 yards). Each gun weighed 20.8 tonnes and fired a shell weighing 118.5 kg (261 lb), with 47-kg (104-lb) charge at 835 m/sec (2740 ft/sec). The 100-mm (3.9-in)/47-cal was mounted in twin Minisini AA mountings elevating to 80°, and was derived from the old 100-mm/50-cal Skoda gun. The gun weighed 20.2 tonnes, with a 138.8-kg (306-lb) shell.

When first completed the ships had level tops to their funnels but in 1940-41 both ships were given prominent caps which improved their looks. In 1937 four of the 100-mm guns were removed and replaced by four twin 37-mm (1.46-in) AA.

Both ships played an active role in the war in the Mediterranean. *Trento* was hit by a bomb during the Fleet Air Arm attack on Taranto in November 1940, but it failed to explode; she was also unscathed during the action off Cape Spartivento later that month. She fired at British cruisers during the pre-

The Swedish cruiser *Tre Kronor* was one of four ships planned in the early 1940s. Launched near the end of the Second World War they were modernized in the early 1950s and received new radar in 1958. *Gota Lejon* was sold to Chile in 1971 where she became fleet flagship under the name *Almirante Latorre*

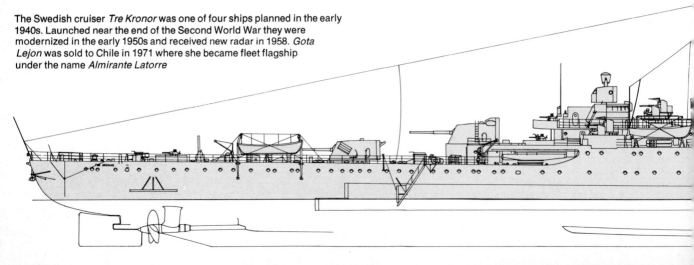

lude to the Battle of Cape Matapan but escaped with the main fleet. On June 15, 1942, she was torpedoed by the British submarine *Umbra* after she had been immobilized by a fire in the engine room. *Trieste* also took part in the various actions in the Mediterranean, and was finally sunk by bombing in Maddalena on April 10, 1943.

Displacement: 10 500 tonnes (standard), 13 540 tonnes (full load) *Length:* 196.96 m (646 ft 2 in) *Beam:* 20.6 m (67 ft 6 in) *Draught:* 5.9 m (19 ft 4 in) *Machinery:* 4-shaft geared steam turbines, 150 000 shp=35 knots *Protection:* 75 mm (3 in) belt, 50 mm (2 in) deck, 100 mm (3.9 in) turrets *Armament:* 8 203-mm (8-in)/50-cal (4×2); 16 100-mm (3.9-in)/47-cal AA (8×2); 8 13.2-mm (0.52-in) machine-guns; 8 53-cm (21-in) torpedo tubes (above water, beam, 4×2); 3 floatplanes, 1 catapult *Crew:* 801

Transall Franco-German aircraft   See **C-160**

'Tribal' British destroyer class (1905-08)
                                   See ***Cossack***

'Tribal' British destroyer class (1935-36)
                                   See ***Alfridi***

'Tribal' British frigate class   See ***Ashanti***

Trident, Lockheed

US submarine-launched ballistic missile. In 1966-67 the United States Department of Defense carried out its STRAT-X study aimed at defining what new strategic missiles would be needed to succeed weapons such as Minuteman and Poseidon. Four avenues of development were recommended: a land-based ICBM, buried in hard-rock silos to make it less vulnerable; a mobile ICBM; a ballistic missile to be launched from fast surface ships; and ULMS (undersea long-range missile system). Only ULMS was pro-

ceeded with, and it has since been renamed Trident.

Lockheed Missiles and Space company, which also developed Polaris and Poseidon, was awarded a development contract for the new weapon in November 1972. What has become Trident is in fact a less advanced missile/submarine combination than had been envisaged in the STRAT-X study and was at one time known as Expo (extended-range Poseidon). The missile, which made its maiden flight in January 1977, is a three-stage weapon which relies heavily on the experience which LMSC built up with its predecessors. Trident is scheduled to become operational on a limited scale in October 1979, when the first of ten converted submarines which previously carried Poseidon puts to sea with the new missile. The definitive launch platform, the *Ohio* Class submarine, is unlikely to be operational before 1981. The new submarines, which carry 24 Tridents each, are considerably quieter than their predecessors and have a more efficient command-and-control system. At least 13 are expected to be built, and this total may be increased.

All three stages of the UGM-93A Trident I (C4) are powered by Thiokol/Hercules solid-propellant rocket motors. The missile employs inertial guidance, and is due to carry the Mk 4 re-entry system containing eight independently targeted RVs each with a thermonuclear warhead of 100 kilotons yield. The Mk 500 Evader manoeuvring re-entry vehicle has been carried by Trident during flight trials, but by the end of 1978 no decision to fit it to operational missiles had been taken.

Trident I may be followed in the mid-1980s by the proposed Trident II (D5), which would have a longer range, carry a greater payload and have an accuracy approaching that of Minuteman. Trident II would be virtually a submarine-launched ICBM, but the time slippage, development problems and cost increase associated with Trident I must cast doubts on a follow-on weapon.

Length: 10.36 m (34 ft) *Diameter:* 1.88 m (6 ft 2 in) *Weight:* 31 750 kg (70 000 lb) *Range:* 7000 km (4375 miles) *Warhead:* Mk 4 MIRV, 8 100-kiloton thermonuclear warheads

Triplane, Sopwith

British fighter aircraft. The advantages of three wings instead of two on a fighting aircraft—narrower chord to improve pilot visibility, and shorter span which, allied to the reduced chord, made for better manoeuvrability—made the Sopwith triplane, successor to the Pup, an outstanding combat aircraft during its relatively brief career in 1917, and its success inspired a rush of German triplane fighters. The Sopwith Triplane's fuselage resembled that of the Pup, but was slightly shorter, and the tailplane, too, was similar. The wings were braced by a single continuous strut on each side. Armament, like that of the Pup, was a single synchronized Vickers machine-gun on top of the forward fuselage, though experimental variations included two Vickers guns, an additional Lewis in the port centre wing and a Vickers angled slightly upwards for attacking from below and behind. Powerplant was a 110-hp Clerget.

The prototype Triplane was completed in May 1916 and underwent operational trials in France the following month. Its success was followed by orders from both the RFC and RNAS, though in the event the RFC's urgent need for fighters in the second half of 1916 led, at the beginning of 1917, to their Triplanes being exchanged, while still under construction, for RNAS Spad VIIs. Eventual production totalled 150, built by Clayton & Shuttleworth as well as Sopwith, the original RFC order for 266 reduced to 120.

The Triplane began to enter service with RNAS squadrons on the Western Front in early 1917, making its operational debut in April of that year. It had been up-engined with the 130-hp Clerget, and it quickly established a formidable reputation, the most remarkable achievement being that of B Flight, 10 Naval Squadron, commanded by Flight Sub-Lieutenant Raymond Collishaw. Between May and July of 1917 the Canadian pilots of 'Black Flight', with their Triplanes named *Black Death*, *Black Maria*, *Black Prince*, *Black Roger* and *Black Sheep*, destroyed a total of 87 enemy aircraft, and in June Collishaw alone shot down 16, including 13 of the latest German single-seat fighters, in a period of only 27 days. However, the Triplane began to be replaced by the Camel in July, and by the end of the year the type had been withdrawn from the Western Front, where it had equipped a total of six squadrons. One Triplane also served in Macedonia,

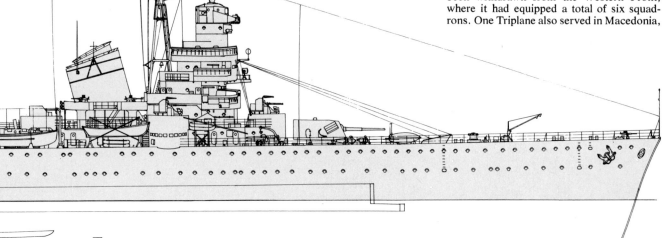

John Roberts

Tripoli

The Sopwith Triplane was a revolutionary design when it appeared on the Western Front in 1916. It is a measure of its success that the configuration was adopted in German and Austrian fighters

where it was piloted by Flight Lieutenant John Alcock, later one of the pilots of the Vickers Vimy which made the first aerial crossing of the Atlantic.

Another Sopwith Triplane produced in 1916 differed radically from the successful fighter. Although the wing configuration and bracing were similar, they were wider and of different construction, while the fuselage and tailplane were based on those of the 1½ Strutter rather than the Pup. The two examples built were powered by Hispano-Suiza eight-cylinder V-type engines in place of the Clerget rotary, one having the 150-hp direct-drive type and the other the geared 200-hp unit. However, while performance was satisfactory, all available Hispano-Suizas had been earmarked for the S.E.5, and the Sopwith design was abandoned.

(Triplane, 130-hp Clerget) *Span:* 8.08 m (26 ft 6 in) *Length:* 5.73 m (18 ft 10 in) *Gross weight:* 699 kg (1541 lb) *Maximum speed:* 188 km/h (117 mph)

(Triplane, 200-hp Hispano) *Span:* 8.69 m (28 ft 6 in) *Length:* 7.06 m (23 ft 2 in) *Gross weight:* not known *Maximum speed:* 193 km/h (120 mph)

Tripoli

Italian torpedo gunboat, built 1885-86. Following the lead taken by the Royal Navy in building torpedo gunboats to counter the threat of torpedo boats, the Italians ordered their first in 1885. *Tripoli* was launched by Castellammare di Stabia on August 25, 1886 and commissioned at the end of that year. In 1897 she was reboiled and converted to oil-firing, and was fitted for minelaying. The armament was reduced to two 3-in (76-mm)/40-cal guns, four 6-pdr (57-mm) QF, with provision for laying 64 mines over the stern. She served in the First World War as a minelayer and was discarded in 1923.

Displacement: 848 tonnes (normal), 970 tonnes (full load) *Length:* 73.4 m (240 ft 10 in) oa *Beam:* 7.88 m (25 ft 10 in) *Draught:* 3.26 m (10 ft 8 in) *Machinery:* 3-shaft reciprocating steam, 2400 ihp=17.5 knots *Protection:* 40 mm (1.57 in) deck *Armament:* 1 4.7-in (120-mm)/32-cal QF; 6 6-pdr (57-mm)/43-cal QF (6×1); 5 1-pdr (37-mm)/20-cal (5×1); 5 14-in (36-cm) torpedo tubes (above water) *Crew:* 105

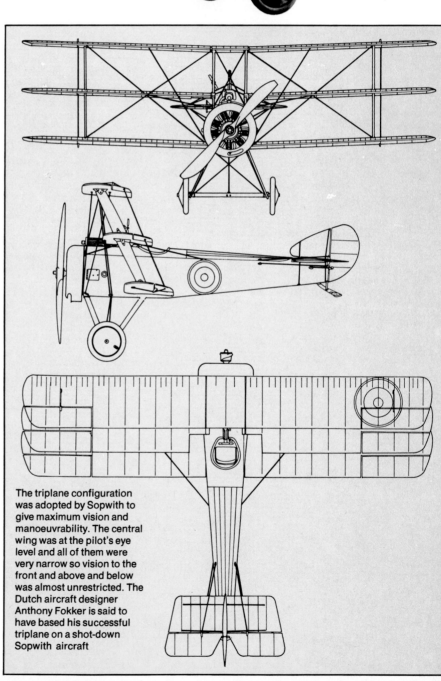

The triplane configuration was adopted by Sopwith to give maximum vision and manoeuvrability. The central wing was at the pilot's eye level and all of them were very narrow so vision to the front and above and below was almost unrestricted. The Dutch aircraft designer Anthony Fokker is said to have based his successful triplane on a shot-down Sopwith aircraft

Triton

British submarine class. The *Triton* or 'T' Class were designed in the early 1930s as replacements for the old boats of the 'L' Class and were intended for service as ocean-going patrol submarines like the earlier *Odin*, *Perseus* and *Rainbow* Classes. In order to build a reasonable number within the restriction placed on overall submarine tonnage by the current international treaty limitations, the displacement was restricted to 1090 tons compared with 1475 tons in the *Rainbow* Class. This was achieved by accepting a lower surface speed, which allowed for a reduction in the diesel plant and therefore the hull structure. However, the *Triton* Class were also of improved construction, with a stronger hull and greater diving speed, and were more heavily armed, having ten tubes instead of eight. All were arranged to fire forward, eight being mounted in the bows, six internally and two in the casing, and two amidships, angled out from the casing abreast the bridge. Only the internal tubes were provided with reload torpedoes.

The first of the class, *Triton*, was ordered under the 1935 Programme, a further 14 being authorized during 1936-38. The war programmes added another 47 to the class but four of these were subsequently reordered as *Amphion* Class submarines and another six, still under construction at the end of the war, were cancelled. (Three of these had been launched, and the incomplete hulls were sold for scrap during 1945-46). The early boats completed with a bulbous casing around the external bow tubes, but this was found to create a bow wave when running at periscope depth which impaired vision, and the casing was given a finer form in later vessels while the earlier units were modified during refits. The vessels ordered from 1939 onwards were fitted with an additional external tube in the casing aft and their midship tubes were moved to a position abaft the conning tower and arranged to fire aft instead of forward. Some of the prewar vessels also had the stern tube added but their midship tubes were not altered. During the middle years of the war a single 20-mm (0.79-in) AA gun was mounted at the rear of the conning tower, and air-warning radar was fitted in the majority of the class. Units under construction were similarly modified. All the 1942 and some of the 1941 Programme ships were of all-welded construction while the majority of the earlier wartime vessels were part-welded. The all-welded hulls provided the advantage of allowing oil to be carried in the ballast tanks to give a greatly extended operational range and most of those all-welded boats which completed before the end of the war were sent to the Pacific and Far East where the great distances involved made such a feature essential.

The *Triton* Class together with the smaller *Swordfish* and *Undine* Class boats provided the bulk of Britain's submarine force during the Second World War, and the earlier vessels saw extensive service in Home Waters, the Mediterranean and the Far East. Fifteen of the class were sunk of which 13 were lost in the Mediterranean. In 1940 *Triad* was lost due to unknown cause, and *Triton* was sunk by the Italian torpedo boat *Clio*. In 1941 *Tetrarch* was lost due to unknown cause. In 1942 *Tempest* and *Thorn* were sunk by the Italian torpedo boats *Circe* and *Pegaro* respectively, and *Talisman*, *Traveller* and *Triumph* were lost due to unknown cause. In 1943 *Turbulent* and *Thunderbolt* were sunk by Italian MA/SBs and the corvette *Cicogna* respectively; the *P.91* and *Trooper* were probably mined; and *Tigris* was lost due to unknown cause. The remaining pair were both lost in Home Waters in April 1940: *Tarpon* was sunk by the German minesweeper *M.6* in the North Sea and *Thistle* was torpedoed by the submarine *U4* off Norway. *Thetis* accidentally sank while on acceptance trials in Liverpool bay in 1939 but was later raised, repaired and commissioned as HMS *Thunderbolt*. *Terrapin* was extensively damaged by Japanese depth charging while operating in the South Pacific in May 1945 and, with the war almost over, she was declared a constructive total loss.

In 1940 the names *Triad*, *Tigris*, *Truant*, *Tetrarch*, *Talisman*, *Torbay* and *Tuna* were given to *N.53*, *N.63*, *N.68*, *N.77*, *N.79* and *N.94* respectively. The 1939 and 1940 Programme ships were initially given the numbers *P.91-99* and the majority entered service with these, but in 1943 all were given full names, except *P.91* which had been lost. *Tasman* was renamed *Talent* in 1945, to replace the original boat of that name.

The original *Talent* and *Tarn* were transferred to the Royal Netherlands Navy in 1944-45, being renamed *Zwaardfisch* and *Tijgerhaai* respectively, and during 1945-55 ten of the class were sold for scrap. *Templar* and *Tantivy* were expended as A/S targets during 1950-51 and *Truculent* was sunk in collision with a merchant vessel in January 1950 (all three were later raised and scrapped). *Taurus* and *Tapir* were temporarily loaned to the Netherlands in 1948 and operated as *Dolfijn* and *Zeehond* respectively until returned in 1953.

During 1951-56 a number of the all-welded boats, *Tabard*, *Taciturn*, *Thermopylae*, *Tiptoe*, *Totem*, *Trump*, *Truncheon* and *Turpin*, underwent major modernization. This involved lengthening the hull by adding a new 6.1-m (20-ft) section (*Taciturn* 4.3 m [14 ft], and *Thermopylae* and *Turpin* 3.7 m [12 ft]) amidships to accommodate a second pair of electric motors and more batteries. In addition the batteries were changed to the new high-capacity type, the external torpedo tubes were removed and the casing and conning tower were streamlined. The overall effect was to increase the displacement by about 200 tons and greatly improve their submerged performance in endurance, quiet running and in speed, which was raised to 15 knots. During 1955-60 *Talent*, *Tireless* and *Token* were given a similar but less extensive modernization in which they were streamlined and given high-capacity batteries but, being riveted vessels, not lengthened. The remaining unmodernized vessels, including the two Dutch boats, were sold for scrap during 1961-66 but the modernized vessels survived into the 1970s. Of these *Totem*, *Turpin* and *Truncheon* were transferred to Israel during 1967-68 and renamed *Dakar*, *Leviathan* and *Dolphin* respectively. *Dakar* was lost due to unknown cause in January 1968, *Leviathan*

HM Submarine *Thunderbolt*, better known as *Thetis* but renamed after she was lost in Liverpool bay in June 1939. She was recommissioned with a new name but finally lost in action in the Mediterranean in 1943 when she was attacked by an Italian corvette off Sicily

Triton

was sold for scrap in the mid-1970s and the *Dolphin*, serving as a training vessel, was the only surviving member of the class in 1978.

Triton (ordered under 1935 Programme), *Triumph* (1936), *Thistle* (1937), *Triad* (1937), *Truant* (1937), *Tetrach* (1939), *Trusty* (1939 Emergency War Programme), *Turbulent* (1939 EW), *Trespasser* (ex-*P92*) (1940), *Taurus* (ex-*P93*) (1940), *Tactician* (ex-*P94*) (1940), *Truculent* (ex-*P95*) (1940), *Templar* (ex-*P96*) (1940), *Tally Ho* (ex-*P97*) (1940), *Tantalus* (1940), *Tantivy* (1940), *Telemachus* (1941), *Talent* (1941), *Terrapin* (1941), *Thorough* (1941), *Tiptoe* (1941), *Trump* (1941), *Taciturn* (1941), *Tapir* (1941), *Tarn* (1941), *Tasman* (1941), *P91* (1940)—built by Vickers-Armstrongs
Tigris (1937), *Torbay* (1939), *Tradewind* (1941), *Trenchant* (1941)—built by Chatham dockyard
Tuna (1937), *Traveller* (1939 EW), *Trooper* (1939 EW), *Tabard* (1942)—built by Scotts
Thunderbolt (ex-*Thetis*) (1939), *Trident* (1936), *Taku* (1937), *Talisman* (1939), *Tempest* (1939 EW), *Thorn* (1939 EW), *Thrasher* (1939 EW)—built by Cammell Laird
Thule (ex-*P325*) (1941), *Tudor* (ex-*P326*) (1941), *Totem* (1942), *Truncheon* (1942)—built by Devonport dockyard
Tireless (1941), *Token* (1941), *Turpin* (1942), *Thermopylae* (1942)—built by Portsmouth dockyard

Triton was launched in 1937. The 1936 Programme boats were launched in 1938; the 1937 boats were launched in 1938-40; the 1939 boats were launched in 1939-40, and the Emergency War Programme boats were launched in 1940-42; the 1940 boats were launched in 1942; the 1941 boats were launched in 1942-45; and the 1942 boats were launched in 1943-45.

Displacement: 1090/1570 tons (surfaced/submerged) *Length:* 74.8 m (245 ft 6 in) pp *Beam:* 8.1 m (26 ft 6 in) *Draught:* 3.7 m (12 ft) *Machinery:* 2-shaft diesel/2 electric motors, 2500 bhp/1450 shp=15/9 knots (surfaced/submerged) *Armament:* 10 (later 11) 21-in (53-cm) torpedo tubes; 1 4-in (102-mm) *Crew:* 60

Triton

Danish corvette class, built 1953-58. The four Danish corvettes of the *Triton* Class were built to an Italian design in Italy for the Royal Danish Navy. Three similar ships were built for the Italian navy and one, *Lynx*, was laid down for the Royal Netherlands Navy but was subsequently transferred back to the Italian navy in 1961 and renamed *Aquila*. A further two vessels were laid down in Italy for the Indonesian navy where they are known as the *Pattimura* Class.

All the vessels have been built under the provisions of the US 'Offshore' Mutual Defense Aid Program (MDAP). Although all the vessels have been built to the same basic design they all vary in details of armament, radar, etc, as well as having slight differences in dimensions. The Italian boats originally mounted two 76-mm (3-in) guns carried fore and aft, but in 1963 these were replaced by two single Bofors 40-mm (1.57-in). It was planned that the vessels should eventually be armed with OTO-Melara 76-mm guns, but

No and name	laid down	launched	completed	builder
Danish vessels				
F.344 *Bellona*	1954	1/55	1/57	Naval Meccanica, Castellammare
F.345 *Diana*	—	12/54	7/55	Cantieri del Tirreno, Riva Trigoso
F.346 *Flora*	1953	6/55	8/56	Cantieri del Tirreno, Riva Trigoso
F.347 *Triton*	1953	9/54	8/55	Cantiere Navali, Taranto
Indonesian vessels				
801 *Pattimura*	1956	7/56	1/58	Ansaldo, Livorno
802 *Sultan Hasanudin*	1957	3/57	3/58	Ansaldo, Livorno
Italian vessels				
F.542 *Aquila* (ex-*Lynx*)	1953	7/54	10/56	Breda Marghera, Venice
F.543 *Albatros*	1953	7/54	6/55	Naval Meccanica, Castellammare
F.544 *Alcione*	1953	9/54	10/55	Naval Meccanica, Castellammare
F.545 *Airone*	1953	11/54	12/55	Naval Meccanica, Castellammare

this has never been implemented. The Italian vessels were designed primarily for A/S duties, and apart from the two triple US Mk 32 A/S torpedo tubes, the Italian vessels were equipped with two Hedgehogs, two depth-charge throwers and a depth-charge rack. The combined search and navigation radar is a single SMA/SPQ-2 model and the hull mounted a sonar QCU-2 set. The radius of action of the Italian ships is quoted as 3000 nautical miles at 18 knots with a bunkerage of 100 tons of diesel fuel.

The three Danish vessels displace some 40 tons less than the Italian boats, dimensions being the same. The armament shows that the role finally chosen for the Danish corvettes is somewhat different from that of the Italian boats, and they have been armed to operate in the restricted coastal waters around the Danish coastline. They have thus retained the 76-mm guns fore and aft, and in addition carry a single Bofors 40-mm mounted on the deckhouse just forward of the after 76-mm guns. They are not very well suited for A/S duties, being fitted with four obsolete depth-charge throwers and two Hedgehogs. The sonar is the same as that in the Italian vessels, but the search radar is the British Plessey AWS-1. The ships were originally rated as corvettes but are now generally regarded as frigates, having an F pennant number.

The two Indonesian boats are somewhat larger than the Italian and Danish boats, displacing some 150 tons more than the Italian boats and being some 6.1 m (20 ft) longer. This was to some extent necessitated by the Indonesian staff requirement that they

should have a higher speed than the Italian and Danish boats. They are equipped with three diesels driving three shafts, compared with the two-shaft diesels in the other ships. The Indonesians have retained the two 76-mm and in addition are armed with a twin 70-cal 30-mm (1.18-in) gun aft. Antisubmarine armament is identical to that of the Danish boats. Bunkerage is the same as the other vessels, but with three diesels the radius of action has been reduced to 2400 nautical miles.

These ships are now considered to be obsolete, and the Danish *Diana* was finally decommissioned for scrap in 1974, and the Indonesian ship *Sultan Hasanudin* (802) is in reserve.

(Danish vessels) *Displacement:* 760 tons (standard) *Length:* 76.3 m (250 ft 4 in) oa *Beam:* 9.6 m (31 ft 6 in) *Draught:* 2.7 m (8 ft 10 in) *Machinery* 2-shaft Fiat 409T diesels, 4400 bhp=20 knots *Armament:* 2 76-mm (3-in); 1 40-mm (1.57-in); 2 Hedgehogs; 4 depth-charge throwers *Crew* 100-110

(Indonesian vessels) *Displacement:* 950 tons (standard) *Length:* 82.4 m (270 ft 4 in) oa *Beam:* 10.4 m (34 ft 2 in) *Draught:* 2.7 m (8 ft 10 in) *Machinery:* 3-shaft Fiat diesels, 6900 bhp=22 knots *Armament:* as Danish vessels *Crew:* 100-110

(Italian vessels) *Displacement:* 800 tons (standard) *Dimensions* and *machinery:* as Danish vessels *Armament:* 2 76-mm (3-in); 1 40-mm (1.57-in); 2 Hedgehogs; 6 Mk 32 A/S torpedo tubes (2×3) *Crew:* 100-110

Triton

US nuclear-powered radar picket submarine. *Triton* was laid down on May 29, 1956, by General Dynamics (Electric Boat) at Groton, launched August 19, 1958, and completed November 10, 1959. She was designed and constructed as a radar picket submarine (SSRN) to provide early warning of aircraft attacks against a carrier task force, submerging when she herself was in danger of attack. A large, retractable air-search antenna was housed in the conning tower, and she was provided with a Combat Information Center and extensive communications. She was fitted with four bow torpedo tubes and two stern tubes.

Because of her size the *Triton* was to have two specially designed S4G pressurized water-cooled nuclear reactors, two steam turbines and two propeller shafts. To test these reactors a prototype reactor (S3G) was specially built ashore by the Atomic Energy Commission. At an overall length of 136.4 m (447 ft 6 in) she was the largest submarine ever built until the *Ohio* Class SSBNs, the first of which was launched in 1977. But, because of her size, there were problems during construction. While on the building slip her bow blocked the railway through the shipyard; a portion had to be cut away to allow the trains to pass, and was replaced just prior to launch. Her stern projected too far out into the river, and the last 15 m (50 ft) of stern section was constructed on an adjacent ship, being joined to the main hull only days before launch. The sail was too high to pass under the shipyard cranes during the launch and the top 3.7 m (12 ft) had to be cut away to be replaced later.

Triton's two reactors give her a maximum of 34 000 shp to produce the high surface speed necessary for operations in conjunction with fast carrier task forces. Her conventional hull configuration gives her excellent seagoing qualities, though submerged speed is a mere 20 knots.

In March 1961 the radar picket programme was abandoned and *Triton* was reclassified as an attack submarine (SSN 586). Subsequently it was proposed that she be operated as an underwater national command post afloat, a role for which her size, nuclear propulsion and large combat information center admirably suited her, but no funds for such a conversion were approved. She was therefore decommissioned May 3, 1969, only ten years after her completion, thus becoming the first nuclear-powered submarine to be placed in reserve.

Displacement: 5940/6670 tons (surfaced/submerged) *Length:* 136.4 m (447 ft 6 in) *Beam:* 11.3 m (37 ft) *Draught:* 7.3 m (24 ft) *Machinery:* 2 pressurized water-cooled S4G nuclear reactors, 2-shaft steam turbines, 34 000 shp=27/20 knots (surfaced/submerged) *Armament:* 6 21-in (53-cm) torpedo tubes (4 bow, 2 stern) *Crew:* 172 as radar picket

Trojan, North American T-28

US basic trainer and light attack aircraft. Developing a replacement for the ubiquitous and long-serving T-6 Texan basic trainer was a challenging task, but North American's NA-159 was good enough to win the US Air

The nuclear-powered radar picket submarine USS *Triton* (SSRN 586) under way in 1959

A T-28A Trojan. Though primarily a trainer it proved a highly efficient ground-attack fighter

Force's design competition not long after the Second World War. In 1948 the company received a contract to build two XT-28 prototypes which followed the same low-wing monoplane configuration as the Texan, with tandem seating for instructor and pupil. They differed from the Texan in being of all-metal construction, having a clear-view canopy, a retractable tricycle landing gear, and more power from an 800-hp Wright R-1300-1A seven-cylinder radial engine.

Maiden flight of the first XT-28 took place on September 26, 1949, and was followed by an initial contract for 266 production T-28A Trojans, subsequently increased to a total of 1194. Deliveries began in April 1950 and were completed during 1953. Two T-28As were evaluated by the US Navy, which subsequently ordered two models for its own training schools. The T-28B, of which 489 were built from 1954 onwards, stepped up the power by utilizing a 1425-hp Wright R-1820-86 Cyclone engine, but otherwise differed little from the air force's T-28A. The 299 T-28Cs were generally similar to the B model, but were fitted with arrester hooks to provide training in deck-landing techniques; the first one flew on September 19, 1955, and the last was delivered some two years later.

From 1958, with the advent of Cessna T-37A jet basic trainers, the USAF began to phase out its T-28As, several of which came on to the civilian market. North American developed a demilitarized version, powered by a 1300-hp Wright R-1820-56S engine and known as the NA-260 Nomad, and several conversions to this standard were made by the Pacific Aeronautics corporation (Pac-Aero). The Hamilton Aircraft company offered a similar conversion (but with a 1200-hp Wright engine) as the T-28-R Nomair, selling six hooked Nomairs to the Brazilian navy in 1962.

Meanwhile, the French Armée de l'Air, increasingly involved in the war in Algeria, had in 1959 evaluated the Nomad prototype as a potential light attack and reconnaissance aircraft. Following this, and the receipt of three PacAero conversions, Sud-Aviation purchased 245 ex-USAF T-28As and converted them to similar standard for the Armée de l'Air, by whom they were known as the Fennec (desert rat). The Fennec was provided with six underwing hardpoints, the inner two carrying a 12.5-mm (0.49-in) gun pod and the outer four a variety of bombs, rockets or other stores. It was used in Algeria and Indo-China.

Tromp

The USAF itself commissioned an armed version in 1961 as the T-28D, and over the next eight years 393 T-28As were converted to this standard by North American and Fairchild Republic. These were purchased with USAF funds and supplied under the Military Assistance Program to South Vietnam, Thailand, the Congo Republic and various South American air forces. The final version, designated T-28D-5, had two underwing guns plus six hardpoints for 1814 kg (4000 lb) of ordnance. An experimental version with increased warload, powered by a 2445-shp Lycoming T55 turboprop engine and having a taller vertical tail, was flown for the first time on February 15, 1963. Three of these YAT-28E prototypes were evaluated between 1964-66, but this version did not go into production.

(T-28A) *Span:* 12.37 m (40 ft 7 in) *Length:* 9.75 m (32 ft) *Gross weight:* 3595 kg (7925 lb) *Maximum speed:* 475 km/h (295 mph)

(T-28D) *Span:* 12.37 m (40 ft 7 in) *Length:* 10 m (32 ft 10 in) *Gross weight:* 3853 kg (8495 lb) *Maximum speed:* 611 km/h (380 mph)

Tromp

Dutch coast-defence battleship, built 1902-06. An improved version of the *Konigin Regentes* Class was authorized in 1901 and launched in 1904 by the Royal Dockyard at Amsterdam. In some other navies she would have been rated as an armoured cruiser, with only two single 24-cm (9.4-in) Krupp guns in turrets forward and aft and 15-cm (5.9-in) guns winged out at the corners of the superstructure. Also known by the full name *Marten Harpertszoon Tromp*, she spent most of her life in the East Indies and was stricken before the Second World War.

Displacement: 5300 tons (normal) *Length:* 100.9 m (331 ft) wl *Beam:* 14.6 m (48 ft) *Draught:* 5.6 m (18 ft 4 in) max *Machinery:* 2-shaft reciprocating steam, 6000 ihp=16.5 knots *Protection:* 152-104 mm (6-4 in) belt, 51 mm (2 in) deck, 254 mm (10 in) conning tower *Armament:* 2 24-cm (9.4-in) L/40 (2×1); 4 15-cm (5.9-in) L/40 (4×1); 10 75-mm (2.95-in) QF (10×1); 4 1-pdr (37-mm); 3 45-cm (17.7-in) torpedo tubes (1 above water, bow; 2 submerged, beam) *Crew:* 344

Tromp

Dutch cruiser class. *Tromp* and her sister *Jacob van Heemskerk* were designed during the early 1930s as a counter to the Japanese destroyers of the *Fubuki* Class which were larger and more powerful than the Dutch destroyers of the East Indies Squadron. Although classed as cruisers they were basically large destroyer leaders expanded to a small cruiser size in order to combine high speed and a relatively heavy armament with sufficient protection to provide defence against destroyer gunfire. This attempt to outclass the Japanese destroyers was probably cheaper than trying to match them on a ship-for-ship basis, which would have required the construction of several new vessels which collectively would have involved much greater expense. The main armament consisted of three twin 150-mm (5.9-in)

guns, two mounted forward and one aft, which could elevate to 60° for use against aircraft. Protection consisted of 16-mm (0.6-in) side plating supported by an internal belt of 32 mm (1.3 in) thickness, a 25-mm (1-in) main deck over the machinery spaces amidships and a 25-mm lower deck over the magazines. Designed speed was 33.5 knots, which, given the better seakeeping qualities of a larger vessel, was sufficient to allow them to keep pace with destroyers, though it was unlikely to allow them to escape from the majority of the larger Japanese cruisers which had design speeds of 33-36 knots. Both ships exceeded expectations and on trials *Tromp* achieved 34.5 knots.

Both vessels were constructed by the Netherlands shipyard in Amsterdam, *Tromp* being laid down in 1936, launched in 1937 and completed in 1938, joining the East Indies Squadron in the following year. *Jacob van Heemskerk* was laid down in 1938 and launched in 1939 but was still fitting out when the Germans invaded Holland in 1940. To avoid her falling into enemy hands she was towed to England in May 1940 and completed by Portsmouth dockyard during 1940-41. As the Dutch guns and mountings were not available she was fitted with four British twin 4-in (102-mm) dual-purpose mountings, three in the place of the 150-mm mounts and one abaft a new tripod mainmast (added to allow the fitting of air-warning radar), controlled from two directors, one on the bridge and one on the after superstructure. She was also fitted with a multiple 2-pdr pom-pom at the after end of the superstructure in place of the two twin 40-mm (1.58-in) mountings. This new armament effectively converted her into a small AA cruiser. Subsequently her pom-pom was replaced by a fifth twin 4-in mounting and both she and *Tromp* had their light AA armaments increased by the addition of several 40-mm and 20-mm (0.79-in) guns. *Heemskerk* was not fitted with torpedo tubes.

After the outbreak of war in the Far East, *Tromp* was employed in defence of the Dutch East Indies until the islands were overrun by the Japanese. She was finally withdrawn after being damaged while attacking a Japanese invasion force. After repairs she was attached to the British Eastern Fleet where she was later joined by *Heemskerk*. With a few exceptions they remained with this force until the end of the war taking part in several operations against the Japanese occupying their island colonies. Both ships were removed from the effective list in the late 1950s and were subsequently scrapped.

Displacement: 3850 tons (standard), 4280 tons (full load) *Length:* 132 m (433 ft) oa *Beam:* 12.4 m (40 ft 9 in) *Draught:* 4.6 m (15 ft) *Machinery:* 2-shaft geared steam turbines, 56 000 shp=33.5 knots *Protection:* 50 mm (1.97 in) sides, 25 mm (1 in) decks, 16 mm (0.6 in) turrets *Armament:* 6 150-mm (5.9-in) (3×2); 4 40-mm (1.57-in) (2×2); 4 12.7-mm (0.5-in) (2×2); 6 53-cm (21-in) torpedo tubes (2×3) *Crew:* 309

Tromp

Dutch guided-missile destroyer class. *Tromp* (F.801) was laid down on August 4, 1971, launched May 2, 1973, and completed May 10, 1975. *De Ruyter* (F.806) was laid down December 22, 1971, launched March 9, 1974,

and completed in June 1976. Both ships were built by De Schelde, Flushing. Designed to replace the aging cruisers of the *De Ruyter* Class, they were built as flagships for the ASW frigate squadrons, and a flush deck with high freeboard was selected for good seakeeping in the North Sea and eastern Atlantic waters in which they are expected to operate.

The COGOG propulsion system is similar to that of the British Type 42 destroyers, with two Olympus gas turbines for boost and two Tyne gas turbines for cruise; the gearing is of Dutch design and manufacture. The large twin uptakes are angled out in order to keep the hot gases clear of the radars.

A twin automatic 120-mm (4.7-in) mounting, removed from one of the older *Holland* Class destroyers, is fitted forward of the bridge, with an octuple launcher for NATO Sea Sparrow missiles above it to provide short-range air defence. Both of these weapons are controlled by the HSA WM 25 director mounted above the launcher. Aft of the tall mainmast is a US Mk 13 Tartar launcher for Standard SM-1 missiles, providing area defence, with two SPG-51 tracker/illuminators. Quadruple launchers for US Harpoon SSMs have recently been fitted on the superstructure immediately forward of the funnel uptakes. Three-dimensional air search and tracking for both these weapons are combined in the massive radome which gives the ships their distinctive appearance. Inside the dome HSA radars of Dutch manufacture are mounted back to back above and below a common platform. For antisubmarine operations they carry a helicopter. A Wasp was carried initially but this will eventually be replaced by a Lynx with its own hangar and maintenance facilities. Two triple banks of Mk 32 torpedo tubes are fitted at upper-deck level amidships. The sonars are of British and US manufacture.

Three ships of the *Tromp* Class were originally projected, but in view of the high cost of the first two ships it was decided to replace the third by an area-defence version of the Standard frigate.

Displacement: 3665 tons (standard), 4300 tons (full load) *Length:* 138.6 m (454 ft 9 in) oa *Beam:* 14.8 m (48 ft 6 in) *Draught:* 4.6 m (15 ft) *Machinery:* 2 Olympus gas turbines, 44 000 hp=28 knots; 2 Tyne gas turbines, 8200 hp=18 knots *Armament:* 2 120-mm (4.7-in) DP (1×2); 1 Standard SM-1 Mk 13 launcher; 1 Sea Sparrow octuple launcher; 2 Harpoon SSM quadruple launchers; 6 Mk 32 A/S torpedo tubes; 1 helicopter *Crew:* 306

Trumper

British homing torpedo. Following the cancellation of the Bowler project in 1942, work started on a new torpedo called Trumper. It was an active homer based on the 21-in (53-cm) Mk 8 and Mk 9 torpedoes. The details of design were settled in 1943 on the basis of acoustic data from the Bowler research, and the General Electric company of Wembley, Middlesex was given a development contract. In the winter of 1943 a trial was conducted against a submarine.

The homing method first used was phase comparison but this was dropped in favour of amplitude comparison, as in the German Zaunkönig. A quartz crystal transmitter and

The Dutch guided-missile destroyer *Tromp*. Vessels in her class are readily recognizable by the distinctive all-weather protective dome which houses complex Dutch-designed HSA radars

mosaic of receiver crystals were mounted inside an oil-filled dome fitted to a specially flattened Mk 8 nose. The two stacks of crystals were paired to give a single broad beam with a spread of about 60°. The target was kept on the edge of the beam to give a lead-angle of about 30°, giving some protection from towed 'foxers' and the target's wake. When the range had been reduced to 155 m (170 yards) Trumper made a 40° turn towards the noise source.

Trumper reached the stage of sea trials in 1945, but the end of hostilities resulted in its cancellation.

Truxtun

US nuclear-powered guided-missile cruiser. The US Navy requested seven oil-burning frigates in the FY 1962 programme; six of them were completed as *Belknap* Class vessels but Congress stipulated that one unit be nuclear-propelled. This was ordered in 1962 as DLGN.35 from New York Shipbuilding, laid down on June 17, 1963, launched as *Truxtun* on December 19, 1964, and completed on May 27, 1967. *Truxtun* carried an identical armament to that of her *Belknap* Class contemporaries, but there was one major difference in layout: the single 127-mm (5-in) Mk 45 gun was fitted forward, with its Mk 68 director above the bridge, and the twin Mk 10 launchers aft, with the two SPG-55 guidance radars above the hangar—the reverse of the placing of these two systems on *Belknap*. As on the latter, the magazine for the Mk 10 launcher could hold Terrier surface-to-surface missiles and Asroc antisubmarine missiles. Two single 76-mm (3-in)/50-cal guns were mounted in tubs projecting from the superstructure amidships. Beneath the tubs were two single Mk 32 torpedo tubes port and starboard housed in the superstructure. Two Mk 25 tubes were

also built into the stern but have not been used. The armament was completed by a DASH (drone antisubmarine helicopter) with its own hangar. This was later replaced, as on the *Belknap* Class, by a manned Seasprite helicopter (LAMPS I).

The sensor outfit was even more advanced than that of the *Belknap* Class. In addition to the large SQS-26 bow sonar, *Truxtun* was fitted with an SPS-40 air-search radar and the new SPS-48 three-dimensional planar radar, with a smaller SPS-10 for surface surveillance. The latter three aerials are mounted on top of tall quadruped lattice masts, which combine with the absence of funnels to give the ship a distinctive appearance.

The propulsion system is identical to that of *Bainbridge*. The turbines give her less power and a lower speed than the *Belknap* Class, but this is more than compensated by the increase in endurance.

The Terrier missile has been superseded by the extended-range Standard missile, which has improved performance. It seems likely that the 76-mm guns may also be replaced by quadruple launchers for Harpoon surface-to-surface missiles in the near future. *Truxtun* has served in the Pacific Fleet since completion. She was redesignated CGN in 1975.

Displacement: 8200 tons (standard), 9200 tons (full load) *Length:* 118 m (387 ft 3 in) *Beam:* 17.7 m (58 ft) *Draught:* 9.4 m (30 ft 9 in) *Machinery:* 2 DG2 nuclear reactors, 2-shaft steam turbines, 60 000 shp=30 knots *Armament:* 1 twin Mk 10 launcher, Standard ER SAMs and Asroc A/S missiles; 1 127-mm (5-in)/54-cal Mk 42 DP; 2 76-mm (3-in) AA; 4 32.4-cm (12.75-in) torpedo tubes, Mk 32 A/S torpedoes; 1 Seasprite helicopter *Crew:* 510

TS-11, PZL-Mielec Polish trainer and light ground-attack aircraft **See Iskra**

TSh-2, Grigorovitch

Soviet ground-attack aircraft. This unequal-span single-bay two-seat biplane was developed by Dmitri P Grigorovitch at the Central Construction Bureau (TsKB) in Moscow in 1930. With the Bureau designation TsKB-21, it was based on the LSh (TsKB-2), which in turn had been inspired by Polikarpov's R-5 light bomber-reconnaissance biplane. The LSh had failed because its engine was to be fully enclosed in an armour casing while crew cockpits were to be protected by an armoured canopy, leaving them restricted vision through louvres and a periscope. The resultant aircraft would be difficult to operate and overweight with consequently poor performance.

Before completion the LSh was converted to the TSh-1 (TsKB-6), the TSh part of the designation standing for heavy ground-attack aircraft. This flew in February 1931 and was followed by two more prototypes, each differing in the method of armour attachment—welding, bolting and riveting. An open cockpit arrangement was preferred, and power was provided by a water-cooled M-17 engine. The armament of TSh-1 was retained in the TSh-2, but the eight fixed PV-1 7.62-mm (0.30-in) forward-firing machine-guns were accommodated in the thickened lower wing instead of in the two detachable four-gun underwing packs utilized by the TSh-1.

Although it was thought that a small batch of TSh-2s had been delivered to the VVS (Soviet air force), this has never been confirmed. Development of armour protection conceived as part of the aircraft structure rather than as 100% additional dead weight continued through the TSh-3 low-wing monoplane with a fixed 'trousered' undercarriage and eventually led to the BSh, better known as the Il-2 Sturmovik.

Span: 15.5 m (50 ft 10 in) *Length:* not known *Gross weight:* not known *Maximum speed:* 215 km/h (134 mph)

Tsukuba

Japanese battleship class. *Tsukuba* and her sister *Ikoma* were laid down during the Russo-Japanese War, and their design was heavily influenced by various factors which emerged from naval operations conducted during the war. Although it was not anticipated that these two ships would be completed to take part in the war, the Japanese wanted to press ahead with their construction to replace expected losses and to help build up a more modern navy.

Japanese designers were convinced that guns of the largest size were most effective, and followed the theories advocated by the Italian designer Vittorio Cuniberti that modern capital ships should be fast and well armoured with a uniform gun calibre. *Tsukuba* and *Ikoma* thus carried a main armament of four 12-in (305-mm) guns in two twin turrets, a main armoured belt of 178 mm (7 in) at its maximum, and a speed of 20.5 knots. These vessels were in effect armoured cruisers, and outclassed all other cruisers then in existence. They laid the basic design foundations for what eventually became known as the battlecruiser. No other naval power built such vessels as these, the contemporary British *Duncan* Class, built some four years earlier, being much slower although with similar armament and protection. The nearest approach was the Italian *Roma* Class, but they carried a mixed-calibre armament of 12-in and 8-in (203-mm) guns. Although a superb design these two ships were obsolete by the time they were completed, for other navies had also learnt the lessons of the Russo-Japanese War, and Britain and Germany had begun construction of battlecruiser-type vessels. They were soon joined by the US, and the balance of power in the Far East gradually began to swing in favour of the US, with her vast industrial potential.

Construction of these two vessels by Kure navy yard was fairly rapid, spurred on mainly by the progress with the Russo-Japanese War and the naval losses suffered by Japan. The ships were majestic looking vessels, the two tall funnels exhausting the 20 Miyabara boilers were well spaced, and the forecastle deck extended aft to just forward of the rear 12-in turret. The secondary 6-in (152-mm) guns were sited in a main-deck battery, but the siting of the lower casemate guns left something to be desired, for their operation was hampered in any seaway. This shortcoming was rectified in *Ikoma* during 1919 when she was refitted, and the 6-in guns resited one deck higher, two of the 6-in being completely removed. Further alterations to the armament during this refit left *Ikoma* with four 12-in, eight 4.7-in (120-mm) and six 3-in (76-mm). She was then used as a gunnery-training tender until 1922 when she was disarmed under the terms of the Washington Treaty and finally broken up in 1924. Although the basic concept of the design proved satisfactory the ships suffered from numerous defects, being the largest warships built in Japan at the time.

At the start of the First World War the two ships were employed hunting for the German Far East Squadron of Admiral von Spee. *Tsukuba* was lost when her magazine exploded when anchored in Yokosuka harbour in the afternoon of January 14, 1917. A total of 305 of the crew were lost. The wreck was subsequently salvaged and broken up.

Displacement: 13 750 tons (normal) *Length:* 144.8 m (475 ft) oa *Beam:* 22.8 m (74 ft 9 in) *Draught:* 7.9 m (26 ft) *Machinery:* 2-shaft vertical triple-expansion, 20 500 ihp=20.5 knots *Protection:* 178-102 mm (7-4 in) main belt, 178-127 (7-5 in) turrets and casemates, 203-152 mm (8-6 in) conning tower, 50 mm (2 in) deck *Armament:* 4 12-in (305-mm) (2×2); 12 6-in (152-mm) (12×1); 12 4.7-in (120-mm); 2 14-pdr (76-mm); 3 3-pdr (47-mm); 3 18-in (46-cm) torpedo tubes *Crew:* 817

Tu-4, Tupolev

Soviet strategic bomber. The aerodynamic and structural advances incorporated in the Boeing B-29 Superfortress made it the most sophisticated strategic bomber of the Second World War, and the United States had refused to supply it to the Soviet Union. Consequently, when three B-29s operating from China landed at Vladivostok during the second half of 1944, the first with battle damage but the others simply short of fuel,

The Japanese battleship *Tsukuba* in 1907. She was lost when her magazine exploded in 1917

Name	laid down	launched	completed
Ikoma	3/05	4/06	3/08
Tsukuba	1/05	12/05	1/07

the Tupolev design bureau was asked not only to build a copy but to provide plans for Soviet production of the type. No fewer than 20 pre-series aircraft were completed before the Tu-4, as it was designated in Soviet service, was ready to enter production towards the end of 1946. The first production aircraft was seen publicly at the Tushino air display in August 1947, and deliveries to the ADD (long-range aviation) began in early 1948, a remarkable achievement considering that all the B-29's complex systems had to be duplicated as well as the structure.

The Tu-4, subsequently designated Bull by NATO, was powered by four 2200-hp ASh-73TK engines and was somewhat lighter than the Superfortress. It remained in service as a front-line bomber until the late 1950s, and subsequently served as a tanker, radar trainer and transport. A number were supplied to China in the mid-1950s, and developments included prototypes of the Tu-70 Cart and Tu-75 transports and the Tu-80 Barge bomber. The Tu-70 and 75, civil and military transports respectively, used new fuselages, while the much larger Tu-85 was comparable to the US Convair B-36, but the imminent arrival of jet-powered types led to its abandonment.

Span: 43.05 m (141 ft 3 in) *Length:* 30.18 m (99 ft) *Gross weight:* 47 600 kg (104 940 lb) *Maximum speed:* not known

Tucker

US destroyer class, built 1913-17. Six destroyers (DD.57-62) were authorized in 1913, followed by six more a year later (DD.63-68). They were an expansion of the preceding *Cassin* Class, but with slightly reduced beam for higher speed, and geared turbines for efficiency.

Tucker (DD.57), *Sampson* (DD.63), *Rowan* (DD.64)—built by Fore River

Conyngham (DD.58), *Porter* (DD.59), *Wilkes* (DD.67)—built by Cramp
Wadsworth (DD.60), *Davis* (DD.65), *Allen* (DD.66)—built by Bath Iron Works
Jacob Jones (DD.61), *Wainwright* (DD.62)—built by New York shipbuilding
Shaw (DD.68)—built by Mare Island navy yard

These were the latest US destroyers in service when war broke out in April 1917, and they were sent across to Queenstown (now Cobh), Ireland, as antisubmarine escorts. *Jacob Jones* was torpedoed by a U-Boat on December 6, 1917. On October 9, 1918 Shaw lost her bow in collision with the troopship *Aquitania* but reached port safely. *Conyngham*, *Porter*, *Davis*, *Shaw*, *Tucker*, *Wainwright* and *Wilkes* were transferred to the coastguard in 1924-26 as *CG.2*, *CG.7* and *CG.21-25*; after their return in 1933 they were scrapped. *Wadsworth* was scrapped in 1936 but *Allen* survived until 1946. She was stationed at Pearl Harbor throughout the Second World War and was used for training.

Displacement: 1090-1110 tons (normal) *Length:* 96.09 m (315 ft 3 in) oa *Beam:* 9.3 m (30 ft 6 in) *Draught:* 2.9 m (9 ft 6 in) *Machinery:* 2-shaft geared steam turbines, 17 000-18 000 shp=29.5 knots *Armament:* 4 4-in (102-mm) QF (4×1); 8/12 21-in (53-cm) torpedo tubes (4×2/3) *Crew:* 100

Tu-2, Tupolev Soviet medium bomber
See **Bat**

Tu-14, Tupolev Soviet light bomber
See **Bosun**

Tu-16, Tupolev Soviet strategic bomber and reconnaissance aircraft See **Badger**

Tu-20, Tupolev Soviet strategic bomber and reconnaissance aircraft See **Bear**

Tu-22, Tupolev Soviet medium bomber
See **Blinder**

Tu-26, Tupolev Soviet strategic bomber and reconnaissance aircraft See **Backfire**

Tu-28, Tupolev Soviet jet intercepter
See **Fiddler**

Tu-85, Tupolev Soviet strategic bomber
See **Barge**

Tu-98, Tupolev Soviet experimental bomber/intercepter See **Backfin**

Tu-114, Tupolev Soviet AWACS aircraft
See **Moss**

Tucumcari

US hydrofoil. The hydrofoil *Tucumcari* was launched by Boeing Aerospace on July 15, 1967, and commissioned on March 7, 1968. She was built to test the feasibility of developing hydrofoils for military use. She was ordered in 1966 and was designed with a fully submerged foil system with a canard configuration. The two after foils supported about 70% of the displacement, while the bow foil supported 30%. When foil-borne, steering was accomplished by the forward foil rotating on its strut about a vertical axis. To maintain the hull at a constant height above the water a wave-height sensing system is used.

A water-jet propulsion system was used in which a powerful pump developed the thrust needed to propel the vessel by ejecting a considerable mass of water at high speed. When foil-borne, sea water was sucked in through openings in the foils and carried in ducts to the pump inlet. Power for the pump was provided by a Rolls-Royce Proteus gas turbine. When hull-borne another water-jet pump, driven by a General Motors diesel, provided propulsion.

The military potential of *Tucumcari* was tested in 1969-70. She carried out a number of coastal patrols off Vietnam which proved that the hydrofoil was capable of operating in rough weather conditions. The following year *Tucumcari* carried out a number of trials for various NATO navies. It was generally felt that she was rather too small to meet a practical NATO requirement, but nevertheless proved the principle and capability of the hydrofoil. As a result of these trials the Italians designed their own slightly larger hydrofoil, *Sparviero*, which was completed in May 1973, while the US designed the 230-ton *Pegasus*.

During the numerous trials carried out with *Tucumcari* she was found to suffer from a lack of lateral stability but the addition of ventilation fences to the surface-piercing struts of the foils overcame this problem. The machine-guns and mortar were removed in 1971 and a 20-mm (0.79-in) gun added. On November 15, 1972, *Tucumcari* ran aground and was severely damaged. The cost of repairs was prohibitive and the ship was scrapped in October 1973.

Displacement: 58 tons *Length:* 22.7 m (74 ft 6 in) *Beam:* 5.9 m (19 ft 6 in) *Draught:* 1.4 m (4 ft 6 in) hull-borne *Machinery:* 1 gas turbine, 3100 hp=40+ knots (foil-borne); 1 General Motors

diesel, 150 hp (hull-borne) *Armament:* 1 40-mm (1.57-in); 4 machine-guns; 1 80-mm (3.1-in) mortar *Crew:* 13

Tullibee

US nuclear-powered submarine. The USS *Tullibee* (SSN.597) was originally planned as a 1000-ton submarine for antisubmarine operations, with good manoeuvrability rather than high speed. A modified *Albacore*-type teardrop hull was used, but the need to increase the size to accommodate the reactor and its shielding led to a submarine over twice the planned size. A new type of pressurized-water reactor, the S2C, with turbo-electric drive was used to power the boat, giving a higher silent speed than in the earlier boats. The whole of the bow was used to house sonar equipment for detecting and tracking enemy submarines, and the four torpedo tubes were therefore fitted amidships position, angled out at 10° from either side of the hull.

Tullibee was laid down on May 26, 1958, launched on April 27, 1960 and commissioned on November 10, 1960. Experience gained with *Tullibee* was incorporated in the later *Thresher* Class, and no further submarines were built to this design.

Displacement: 2317/2640 tons (surfaced/submerged) *Length:* 83.2 m (273 ft) oa *Beam:* 7.2 m (23 ft 6 in) *Draught:* 6.4 m (21 ft) *Machinery:* 1-shaft S2C nuclear reactor, 1-shaft turbo-electric, 2500 shp=15/15 knots (surfaced/submerged) *Armament:* 4 21-in (53-cm) torpedo tubes *Crew:* 87

Tumleren

Danish torpedo boat class, built 1911. At the same time as a prototype torpedo boat (*Söridderen*) was ordered from the British firm Yarrow, the same specification was put out to the German firm Schichau. The lead ship *Tumleren* was built in Germany, while the *Vindhunden* and *Spaekhuggeren* were built in the Royal Dockyard at Copenhagen. The layout was reminiscent of the later *A.1*-type torpedo boats built for the German navy in 1915, with a single funnel, and a well deck between bridge and forecastle. As in the *Söridderen* Class there were single guns forward and aft, single torpedo tubes sided in the well deck, a bow tube and single tube sided aft.

The three boats were renumbered *19, 18* and *17* respectively in 1920, then *C.1-3* in 1923 and finally *N.1-3* in 1929. All three were scrapped in 1935.

Displacement: 295 tons (normal) *Length:* 56.4 m (185 ft) wl *Beam:* 5.8 m (19 ft) *Draught:* 2.2 m (7 ft 3 in) *Machinery:* 2-shaft steam turbines, 5000 shp=27.5 knots *Armament:* 2 75-mm (2.95-in) QF (2×1); 5 45-cm (17.7-in) torpedo tubes (1 bow, 4 deck) *Crew:* 33

Tumult

British destroyer class. The vessels of the *Tumult* Class formed the 6th Destroyer Flotilla of the Emergency War Programme and were of identical design to the previous *Savage* Class except that they were not fitted for Arctic service. They were laid down in

1941, launched in 1942 and completed in 1943. The designed AA armament consisted of a twin 40-mm (1.57-in) mounting amidships and four twin 20-mm (0.79-in) mountings, two abaft the funnels and one in each of the bridge wings. At the time of completion the twin 40-mm was in short supply, so *Tyrian*, *Tuscan*, *Tumult* and *Troubridge* carried two single 20-mm and *Tenacious* two twin 20-mm mountings in its place. These weapons were later replaced by the proper mounting. In addition *Tumult* was completed with an experimental arrangement of two fixed torpedo tubes, mounted on the upper deck abreast the funnel, instead of her forward bank of revolving tubes. After trials these were removed and the ship reverted to the standard tube outfit.

On completion the class were formed into the 24th Destroyer Flotilla and sent to the Mediterranean where they operated until late in 1944 when they were earmarked for the British Eastern Fleet. Before being transferred they were refitted to improve their AA defence and had their twin 20-mm mountings replaced by four or five 40-mm or 2-pdr singles, except *Tyrian* which retained the 20-mm guns in her bridge wings. Early in 1945 they sailed for the Indian Ocean where instead of joining the Eastern Fleet they were attached to the newly formed British Pacific Fleet with which they operated until after the war.

In 1946 the class was placed in reserve except for the *Troubridge*, which served as leader to the 3rd Destroyer Flotilla, Mediterranean, during 1946-49. During the 1950s the entire class was converted into fast antisubmarine frigates which extended their lives until the late 1960s when the majority were sold for scrap.

See also *Rapid* and *Tenacious*.

Teazer, Tenacious—built by Cammell Laird
Termagant, Terpsichore—built by Denny
Troubridge, Tumult—built by John Brown
Tuscan, Tyrian—built by Swan Hunter

Displacement: 1800 tons (standard), 2500 tons (full load) *Length:* 110.6 m (362 ft 9 in) oa *Beam:* 10.9 m (35 ft 9 in) *Draught:* 3.05 m (10 ft) *Machinery:* 2-shaft geared turbines, 40 000 shp=36 knots *Armament:* 4 4.7-in (120-mm); 2 40-mm (1.57-in); 8 20-mm (0.79-in) (4×2) ; 8 21-in (53-cm) torpedo tubes (2×4) *Crew:* 179

Tupolev Soviet aircraft See **Backfin, Backfire, Badger, Barge, Bat, Bear, Blinder, Bosun, Fiddler, MDR-2, MDR-4, Moss, TB-1, TB-3, Tu-4**

Turbine

Italian destroyer class, built 1925-28. Eight improved *Nazario Sauro* Class destroyers were ordered in 1925.

Aquilone, Turbine—built by Odero, Sestri Ponente
Borea, Espero, Ostro, Zeffiro—built by Ansaldo
Euro, Nembo—built by Cantieri del Tirreno, Riva Trigoso

Most of the class were early Second World War losses. *Espero* was sunk in action with

Turbo-Porter, Pilatus

British cruisers on June 28, 1940, and *Zeffiro* was torpedoed by an aircraft on July 5. On July 20, 1940, *Nembo* and *Ostro* were also sunk by aircraft torpedoes, and on September 17 *Aquilone* was sunk by mine and *Borea* by bombing. *Euro* was sunk by a German bomb on October 1, 1943, while *Turbine* was recommissioned by the Germans as *TA.14* and sunk by US air attack on September 15, 1944.

Displacement: 1090 tonnes (standard), 1700 tonnes (full load) *Length:* 93.2 m (305 ft 9 in) oa *Beam:* 9.2 m (30 ft 2 in) *Draught:* 3 m (9 ft 10 in) *Machinery:* 2-shaft geared steam turbines, 40 000 shp=36 knots *Armament:* 4 120-mm (4.7-in)/45-cal (2×2); 2 2-pdr (40-mm)/39-cal AA (2×1); 2/4 13.2-mm (0.52-in) machine-guns; 6 53-cm (21-in) torpedo tubes (2×3) *Crew:* 179

An Italian *Turbine* Class destroyer. Most of the class were sunk early in the Second World War

Turbo-Porter, Pilatus

Swiss multipurpose utility aircraft. Although the great majority of the 400-plus Turbo-Porters and piston-engined Porters have been sold by Pilatus (and Fairchild, who built them under licence) to civilian customers, a number of the world's air forces employ this superb STOL aeroplane for all kinds of transportation jobs, often in extremely difficult terrain and without recognized airstrips. Among them are Australia (army), Austria, Bolivia, Chad, Colombia, Ecuador, Israel, Peru, Sudan and Thailand.

Nominally a ten-seat transport (or equivalent weight of cargo), the piston-engined Porter first flew in 1959 and the turboprop version about two years later. Fairchild produced 15 of a special counter-insurgency version for the US Air Force's Credible Chase programme in Vietnam. Known as the AU-23A Peacemaker, it had a 650-shp AiResearch TPE 331-1-101F turboprop (most Turbo-Porters have a Turboméca Astazou or Canadian Pratt & Whitney PT6A in the 500-550-shp range) and was armed with side-firing 20-mm (0.79-in) XM-197 cannon or 7.62-mm (0.30-in) Miniguns. One fuselage and four underwing pylons could carry an external load of up to 907 kg (2000 lb) of bombs, rockets, napalm, smoke grenades, flares, camera pods or other stores; the cabin was often occupied by psychological warfare broadcast and leaflet-dropping equipment, and other sensors. After the US withdrawal from South-East Asia the USAF transferred 14 of its Peacemakers to the Royal Thai Air Force, to whom it supplied a further 20 similar aircraft in 1975-76.

(AU-23A Peacemaker) *Span:* 15.14 m (49 ft 8 in) *Length:* 11.23 m (36 ft 10 in) *Gross weight:* 2767 kg (6100 lb) *Maximum speed:* 280 km/h (174 mph)

Turbulent

British destroyer class. In 1914 four destroyers were ordered by Turkey from the British shipbuilders Hawthorn Leslie, but the First World War began before they could be laid down and work on them was abandoned. A large amount of the material required had been assembled, so in November 1914 the Admiralty reordered the four ships with the design slightly modified to suit British requirements. They were originally to be named *Napier, Ogre, Offa* and *Narborough*, but in February 1915 (when the names were allotted to *Matchless* Class ships) they were renamed *Talisman, Turbulent, Trident* and *Termagant*. They were laid down during December 1914 and January 1915 and launched between July 1915 and January 1916. In design they resembled slightly enlarged *Matchless* Class destroyers but carried a heavier gun armament having five instead of three 4-in (102-mm) guns. Two of these weapons were mounted abreast the bridge on the forecastle, one on a bandstand between the first and second funnels, and two aft, one being raised on a platform.

All four completed early in 1916, *Termagant* and *Turbulent* joining the battlecruiser force of the Grand Fleet and the remaining pair joining the Harwich Force. Both the Grand Fleet ships took part in the Battle of Jutland and during the night actions on the morning of June 1, 1916, *Turbulent* was sunk when her flotilla ran across the head of the German line. After Jutland, *Termagant* joined her sisters at Harwich where the three were employed with the submarine flotillas. In 1917 they transferred to the 6th Destroyer Flotilla at Dover and spent the rest of the war patrolling the Channel defences. In 1919 they were placed in reserve and in 1921 they were sold for scrap.

Displacement: 1098 tons (load) *Length:* 94.2 m (309 ft) oa *Beam:* 8.7 m (28 ft 7 in) *Draught:* 2.9 m (9 ft 6 in) *Machinery:* 3-shaft direct-drive steam turbines, 25 000 shp=34 knots *Armament:* 5 4-in (102-mm) (5×1); 4 21-in (53-cm) torpedo tubes (2×2) *Crew:* 102

Turunmaa

Finnish corvette class. Ordered in 1966 from the Wärtsila shipyard, Helsinki, both ships were laid down in March 1967. *Turunmaa* was launched on July 11, 1967, and completed on August 29, 1968. *Karjala* was launched on August 16, 1967, and completed October 21, 1968. Small and compact, with a low flush-decked hull, topped by a tall superstructure with an enclosed bridge, the *Turunmaa* Class were designed primarily for trade protection. The requirement for good endurance at cruising speed combined with a capability for bursts of high speed resulted in a novel propulsion system. Three small Mercedes-Benz diesels, each with a rating of 1330 bhp, drive three shafts for a cruising speed of 17 knots. On the centre shaft aft of the diesel is an Olympus gas turbine with a rating of 22 000 hp which is used to boost speed to 35 knots. This was only the second installation of the Olympus turbine (the first was on HMS *Exmouth*), and the ships were apparently still running in 1979 with the original turbines.

The armament is conventional. A single 120-mm (4.7-in) Bofors dual-purpose gun, with an elevation of 80° and a rate of fire of 80 rds/min is mounted forward of the bridge. Two single 40-mm (1.57-in) Bofors AA guns are carried, one on the after end of the superstructure and the other on the stern, and there is also a twin 30-mm (1.18-in) mounting aft of the single mast. For fire control against ships or aircraft a Dutch HSA M-22 radome is fitted above the bridge. The armament is completed by two depth-charge projectors. To counteract the considerable topweight Vosper Thornycroft fin stabilizers are fitted.

Displacement: 660 tons (standard), 770 tons (full load) *Length:* 74.1 m (243 ft) oa *Beam:* 7.8 m (25 ft 6 in) *Draught:* 2.6 m (8 ft 6 in) *Machinery:* 1-shaft Olympus gas turbine, 22 000 hp=35 knots, 3-shaft Mercedes-Benz diesels, 3990 bhp=17 knots *Armament:* 1 120-mm (4.7-in) DP; 2 40-mm (1.57-in) AA (2×1); 1 30-mm (1.18-in) AA (1×2); 2 depth-charge projectors *Crew:* 70

'Turya'

Soviet hydrofoil class. These hydrofoils, of which it is estimated that about 30 are in service, have been developed from the basic 'Osa' patrol boats, large numbers of which are in service. Dimensions are the same as the 'Osas' but displacement has been increased by some 35 tons. They appear to be a hydrofoil version of the standard 'Stenka' displacement-hull patrol craft, also developed from the 'Osa'.

The 'Turya' Class have been developed from the outset as a military hydrofoil, whereas the earlier 'Pchela' Class were developed for use by the frontier guard. They carry a fairly standard armament for an older type of patrol boat of four torpedo tubes and guns. They do show one unusual feature in that there appears to be a form of VDS fitted on the transom stern. Although the hydrofoils are fitted with sonar they appear to lack any form of antisubmarine armament. They would probably be able to co-operate with shore-based helicopters in an A/S role. It is possible that the 16-in (41-cm) A/S torpedo will replace the 21-in (53-cm). The main search radar is a Pot Drum and fire control is exercised through Drum Tilt. The 'Turya' Class vessels began to enter service in 1973, and production is estimated at about 4-5 a year.

Displacement: 200 tons (standard), 230 tons (full load) *Length:* 39.2 m (128 ft 8 in) *Beam:* 7.6 m (25 ft) *Draught:* 1.8 m (5 ft 10 in) *Machinery:* 3 diesels, 14 000 hp=40 knots *Armament:* 2 57-mm (2.24-in) (1×2); 2 25-mm (1-in) (1×2); 4 21-in (53-cm) torpedo tubes *Crew:* 30

Tutor, Canadair CL-41

Canadian jet basic trainer and light ground-attack aircraft. The CL-41 is an all-Canadian aeroplane, its airframe having been designed by Canadair and its J85 turbojet by the Montreal branch of the US aero-engine giant, Pratt & Whitney. Canadair first proposed the CL-41 to the Canadian government in 1958, but met with a lukewarm response. The project then lay dormant for more than a year before the company decided to go ahead without government funding, eventually flying the first of two prototypes on January 13, 1960; this was powered by a 1089-kg (2400-lb) st JT12A-5 turbojet engine.

Its economical operation and excellent flying qualities soon impressed the Royal Canadian Air Force, and Canadair's persistence was rewarded with a contract for 190 production CL-41As, powered by the 1195-kg (2633-lb) st J85-CAN-40 turbojet. Deliveries began in October 1963 and were completed during 1966, the RCAF introducing 'all-through' jet training on these aircraft in early 1965. It is this trainer model, with the RCAF (now Canadian Armed Forces) designation CT-114, which has the name Tutor. About half the original number were still in service 12 years later, most of them with No 2 Flying School at Moose Jaw, Saskatchewan, and others with the CAF Snowbirds aerobatic display team. Some Royal Netherlands Air Force pilots train in Canada on the Tutor.

Like most jet trainers, the CL-41 was fully capable of doubling as a light attack aircraft, and a CL-41G prototype flew in June 1964 with a 1338-kg (2950-lb) st J85-J4 engine. It had no built-in armament, but six underwing points enable it to carry up to 1814 kg (4000 lb) of bombs, napalm, gun or rocket pods, Sidewinder missiles or drop tanks. Twenty CL-41Gs were supplied to the Royal Malaysian Air Force, by whom they are known as the Tebuan (wasp), between 1967-69, and these still equip two squadrons.

(CL-41A) Span: 11.13 m (36 ft 6 in) *Length:* 9.75 m (32 ft) *Gross weight:* 3355 kg (7397 lb) *Maximum speed:* 782 km/h (486 mph)

Twin Beech, Beechcraft

US military aircraft. Some half-dozen basic Beechcraft light twins are currently used by many of the world's air forces. The oldest of these, still used by about 20 countries, is the prewar Model 18 and its wartime counterpart, the C-45 Expeditor. Nearly 7100 were built between 1937-59, and in the late 1970s several hundred remained in service in various guises. Japan had over 100 for communications and various aircrew training duties. The other major operators were the US Air Force, which used the C-45G and H as six-seat utility transports, and the US Navy with the photographic RC-45J and the TC-45J trainer. The powerplant is comprised of a couple of 450-hp Pratt & Whitney Wasp radial engines.

Smallest of the postwar Beech twins is the B55 Baron (260-hp Continental IO-470 piston engines), selected in 1965 by the US Army as an instrument trainer under the designation T-42A Cochise. Sixty-five were ordered, plus another five for Turkey, and 12 standard Barons were supplied to the Spanish air force.

Beech's Twin-Bonanza and Queen Air serve in several piston-engined U-8 versions (named Seminole) with the US Army, the final model being the U-8F (71 built). The six-passenger commercial Queen Air (380-hp Lycoming IGSO-540s) is used by the Japan Maritime Self-Defence Force, for transport and navigation training, and by the air forces of Uruguay and Venezuela. Its larger brother, the King Air, with 550-680-shp P&WC PT6A series turboprops, serves with the US Army as the U-21A and U-21G Ute general-purpose light transport (ten troops, three stretchers or equivalent cargo), and exists in RU-21A/B/C/D/E models for electronic or other reconnaissance duties. The U-21F corresponds to the larger King Air 100; another King Air 90 model (over 60 ordered) is the US Navy's T-44A pilot trainer. The US Air Force has a King Air 90 for VIP transport use as the VC-6B, and the Spanish air force received ten King Air 90s as instrument trainers and liaison aircraft.

The larger, pressurized and T-tailed Super King Air (850-shp PT6A-41 turboprops) is used in quantity (over 100) by all three US services as the C-12A (army name Huron), and three special electronic intelligence RU-21Js, bristling with huge antennae above and below the aircraft, were built for the army's Cefly Lancer programme. The Irish Army Air Corps and Japan Maritime Safety Agency have a coastal-patrol version of the Super King Air, known as the Maritime Monitor 200T.

The largest Beech twin to serve with a military operator is the B99 Airliner, of which the Chilean air force received nine and the Royal Thai Army one. This 15-passenger transport is powered by two 680-shp PT6A-27 turboprops.

(U-8F Seminole) Span: 13.97 m (45 ft 10 in) *Length:* 10.82 m (35 ft 6 in) *Gross weight:* 3493 kg (7700 lb) *Maximum speed:* 385 km/h (239 mph)

(U-21F Ute) Span: 13.97 m (45 ft 10 in) *Length:* 12.17 m (39 ft 11 in) *Gross weight:* 5216 kg (11 500 lb) *Maximum cruising speed:* 459 km/h (285 mph)

(C-12A Huron) Span: 16.61 m (54 ft 6 in) *Length:* 13.33 m (43 ft 9 in) *Gross weight:* 5670 kg (12 500 lb) *Maximum speed:* 536 km/h (333 mph)

Twin Mustang, North American P-82

US Air Force long-range escort and night fighter. North American's P-51 Mustang had proved such a superb long-range escort fighter during the Second World War in Europe that it was natural for the company to be approached when an even longer-range type was required for similar duties in the Pacific theatre. Other requirements were for a crew of two, to reduce pilot fatigue on long missions, and twin engines as an additional safety measure. While other contenders pursued all-jet or jet-and-turboprop designs, North American proposed an ingenious and much simpler solution: a 'twin' Mustang. This solution won the day, and the result, later officially named Twin Mustang, proved

A North American P-82C Twin Mustang. Two pilots reduced crew fatigue on long missions

Rockwell International

to be the last propeller-driven fighter ordered in quantity by the air force.

Design began in January 1944, and the first of two XP-82 prototypes made its initial flight on April 15, 1945. Essentially, each comprised two P-51H Mustang fuselages, with one port wing and one starboard wing, joined together by a new wing centre section and central tailplane/elevator. Both cockpits were retained, the pilot sitting in the port-side fuselage and the copilot in the starboard one. One retractable main wheel and one tail wheel in each fuselage comprised the landing gear, and the two 1380-hp Packard Merlin V-1650-23/25 V-type engines drove 'handed' (ie, opposite-rotating) propellers to cancel out engine torque. An XP-82A was also tested, with non-handed 1500-hp Allison V-1710-119 engines, but the XP-82 arrangement was preferred, and 500 P-82Bs to this configuration were ordered. With end-of-war cancellations only 20 of this model were completed. They were armed with six 0.5-in (12.7-mm) machine-guns in the wing centre section (with 300 rounds per gun), and had four points under the outer wings each able to carry rockets, drop tanks, or a 454-kg (1000-lb) bomb; additional guns in a pod could be hung under the centre section.

Two P-82Bs were modified as prototype night fighters, being redesignated P-82C and P-82D according to the radar installed (SCR-720 and APS-4 respectively). The radar was housed in a long underwing centreline pod which projected ahead of the twin fuselages, and its operator took over the copilot's seat.

Production to meet postwar needs followed in 1946. Three versions were ordered, all with 1600-hp Allison V-1710-143/145 handed engines: 100 P-82Es, 100 P-82Fs and 50 P-82Gs (changing to F-82E/F/G in June 1948, a month after deliveries began). The F-82E fulfilled the original long-range escort role, with a normal range of 4020 km (2500 miles); it served with one wing of Strategic Air Command. The F-82F (APS-4 radar) and F-82G (SCR-720) served as night and all-weather fighters, mainly with Air Defense Command as successors to the Northrop P-61 Black Widow. Some of these, stationed in Japan when the Korean war broke out in June 1950, were among the first USAF aircraft to enter combat during that conflict. On June 27, 1950, the first official air-to-air victory of the war was credited to an F-82G of the 68th Fighter (All-Weather) Squadron. Deliveries of the F-82F and G totalled 91 and 45 respectively; the remaining 14 night fighters, allocated for service in Alaska, were fitted out with special 'winterization' equipment and designated F-82H.

(F-82E) *Span:* 15.62 m (51 ft 3 in) *Length:* 11.91 m (39 ft 1 in) *Gross weight:* 11 278 kg (24 864 lb) *Maximum speed:* 748 km/h (465 mph)

(F-82F) *Span:* 15.62 m (51 ft 3 in) *Length:* 12.85 m (42 ft 2 in) *Gross weight:* 11 888 kg (26 208 lb) *Maximum speed:* 740 km/h (460 mph)

Typhon

US Navy antiaircraft missile. Typhon was intended to replace Tartar, Terrier, and Talos, but was cancelled on grounds of excessive cost, though its technology evolved into the Aegis system. Typhon began

as a pair of projects, Super Tartar and Super Talos, in 1958 and was built around a huge new SPG-59 long-range missile-control radar. Both weapons were to use the same fire-control system, but otherwise they differed: Super Tartar was a new dual-thrust rocket, to use the standard Tartar launching system; Super Talos used advances in ramjet technology to achieve Talos (or better) range performance on Terrier dimensions and was to be fired from a slightly modified Mark 10 launcher. In effect Super Tartar would well exceed Terrier performance; it was hoped that these small but powerful missiles could be carried aboard frigates, and even destroyers, in large numbers. Thus great economies could be expected: fewer missile ships would be required, and these few ships could be smaller than existing missile cruisers. Moreover, the very-long-range SPG-59 was an electronic scanning radar (Luneberg lens) which could engage several targets simultaneously and so counter the emerging Soviet saturation missile-attack tactics of the late 1950s.

In 1959 both Super projects were amalgamated under the new name Typhon in order to avoid misunderstandings which had cut their budgets. At the time the existing naval antiaircraft missiles were proving far less effective than had been hoped; one 1962 navy report suggested that all $6 billion which had been spent since 1945 had been wasted, as at that time there was no existing missile ship which could be considered truly operational. However, although the existing '3-T' weapons did not meet their specified performance, that performance in turn could not counter the expected Soviet threat, which at this time consisted mainly of Badger bombers dropping cruise missiles at ranges as great as 100 nautical miles. The theory of Typhon was presumably that the long-range component of the system would try to attack the Badgers, while the shorter-range weapon would kill missiles leaking through; in addition, it would be suitable for mounting aboard missile destroyers which could form a distant screen for the carrier task force.

Unfortunately, the initiation of a new missile project just when the existing missiles were in serious trouble drew the best personnel away from the latter, which in any case were the systems the navy would have to live with for some time to come. In addition the big new Typhon project drew from limited funds which might have gone into '3-T' cures. Finally, as the Typhon project continued, it became obvious that even though the long-range missile would fit a relatively small launcher, the SPG-59 radar would force up the size and cost of the launching ship; at one point it was found that this radar consumed so much power that in a conventionally powered ship its operation would markedly reduce cruising range. Consequently most projects for Typhon ships called for nuclear power, which again raised costs considerably.

Both cruiser and frigate designs were pursued, the latter distinguishable by its 'small' SPG-59, with 3400 rather than 10 000 elements. Even the frigate was huge: on 9700 tons (full load) only one long-range and two medium-range (ex-Super Tartar) launchers, plus two of the old 5-in (127-mm)/38 guns, could be accommodated. A cruiser, with the

big radar and three medium-range launchers, would have come to 16 100 tons. However, in 1961 it appeared that such ships would be exceptionally more effective than the large Talos and Terrier ships just entering service, and Typhon ships figured in early versions of the FY 63 and FY 64 budgets.

In fact in order to save the programme despite increases in its cost, the navy abandoned the long-range version in 1962, adopting instead a boosted version of the medium-range Typhon—a shift which foreshadowed the use of a common missile in the later Standard programme. Even so, rising costs in the face of the need to fix the '3-Ts' doomed the programme. On December 13, 1963, Secretary of Defense McNamara deleted a Typhon ship from the FY 65 navy programme; earlier versions had been delayed to that year because of slippage in radar development. Shortly thereafter he cancelled the Typhon missile programme, replacing it in the navy development budget by an Advanced Surface Missile System (ASMS) which in turn became Aegis. The only SPG-59 completed was mounted for tests aboard the missile test-ship *Norton Sound*.

Typhon (long-range) would have extended fleet air defence cover out to about 160 km (100 miles); it was intended to counter saturation by a combination of range and multiple missile-handling capability. By way of contrast, more recent systems, which face much the same threat, operate at shorter range but employ much faster-firing launchers. One reason for the adoption of shorter-range systems is a change in the Soviet threat: the SS-N-7 submerged-launch antiship missile pops up at short range and gives little warning time. In effect it would have been the province of Typhon (medium-range), effective within about 50 km (30 miles); Standard is the true descendant of the latter.

A Hawker Typhoon armed with rockets. As a ground-attack fighter it was devastatingly successful during the fighting in Normandy and north-west Europe. A full salvo of rockets was the equivalent of a broadside from an 8-in (203-mm) cruiser. With armour-piercing warheads the Typhoon was a very valuable tank-killer capable of destroying the heaviest German tanks

Typhoon, Hawker

British fighter-bomber. Pushed into service prematurely, before its engine could be fully developed, the Typhoon was an initial failure in its designed role of an intercepter. But as engine power improved and the aircraft was switched to low-level work its advantages showed through: at one stage it was the only RAF aircraft capable of catching the low-flying Focke-Wulf Fw 190 sneak raiders, and it went on to achieve fame in the ground-attack role.

The Typhoon was designed as a successor to the Hurricane to Specification F.18/37, and in construction combined the traditional Hawker box girder for the front fuselage (including the cockpit) with a stressed-skin, monocoque-shell rear fuselage attached at four points. Early versions had a framed canopy with a door in the manner of the motor car, but a bubble sliding canopy was soon introduced. Each wing was attached directly to the fuselage, while the undercarriage retracted inwards and had a wide track.

The powerplant, which was the initial cause of the Typhoon's problems, was the Napier Sabre I, a 24-cylinder H-type engine rated at 2100 hp, which proved most unreliable. It was soon replaced with the more reliable Sabre IIA, rated at 2180 hp, which was in turn followed by the Sabre IIB, rated at 2200 hp and the IIC, rated at 2260 hp. Most aircraft were fitted with a three-bladed propeller, but late aircraft had four blades.

The original specification had called for an armament of 12 0.303-in (7.7-mm) machine-guns, and a few aircraft were so fitted and designated Typhoon Mk IA. The more usual armament was, however, amended to four 20-mm (0.79-in) Hispano cannon and designated Mk IB. As the change of role to ground attack progressed, the wing was progressively modified to carry a pair of 113-kg (250-lb) bombs, then 227-kg (500-lb) and finally 454-kg (1000-lb) bombs. It eventually carried eight 3-in (7.6-cm) rocket projectiles, each with a 27-kg (60-lb) warhead, which had powerful armour-piercing ability.

The first Typhoon prototype flew on February 24, 1940, and the first production aircraft did not fly until May 27, 1941. Once Hawkers had completed the prototypes and 15 early production aircraft, the remaining 3330 aircraft were built by Glosters. Several Mk IBs were fitted with either two vertical cameras in the rear fuselage or a cine camera in place of the port inner cannon, and used for fighter-reconnaissance duties under the designation FR.IB. A single night-fighter model, the NF.IB was tried out with AI Mk IV radar, but was not a success.

The RAF took delivery of their first Typhoons in July 1941, and the first units to be issued with the type were 56 and 609 Squadrons, based at Duxford. As intercepters the Typhoons showed a disappointing performance at high altitude and had a very poor rate of climb, and the type was almost withdrawn from service. The switch to low-level opera-

tions soon proved the aircraft's worth, and 609 Squadron operating from Manston shot down four Fw 190s in a week in 1942.

Gradually the Typhoon slipped into the fighter-bomber role against enemy shipping in the English Channel, and in offensive sweeps across occupied Europe. They soon became famous for their success in 'train-busting', with as many as 150 locomotives per month being claimed by the middle of 1943. By 1944 the build-up for the invasion saw the increase of Typhoon squadrons and the introduction of the rocket armament. Before Operation Overlord, rocket-armed Typhoons destroyed two major German radar stations at Dieppe/Caudecote and Jouourg near Cap de la Hague. As the invasion moved inland Typhoons proved remarkably effective in countering the German Panzer divisions at Caen and Falaise, destroying 137 tanks in one attack.

Typhoons also operated against pinpoint targets, and successes included the killing of two German generals and over 70 staff officers in the headquarters of the 15th Army at Dordrecht on October 24, 1944; and the wounding of Rommel during an attack on his staff car on July 17, 1944. Typhoon support of the Allied armies continued to the end of the war.

(Mk IB) *Span:* 12.67 m (41 ft 7 in) *Length:* 9.75 m (32 ft) *Gross weight:* 6341 kg (13 980 lb) *Maximum speed:* 663 km/h (412 mph) at 5790 m (19 000 ft)

U-Boats

U-Boats

Austro-Hungarian submarines. The Austro-Hungarian navy was comparatively late in ordering submarines, their first not being launched until 1908. Initially they were known simply by a number in Roman style, and later the U designator was added but by the middle of the war the roman numerals had given way to Arabic ones, thus duplicating the numbers of some of the German boats.

At the outbreak of war the Austrian submarine fleet consisted of seven boats. Of these the first six belonged to three different types each pair being built at either Fiume or Pola. *I-IV* were badly over-engined and

suffered from excessive vibration when running at high speed on the surface with their Körting paraffin engines. They were all fitted with three 45-cm (17.7-in) torpedo tubes. As commander of *V* Kapitänleutnant von Trapp was responsible for sinking the French armoured cruiser *Leon Gambetta* in the Strait of Otranto on April 27, 1915, with two torpedoes fired during a daring and skilful night attack.

In 1914 an order for the next five submarines *(VII-XI)* was awarded to the Ger-

mania yard at Kiel. They were to have been larger diesel-engine boats armed with five 50-cm (19.7-in) torpedo tubes, but they were taken over by the Germans and eventually commissioned as *U66-70*.

Thus the seventh boat of the Austrian navy at the outbreak of war was *XII*, built originally as a private venture by Whithead's at Fiume, and added to the Austrian navy in late 1914. She was sunk off Venice on August 11, 1915, and later salvaged by the Italians. No submarine was numbered *XIII*, but *XIV* was

AUSTRO-HUNGARIAN SUBMARINES

	I, II	*III, IV*	*V, VI*	*XII*
Displacement (tons) (surface/submerged)	230/270	240/300	236/273	236/290
Length (m/ft)	30.5/100	44/144.5	32/105	32.3/106
Beam (m/ft)	3.5/11.5	3.8/12.5	4.3/14	4.3/14
Draught (m/ft)	—	3/9.84	—	4.1/13.5
Speed (knots) (surfaced/submerged)	12/7	12/8.5	11.5/9	11.5/9
Range (nautical miles)/ at speed (knots)	—	1200/9	1000/11	1000
Torpedo tubes	3 45-cm (17.7-in)	3 45-cm	3 45-cm	2 45-cm (bow)
Guns	—	1 11-pdr	none	1 6-pdr

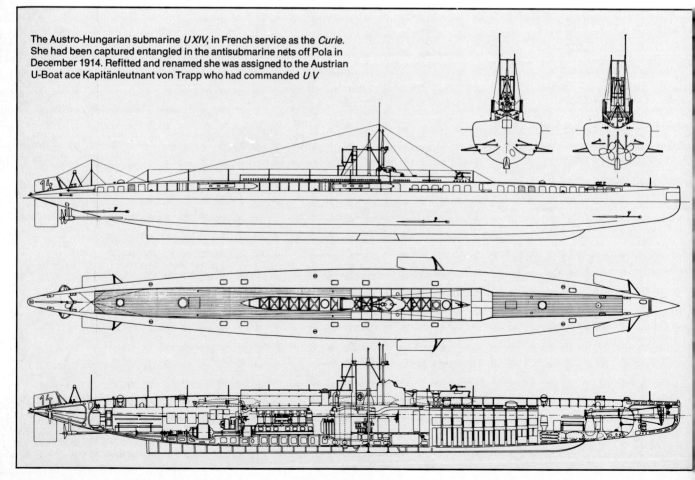

The Austro-Hungarian submarine *U XIV*, in French service as the *Curie*. She had been captured entangled in the antisubmarine nets off Pola in December 1914. Refitted and renamed she was assigned to the Austrian U-Boat ace Kapitänleutnant von Trapp who had commanded *U V*

he French submarine *Curie* which became caught in the nets off Pola in December 1914, was refitted and entered into the navy and given to command by von Trapp.

By early 1915 the Germans had developed the small Type UB coastal submarines and Type UC small minelayer which could be built rapidly and, if necessary, transported by rail in section for assembly elsewhere. Some of the UB-Boats were taken to Pola for assembly and initially manned by their German crews. In June 1915 they began to be formally handed over to the Austrians, *UB 1* becoming *X* and *UB 15* as *XI*. Later in the year three of the Type UC became *XV*, *XVI* and *XVII*. *XVIII* was the Italian *Giacinto Pullino* which was captured in August 1916, refitted and entered into the Austrian navy.

XIX-XXIII were five boats completed in Austrian dockyards in 1917 and were generally similar to the Danish *Havmanden* Class. *XXIV-XXVIII* were completed in 1918. From time to time other boats were transformed or loaned from the Germans, mostly the Types UB or UC, and in 1916 *UB 43* became the *XLIII*. In some cases the flag change may have been nominal with the original German crew staying with the boat, which later reverted to the German navy. This may, in part, have been due to the complication that until August 1916 Italy was at war with Austria-Hungary but not with Germany. With transfer of flag the boats were given Austrian numbers with, among others *UB 48* becoming *LXXIX* and *UB 105* becoming *XCVII*.

During the war the Austrians lost seven submarines, including both *III* and *VI* of the prewar boats. Two more were badly damaged.

J-Boats (1905-18)

German submarines. The Germans were among the last of the major powers to start building submarines for their own navy. Like the British, they were content to let others spend money experimenting and evaluating this new weapon, and then avoiding the early mistakes to start their own construction programme only when there was a proven use for these vessels. But, unlike the British, they saw no value in building submarines that would only be a means of defending their own coast and bases, since other arms were available for this task. To carry out their duties the German naval staff decided that the submarine must be able to operate in what was regarded as the principal sphere of action for the German fleet—the North Sea.

This in turn required the submarines to have an appropriately large radius of action, the ability to stay at sea in the weather likely to be met with in the winter in the North Sea, and importantly an engine able to give the boat an adequate surface speed and reliable enough for it to operate at a distance from any base or support. Meanwhile German shipbuilding yards were keeping in touch with progress in submarine development by building submarines for sale to foreign powers. One such was *Forel* built at Kiel for Russia, which after trials was transported by rail to Vladivostok for use against Japan.

On February 14, 1905, the contract for the first submarine for the German navy (*U 1*) was awarded to the Germania yard at Kiel. The submarine would be of 238 tons surfaced displacement, armed with one 45-cm (17.7-in) bow torpedo tube and powered with the Körting kerosene engine—a considerable advance on the small *Forel* so recently completed at that yard. Despite the tendency of the Körting engine to emit clouds of white exhaust smoke which was visible for miles, the gasoline engine used in British submarines was not countenanced by the German designers because of the dangers from gasoline fumes. *U 1* was completed in December 1906, and meanwhile the contract for a second and larger boat had been awarded to the Imperial dockyard at Danzig. In August 1907 two more submarines, *U 3* and *U 4*, were ordered; those were slightly larger again than *U 2*.

Trials showed that *U 1* did not meet the requirements for North Sea operations, but she had nevertheless proved the overall idea for submarines for the German navy and this allowed further development to proceed. The Körting engine was not reliable enough, but the diesel engine was still even less reliable, though one of these German-invented engines was installed by the French in their submarine *Aigrette* as early as 1902. To the Germans it was apparent that the Körting engine would have to be used, at least for the time being. The naval staff laid down four main criteria that would have to be met in new construction: a surface speed of 15 knots, with 10.5 knots dived; 2000 nautical miles surfaced endurance; four torpedo tubes, the two bow tubes to be capable of being reloaded; and capability of supporting a crew of 20 with 72 hours' air supply. The next 14 boats were all built with these criteria in mind, though not necessarily fulfilling them. As a result of exercises in 1912, when many of these boats remained at sea for 11 days, it was considered that they could sustain successfully a war patrol of five days at a range of 300 nautical miles from their base, equivalent to a distance from Heligoland to the centre of the east coast of England, or to the eastern part of the English Channel. It was therefore appropriate that they also took part in the first U-Boat sweep of the war, and would also sustain the first casualties. On August 9, 1914, *U 15* was rammed and sunk by HMS *Birmingham*; *U 13* never returned

U 1-4

Number	*U 1*	*U 2*	*U 3-4*
Displacement (tons) (surfaced/submerged)	234/278	335/423	414/502
Length (m/ft)	42.4/139	45.4/149	51.2/168
Beam (m/ft)	3.7/12.14	5.5/18	5.5/18
Draught (m/ft)	3.2/10.5	3/9.84	3/9.84
Speed (knots) (surfaced/submerged)	9/8.5	13/9	11.5/9.5
Range (nautical miles)/ at speed (knots)	1400/8	2500/9	3000/9
Torpedo tubes/no of torpedoes	1 45-cm (17.7-in) (bow)/3	4 45-cm (2 bow, 2 stern)/6	4 45-cm (2 bow, 2 stern)/6
Guns	none	none	none

U 1 was the first submarine to be built for the German navy. Her design was based on three earlier vessels built by Krupps for the Russians from French specifications

U-Boats (1905-18)

U 5-18

Number	U 5-8	U 9-12	U 13-16	U 17-18
Displacement (tons) (surfaced/submerged)	497/626	425/601	516/634	555/680
Length (m/ft)	57.3/188	57.3/188	57.9/190	62.3/204.4
Beam (m/ft)	5.5/18	6/19.68	6.1/20	6/19.68
Draught (m/ft)	3.4/11.15	3.5/11.5	3.5/11.5	3.5/11.5
Speed (knots) (surfaced/submerged)	13.5/10.25	14.25/8	14.75/10.75	14.75/9.5
Range (nautical miles)/ at speed (knots)	3360/8.6	3360/8.6	1900/14.25	1910/14.5
Torpedo tubes/no of torpedoes	4 45-cm (2 bow, 2 stern)/6	4 45-cm/6	4 45-cm/6	4 45-cm/6
Guns	1 37-mm (1.46-in)	1 37-mm	1 37-mm	1 37-mm

U 19-114

Number	U 19-22	U 31-41	U 51-56	U 93-98	U 105-114
Displacement (tons) (surfaced/submerged)	650/837	685/878	712/902	837/998	798/996
Length (m/ft)	64.2/210.6	64.8/212.6	65.2/214	71.8/235.6	71.8/235.6
Beam (m/ft)	6.1/20	6.3/20.67	6.4/21	6.4/21	6.4/21
Draught (m/ft)	3.6/11.81	3.6/11.81	3.6/11.81	3.9/12.79	3.9/12.79
Speed (knots) (surfaced/submerged)	15.5/9.5	16.5/9.5	17.9/9	16.75/8.5	16.5/8.5
Range (nautical miles)/ at speed (knots)	5300/8	8790/8			
Torpedo tubes/ no of torpedoes	4 50-cm (19.7-in) (2 bow, 2 stern)/9	4 50-cm/6	4 50-cm/6	6 50-cm (4 bow, 2 stern)	6 50-cm
Guns	1 86-mm (3.4-in) (2 from 1916); 1 105-mm (4.1-in) in U 19	1 86-mm (2 later)	1/2 86-mm or 1 105-mm	1 86-mm (1 105-mm in U 96-98)	1 86-mm; 1 105-mm

from that first patrol on August 12, a possible accidental victim of a German mine. On the other hand U 9 sank the three British cruisers Aboukir, Cressy and Hogue early on the morning of September 22. This remarkable feat was repeated on October 15 when the same submarine sank the cruiser Hawke.

The U 19 Class, which followed, represented a big step forward. Not only were they fitted with a reliable diesel engine, but also with the larger 50-cm (19.7-in) torpedo tubes. Boats were then enlarged and improved progressively as each new batch was ordered: they became longer and displaced more; they had more powerful diesel engines, increased range; and eventually they had their armament increased to six torpedo tubes (four bow and two stern). This evolution covered boats up to U 116 with the exception of a new class of ocean minelayer designated UE, which unlike the coastal minelayers of the UC Type received U numbers. U 42 never saw service in the German navy, having been ordered in Italy to evaluate the capability of a foreign yard to build submarines. The boat had not been delivered when Italy entered the war, and was taken over for the Italian navy as Ballila. Five submarines being built in Germany for the Austro-Hungarian navy were taken over for the Germans on the outbreak of war and numbered U 66-70.

Later in the war larger boats were ordered, but by this time building times were extended to over two years as pressures increased on the German industrial capacity, and most of the boats were never completed. A few of these boats were also named, commemorating earlier heroes of the German submarine service. Thus U 140 was to have been called Kapitän Leutnant Weddigen after the commander of U 9 who sank the four British cruisers in 1914 and was later killed in U 29.

On July 9, 1916, a German submarine surfaced off the US coast and went on to berth in Baltimore. This was Deutschland, an unarmed merchant submarine and the first of several to run the Allied blockade with cargo to and from the United States. Her arrival was undoubtedly a vast propaganda success which greatly outweighed the value of her cargo. Deutschland made one more trip, but the second boat Bremen never arrived. A third boat, Oldenburg, was converted to a warship before completion, and Deutschland was later similarly converted. These cruiser-type of U-Boats were armed with two bow torpedo tubes and a gun armament which included 2 15-cm (5.9-in) guns. They were numbered from U 151 (ex-Bremen) to U 157, Deutschland becoming the U 155. Later in the war an improved type of U-Cruiser was planned as the UD Type, armed with six torpedo tubes and a heavy gun armament. UD 1 was laid down but never launched.

Following the German occupation of most

f Belgium in 1914 the navy found them-
elves in possession of potential submarine
ases at either Bruges or Zeebrugge, which
vere very much nearer the scene of opera-
ons than Heligoland or the other German
ases. Together with the availability of 60-hp
our-cylinder diesel engines this led to the
ery rapid production of some small coastal
ubmarines. They were designed and ordered
n November 1914 and were in service by
arly 1915. These boats were only 27 m (88 ft
in) long, displaced 127 tons on the surface
nd were armed with two torpedo tubes.
hese Type UB submarines were small
nough even to be transported in sections by
ail and assembled on arrival, so some boats
vere assembled in such distant ports as
ruges in Belgium, Pola on the Adriatic, and
'arna on the Black Sea. *UB 1*, having been
nally assembled at Pola, operated for a
vhile with a German crew in the Adriatic
efore being handed over to the Austrians in
une 1915 as submarine *X*.

A second series increased both the size and
he operational use of these small submarines, while the Type UB III in 1917-18
vere bigger again with a surfaced displace-
nent of 520 tons and were 55.5 m (182 ft)
ong. The torpedo armament was increased to
ive torpedo tubes, making them larger and
nore formidable boats than the original seagoing boats with which Germany had started
he war. These Type UB III boats were
onsidered to be such a success that the
esign of the equally successful Type VII U-
3oat of the 1938-45 era incorporated many of
heir features.

Germany undertook extensive minelaying
perations, and for this purpose specialist
ninelaying submarines were evolved. At the
ame time as the Type UB submarine was
eveloped for coastal operations, so a small
ninelayer was designed, the Type UC. There
vere two later variants, the UC II series in
916 and the UC III series in 1917. The main
lifferences were in the number of mines
:arried, and of course the size of the boat,
he increased displacement resulting in
mprovements to both seakeeping qualities
nd range of operations. The UC I boats were
itted only as minelayers, and were small
nough to be transported by rail for final
assembly. Once they had laid their mines
hey had no means of either offence or
lefence, and later types were also fitted with

U 135-167

Number	U 135-138	U 139-141	U 160-167
Displacement (tons) (surfaced/submerged)	1175/1534	1930/2483	821/1000
Length (m/ft)	83.5/274	94.8/311	71.6/235
Beam (m/ft)	7.3/24	9.1/29.86	6.2/20.3
Draught (m/ft)	4.2/13.78	5.3/17.39	4.1/13.5
Speed (knots) (surfaced/submerged)	17/8	15.75/7.5	16/8
Torpedo tubes/ no of torpedoes	6 50-cm (4 bow, 2 stern)	6 50-cm (4 bow, 2 stern)	6 50-cm (4 bow, 2 stern)
Guns	1 150-mm (5.9-in)	2 150-mm (also 2 86-mm in *U 141*)	1 105-mm (2 in *U 160*)

CRUISER TYPES

Number	U 151-157	UD 1
Displacement (tons) (surfaced/submerged)	1512/1875	3800/4500
Length (m/ft)	64.9/213	125/410
Beam (m/ft)	8.8/29	6.1/20
Draught (m/ft)	5.6/18.4	not known
Speed (knots) (surfaced/submerged)	12.5/5.25	not completed
Torpedo tubes/ no of torpedoes	2 50-cm (bow)	6 50-cm (4 bow, 2 stern)
Guns	2 150-mm; 2 86-mm	2 150-mm; 2 86-mm

U 155 at sea. She was formerly the mercantile submarine *Deutschland* and in this role she had made two trips in 1916 to the United States. She was converted after the US entry into the war

U-Boats (1905-18)

The German minelaying submarine *UC 26,* showing the forward mine-wells, with torpedo tubes and handling rooms in blue, crews' quarters in yellow and engines in red. The mauve area is the control room and conning tower

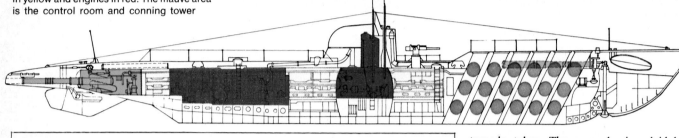

TYPE UB

Type	UB I	UB II	UB III
Displacement (tons) (surfaced/submerged)	127/142	263/292	516/651
Length (m/ft)	28/92	36.1/118.4	55.5/182
Beam (m/ft)	3/9.84	4.4/14.4	5.8/19
Draught (m/ft)	3/10	3.7/12	3.7/12
Speed (knots) (surfaced/submerged)	6.5/5.5	9/5.75	13.5/8
Torpedo tubes/ no of torpedoes	2 45-cm (17.7-in) (bow)	2 50-cm (bow)	5 50-cm (4 bow, 1 stern)
Guns	none	1 4-pdr (1 105-mm later)	1 86-mm (1 105-mm in some)

torpedo tubes. The moored mines laid by these boats were dropped from vertical shafts through the keel, water ballast being taken on to maintain trim. The capture of *UC 5* and a diver's inspection of the wreck of *UC 2* gave the British the first clue as to the source of the increased German mining campaign, and led to the modification of some of the British 'E' Class to act as minelayers.

The small number of oceangoing minelayers of the UE Type were armed with torpedo tubes and carried their mines in two horizontal shafts running the length of the boat, the mines being laid through two doors at the stern. The later boats of this type were of over 1000 tons surface displacement and had a range sufficient to operate off the US coast.

A final series of Type UF small coastal submarines was planned. They would have been similar in size to the UB II boats of 1915 with four or five 50-cm torpedo tubes and one gun. None were completed.

TYPES UC and UE

Type	UC I	UC II	UC III	UE I	UE II
Number	*UC 1-15*	*UC 16-79*	*UC 90-114*	*U 71-80*	*U 117-126*
Displacement (tons) (surfaced/submerged)	168/183	417/493	491/571	755/832	1164/1512
Length (m/ft)	34/111.5	49.4/162	56.5/185.37	56.8/186.35	81.5/267.4
Beam (m/ft)	3.1/10.17	5.2/17	5.7/18.70	5.9/19.36	7.5/24.6
Draught (m/ft)	3/10	3.7/14	3.8/12.5	4.8/15.75	4.2/13.78
Speed (knots) (surfaced/submerged)	6.25/5.25	11.5/7	11.5/6.5	10.5/8	14.75/7
Torpedo tubes/ no of torpedoes	none	3 50-cm (2 bow, 1 stern)	3 50-cm (2 external amid, 1 stern)	2 50-cm (bow, external)	4 50-cm (bow)
Mine chutes/mines	6/12	6/18	6/14	2/38	2/42
Guns	1 MG	1 3.4-in (86-mm)	1 3.4-in (4.1-in in some boats)	1 3.4-in	1 5.9-in (150mm) (*U 117* 1 5.9-in, 1 3.4-in)

-Boats (1935-45)

German submarines. Under the terms of the Treaty of Versailles Germany was not allowed to retain or build any submarines so that at the outbreak of war in 1939 the German U-Boat fleet was comparatively modern, all the vessels having been built since 1935. Between 1919 and 1934 German submarine technicians had not been idle, and among those submarines built in various European shipyards to German design and with German technical assistance were *Gür* built in 1932 for the Turkish navy, and *Vesikko* built in 1933 for Finland. *Gür* was 72.4 m (237 ft 6 in) long and displaced 750 tons (surfaced) and 960 tons (submerged), and was armed with six torpedo tubes (four bow and two stern) and one 4-in (102-mm) gun. *Vesikko* was a smaller boat of only 250 tons (surfaced) and 300 tons (submerged); it was 40.8 m (134 ft) long, and armed with three bow 53-cm (21-in) torpedo tubes and a small gun.

Thus *Gür* provided a prototype for an ocean-going submarine, while *Vesikko* was the forerunner of the coastal submarines. In order to get the building programme under way as rapidly as possible to fulfil the need to have submarines at sea and to train future crews, it was the coastal submarines of Type II, as they were to be known, that were the first to be laid down. The first such boat for the German navy, called *U 1*, was launched in Kiel in June 1935, the remainder following shortly afterwards. Types IIB and IIC were similar, but were larger and carried additional fuel to increase their range. Type IID boats were introduced in 1940; they were still larger; and were fitted with saddle tanks to increase their range further. Although used for operations early in the war these boats were soon relegated to training duties, an

essential part of the enormous expansion programme that the U-Boat arm was to undertake.

Meanwhile the Type I, of which only two boats were built, gave the German navy a capability of operations in the Atlantic. Basically the same design and performance as *Gür*, these two boats in turn were to become the prototype, with the *UB 48* Class of 1917, of a new series of ocean-going submarines, the Type VII. This type, with its several variants, was undoubtedly the mainstay of the German submarine fleet throughout the war. The variants retained many structural characteristics of the original Type VII but were designed either for better performance or for more specialized roles. The first Type VIIA was *U 27*, launched in 1936, designed for operations in the Atlantic. It had good seakeeping qualities and easy handling both on the surface and submerged, and carried the best possible torpedo armament that could be fitted into a submarine of less than 65 m (213 ft) in length and only 626 tons surfaced displacement. Inevitably this was achieved at the expense of other factors, and habitability was spartan, to say the least. The Type VIIAs are distinguished by their single external torpedo tube aft. *U 30,* a boat of this type, was responsible for sinking the liner *Athenia* early in the war.

U 45, the first Type VIIB, was launched in April 1938. The type had increased size and displacement to accommodate higher-performance engines and more fuel. The stern torpedo tube was made internal with the hull. The *U 47* commanded by Korvetten-Kapitän Günther Prien entered Scapa Flow in 1939 and sank *Royal Oak*, and later was to sink many thousands of tons of Allied shipping in the Atlantic.

The Type VIIC, introduced in 1940, had a further increase in displacement and fuel

capacity, more torpedo reloads, and a better AA armament. Contracts were placed for 688 boats of this type, though later some of these were cancelled and others were destroyed by enemy action during construction. The Type VIIC-41 differed only in that it had a stronger hull to give a greater diving depth. Eight boats of this type were to have been completed for the Italian navy, but they were taken into commission by the Germans themselves following the Italian surrender. *U 573* was interned in Spain at Cartagena after being badly damaged by depth charges dropped from an RAF aircraft in 1942. The following year she was sold to Spain and renumbered *G.7. U 570* surrendered after being damaged by an RAF aircraft south of Iceland, and later was commissioned as HMS *Graph*. Orders for a second variant, the Type VIIC-42, were cancelled to allow production to concentrate on newer types. Had it entered service it would have had increased range and an even greater diving depth.

A minelaying variant, the Type VIID, was introduced in 1942. The six boats of this type had a 9.8-m (32 ft 2-in) section added into the hull aft of the conning tower to take five free-flooding mine chutes carrying a total of 15 moored mines similar to those carried by surface minelayers. In the Type VIIF this extra section was adapted to carry 25 torpedoes to replenish other submarines already on patrol. Four boats of this type were built, and they carried additional fuel to increase their range. In addition to the replenishment torpedoes for other boats they had their own establishment of torpedoes to carry out their own operations.

A total of 705 boats of the Type VII variants had entered service by the time of the surrender in 1945, and of these, 437 were lost in action. The *U 977* (Type VIIC) left Norway rather than surrender, and after a

TYPES I and II

Type	IA	IIA	IIB	IIC	IID
Numbers	*U 25, 26*	*U 1-6*	*U 7-24, 120, 121* (ex-Yugoslav)	*U 56-63*	*U 137-152*
Displacement (tons) (surfaced/submerged)	862/983	254/303	279/329	291/341	314/364
Length (m/ft)	72.5/238	41.1/135	42.7/140	44.2/145	44.2/145
Beam (m/ft)	6.2/20.3	4.1/13.5	4.1/13.5	4.1/13.5	4.9/16
Draught (m/ft)	4.3/14	3.8/12.5	3.9/12.8	3.8/12.75	3.9/12.8
Speed (knots) (surfaced/submerged)	18.5/8.25	13/7	13/7	12/7	13/7
Fuel (tons)	96	12	21	23	38
Range (nautical miles)/ at speed (knots)	7900/10	1500/10	2700/10	2900/10	4400/10
Torpedo tubes/ no of torpedoes	4 bow, 2 stern/14*	3 bow/5 (normal), 6 (max)*	3 bow/5 or 6*	3 bow/5 or 6*	3 bow/5 or 6*
Guns	1 10.5-cm (4.1-in); 1 20-mm (0.79-in) AA	1 20-mm (0.79-in) AA	2/3 20-mm (0.79-in) AA	2 20-mm (0.79-in) AA	1 20-mm (0.79-in) AA

For notes see page overleaf

U-Boats (1935-45)

TYPE VII

Type	VIIA	VIIB	VIIC	VIIC-41	VIIC-42	VIID	VIIF
Numbers	U 27-36	U 45-55, 73-76, 83-87, 99-102	U 69-72, 77-82, 88-98, 132-136, 201-212, 221-232, 235-458, 465-486, 551-683, 701-779, 821-836, 901-908, 921-930, 951-1058, 1063-1065	U 1101-1220, 1271-1279, 1301-1308	Cancelled	U 213-218	U 1059-1062
Displacement (tons) (surfaced/submerged)	626/745	753/857	769/871	769/871	990/1050	965/1080	1084/1181
Length (m/ft)	64.9/213	66.9/219.5	67.5/221.5	67.5/221.5	68.7/225.7	77/252.6	78/256
Beam (m/ft)	5.9/19.4	6.2/20.3	6.2/20.3	6.2/20.3	6.2/20.3	6.4/21	7.3/24
Draught (m/ft)	4.4/14.4	4.7/15.4	4.7/15.4	4.7/15.4		5/16.4	5.2/17
Speed (knots) (surfaced/submerged)	17/8	18/8	17.75/7.5	17.75/7.5	Est 18.5 max	16.75/7.25	17.5/8
Fuel (tons)	67	108	114	114	Planned 180	170	199
Range (nautical miles)/ at speed (knots)	4300/12	6500/12	6500/12; 8850/10		About 12 600	8100/12	9500/12
Torpedo tubes/ no of torpedoes	4 bow, 1 stern/11**	4 bow, 1 stern/14**	4 bow, 1 stern/14**	4 bow, 1 stern/14**	/12**	4 bow, 1 stern/12**; 15 mine chutes/ 15 mines	4 bow, 1 stern/39
Guns	1 3.5-in (89-mm); 1 20-mm (0.79-in)	1 37-mm (1.46-in); 2 20-mm	1 37-mm; 2 20-mm***	1 37-mm: 2 20-mm		1 37-mm; 2 20-mm	1 37-mm; 2 20-mm

continuous submerged passage of 66 days reached Argentina on August 17, 1945, where her crew were interned.

The big sister of the Type VII was the Type IX which had a greater range and better habitability. It was designed for operations in distant waters and possessed good seakeeping qualities. The first boat, U37, was commissioned in August 1938 only three months after being launched. The Type IXB built shortly afterwards carried an extra 11 tons of fuel. The Types IXC and IXC-40, which differed only slightly from each other, again increased the fuel capacity and range of the boats. Contracts for some of these boats were cancelled in 1944 in order to concentrate production on the new Type XXI. U511 was handed over to Japan in 1943 and became the RO500; U 1224 similarly became RO501 in 1944, but was sunk north-west of the Cape Verde Islands by a US destroyer while on passage to Japan.

As the Allied blockade on Germany tightened there arose a requirement for a submarine to carry small cargoes of vital materials from the Far East to Germany. The Type IXC design was therefore modified by being lengthened by 7.6 m (25 ft) and given a cargo capacity of 252 tons. The Type IXD 41 which resulted sacrificed all its own torpedo armament and some of its battery capacity to achieve this while a later version, the Type IXD-42, reverted to having its own torpedo armament. This last series of boats may be regarded as the final series of the conven-tional submarine to join the German navy. Apart from its ability to carry vital cargo from the Far East it also had the greatest range of any German submarine of over 31 500 nautical miles. U 195 was transferred to Japan as I 506, while U 181 and U 862 became the I 501 and the I 502.

A small number of Type XB submarines

U 236, a German Type VII submarine, one of the standard designs during the Second World War. U 236 was one of the Type VIIC submarines, the third version, and entered service in January 1943. Damaged in an attack at the end of the war she had to be scuttled by her crew

TYPE IX

Type	IX	IXB	IXC	IXC-40	IXD-41	IXD-42
Numbers	U 37-44	U 64-65, 103-111, 122-124	U 66-68, 125-131, 153-166, 171-176, 501-524, 841-846, 853-858, 865-870, 877-881, 889, 1221-1238	U 167-170, 183-194, 525-550, 801-806	U 180, 195	U 177-179, 181, 182, 196-200, 847-852, 859-864, 871-876
Displacement (tons) (surfaced/submerged)	1032/1153	1051/1178	1120/1232	1144/1257	1610/1799	1616/1804
Length (m/ft)	77/252.6	77/252.6	72.2/237	72.2/237	88/289	88/289
Beam (m/ft)	6.6/21.6	6.9/22.6	6.9/22.6	6.9/22.6	7.5/24.60	7.5/24.60
Draught (m/ft)	4.7/15.5	4.7/15.5	4.7/15.5	4.7/15.5	5.6/18.37	5.6/18.37
Speed (knots) (surfaced/submerged)	18.25/7.75	18.25/7.25	18.25/7.25	18.25/7.25	16.5/7	19.25/7
Fuel (tons)	154	166	208	214	203	442
Range (nautical miles)/ at speed (knots)	10 500/10	12 000/10	13 450/10	13 850/10	12 750/10	23 700/12; 31 500/10
Torpedo tubes/ no of torpedoes	4 bow, 2 stern 22*	4 bow, 2 stern/22*	4 bow, 2 stern/22*	4 bow, 2 stern/22*	nil; 252 tons cargo	4 bow, 2 stern/24*
Guns	1 10.5-cm; 1 37-mm AA; 1 20-mm AA***	1 37-mm AA; 4 20-mm AA****	1 37-mm AA; 4 20-mm AA****	1 37-mm AA; 4 20-mm AA****	1 37-mm AA; 4 20-mm AA	1 37-mm AA; 20-mm AA****

TYPES X and XIV

Type	XB	XIV
Numbers	U 116-119, 219, 220, 233, 234	U 459-464, 487-490
Displacement (tons) (surfaced/submerged)	1763/2177	1688/1932
Length (m/ft)	90.4/296.6	67.5/221.5
Beam (m/ft)	9.3/30.6	9.4/30.84
Draught (m/ft)	4.7/15.4	6.6/21.7
Speed (knots) (surfaced/submerged)	17/7	15/6
Fuel (tons)	368	203 plus 517 as cargo
Range (nautical miles)/ at speed (knots)	14 450/12	12 350/10; 9300/12
Torpedo tubes/ no of torpedoes	2 stern/15*; 30 mine chutes/66 mines	nil, 4 as cargo
Guns	1 37-mm AA; 4 20-mm AA	2 37-mm AA; 2 20-mm AA

were built as large ocean-going minelayers, the Type XA never having left the drawing board. The mines were stowed in six internal mine chutes aft of the forward torpedo tubes, three mines in each chute, and two mines in each of 24 external chutes arranged either side of the boat amidships. Torpedo reloads were stowed both internally and externally. The boats had a range in excess of 14 000 nautical miles, and they were later increasingly used for cargo-carrying missions. *U 219* was in Penang at the time of the German surrender and was captured by the Japanese who renumbered her *I 505*.

The Type XIV were tanker U-Boats derived from the Type VIIC. They were used to supply fuel to other submarines to increase their time on patrol, and for this purpose they carried an additional 203 tons of fuel. They had no torpedo tubes of their own though they carried four torpedoes for transfer to other boats.

From the early stages of the war the German naval staff were interested in producing a 'true submarine' able to travel fast underwater and needing no more than the very minimum time on the surface. This became increasingly important as Allied air power made it increasingly unsafe for German submarines to remain on the surface. One answer was to fit *Schnorkel* (snorkel) tubes to all new construction, and also to

* Indicates that mines could be carried in lieu of some or all of the torpedoes
** Indicates that the torpedo load could be varied so that a mixture of torpedoes and mines could be carried, the mines being launched through the torpedo tubes and carried at the expense of the torpedo armament
*** Some boats carried up to 8 20-mm
**** Indicates that the armament varied with time

U-Boats (1935-45)

EXPERIMENTAL and TURBINE-POWERED

Type Numbers	V 80	V 300 U 791 (not completed)	XXVIIA U 792-795	XXVIIB U 1405, 1406, 1407	XXVIIG None	XXVIIK U 798 (not completed)
Displacement (tons) (surfaced/submerged)	80	655/725	236/259	312/357		
Length (m/ft)	26/85.30	52.1/171	34/111.5	41.5/136.15	39.5/129.6	40.7/133.5
Beam (m/ft)	2.6/8.5	4/13	3.4/11.15	3.4/11.15	3.4/11.15	3.4/11.15
Draught (m/ft)	7.25	18/59	15/49.2	14/46	14/46	16/52.5
Speed (knots) (surfaced/submerged)	not known	19 planned	26	21.5	21.5	14/16
Fuel (tons)	not known	Perhydrol 98	Perhydrol 40; O.F. 14	Perhydrol 55; O.F. 20	Perhydrol 55	Ingolin 55; O.F. 26
Range (nautical miles)/ at speed (knots)	not known	205/19	80/26	114/20	not known	114/20
Torpedo tubes/ no of torpedoes	none	2 bow/6	2 bow/4	2 bow/4	2 bow/4	none
Guns	none	none	none	none	none	none

existing boats. The snorkel was a prewar Dutch idea for ventilating the submarine and was adapted by the Germans to enable the submarine to use its diesel engines while dived. It consisted of a long tube hinged at the bottom so that it would fit flush with the deck when not in use, but when raised would project above water while the submarine was at periscope depth. The head of the tube had a float valve which closed when it was dipped below the surface or covered by a wave. The alternative was some form of closed-cycle engine, and in this direction the most promising development was the turbine designed by Professor Walter and fitted in the submarine *V 80* in 1940. The system relied on the breakdown of a high concentration of hydrogen peroxide (perhydrol) in a catalyst chamber to form oxygen and steam. The oxygen was then used to ignite fuel oil which was mixed with it, and the resulting high-pressure gas mixture was able to drive a turbine. The greatest difficulties lay in the manufacture and storage of the hydrogen peroxide, which decomposes, sometimes violently, in the presence of the slightest impurities. *V 80,* a small submarine of only 80 tons, was designed to test the feasibility of the system. A larger design, based on a Type VIIC hull, was numbered *V 300* (later *U 791*) and carried torpedo tubes. She never completed and was scrapped in 1944. A further design, *V 301*, was based on a new hull shape but never got further than the drawing board.

The next stage was the construction of four small Type XVIIA submarines which were launched in 1943. They were used initially to test out the system, and it was hoped that they would later become operational. As armament they were fitted with two bow torpedo tubes. They had one shaft with two Walter geared turbines which it was hoped would give a submerged speed of around 26 knots. They also had standard diesel-electric drive for normal propulsion. Two variants, Types XVIIB and XVIIG, had only one of the Walter turbines, but this still gave a designed maximum speed of a little over 20 knots. None of the Type XVIIGs were completed, and though other boats of this Type carried out extensive trials they never became operational. *U 1407* (Type XVIIB) was taken over by the Royal Navy at the end of the war. She commissioned as *Meteorite* and carried out further development trials before being scrapped in 1950. These postwar trials led in turn to the building of the two submarines of the *Explorer* Class for the RN using the same propulsion techniques.

Because of the slow development of the Walter turbine the Type XVIIK was planned to give the necessary fast underwater speed and some immunity from air attack. This would have had the Type XVIIB hull with a closed-cycle diesel engine. Cylinders of compressed air to give the boat adequate endurance took up too much space, and in the first instance the boats were purely experimental and no torpedo armament was fitted. A speed of about 16 knots was expected, but none of the boats was completed.

The Type XXI was a fundamentally new sort of submarine with a very streamlined hull and high-capacity batteries to give great submerged speed and endurance. The design was suggested at a conference in Paris in November 1942 as an alternative to the Walter turbine boats which were taking so long to develop, and by June 1943 the preliminary design work was complete. The planned submerged speed was 18 knots for 90 minutes, a tremendous advance on any existing submarine's performance and one that would have caused formidable problems to

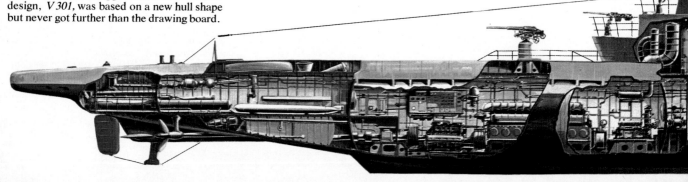

One of the 14 Type IXB ocean-going submarines built during the war. They had superior endurance compared to the Type VII but had a longer building time. They sank, on average, as high a tonnage as U-Boats operating nearer to Britain

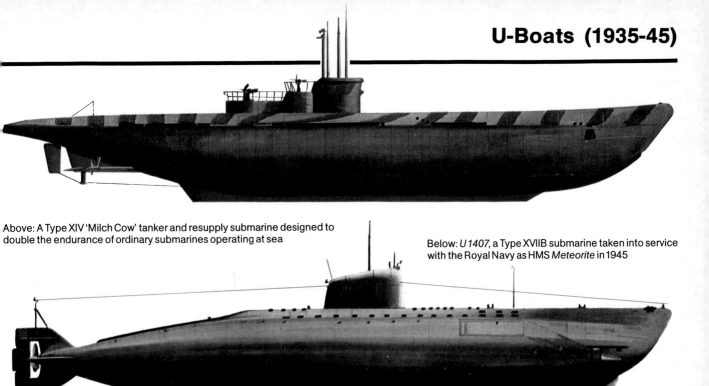

Above: A Type XIV 'Milch Cow' tanker and resupply submarine designed to double the endurance of ordinary submarines operating at sea

Below: *U 1407*, a Type XVIIB submarine taken into service with the Royal Navy as HMS *Meteorite* in 1945

the Allied navies had the Type XXI become operational in any numbers earlier in the war. Additional advantages of this type of U-Boat were a deep-diving capability, a fast silent speed and rapid torpedo reloading. The underwater armament was six bow tubes with 23 torpedoes. It was planned to give these boats a defensive AA armament of a quadruple 30-mm (1.18-in) gun of a new design, but because of production problems few were fitted and most boats had the standard 20-mm (0.79-in) weapon. To speed production the hull was prefabricated in eight all-welded sections in different shipyards away from the main bombing targets of the Allied forces. After transporting the sections to the launching slip they could be welded together rapidly and the boat launched, after spending a minimum time on a vulnerable launching slip.

The size of the Type XXI made it unsuitable for operations in the North Sea or English Channel. The Type XXIII was evolved incorporating many of the ideas of the Type XXI but with coastal characteristics and prefabricated in only four sections. The armament consisted of only two torpedo tubes. In order to maintain a clean streamlined hull shape the conventional deck casing was dispensed with.

In August 1943 the Types XXI and XXIII were ordered and to give them due priority the contracts for the Type VIIC-42 were

cancelled. Despite the dispersal of the prefabrication yards, production delays and the Allied bombing combined to defer the operational dates for both types. Fourteen Type XXIs alone, some of which were almost

ready for operations after long workup and crew training, were destroyed in Bremen, Hamburg and Kiel between mid-February and mid-April 1945. The first and only Type XXI to become operational was the *U 2511*

TYPES XXI and XXIII

Type	XXIA	XXIII
Numbers	U 2501-2564, 3001-3060, 3501-3542	U 2321-2371, 4701-4712
Displacement (tons) (surfaced/submerged)	1621/1819	232/256
Length (m/ft)	72.2/237	34.9/114.5
Beam (m/ft)	6.6/21.77	3/10
Draught (m/ft)	6.2/20.3	3.7/12
Speed (knots) (surfaced/submerged)	15.5/17	9.75/12.5
Fuel (tons)	250	18
Range (nautical miles)/ at speed (knots)	15 500/10	4300/6
Torpedo tubes/ no of torpedoes	6 bow/20	2 bow/2
Guns	2 30-mm (1.18-in) AA	none

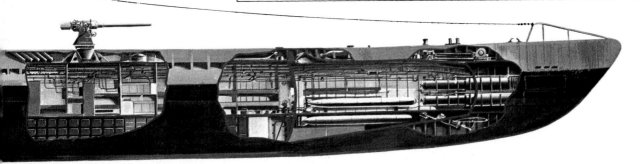

U-2, Lockheed

which sailed from Hamburg on March 18, 1945. She was then delayed with defects, and it was not until April 30 that she left her Norwegian base to commence operations. She was ordered to return to her base on May 4 for the surrender without having made any attacks on shipping.

The first Type XXIII, *U2321*, was launched in Hamburg in April 1944, but it was January 31 and February 6, 1945, before the *U2324* and *U2322* respectively left their base at Kristiansand for the first operational patrols. In all five boats carried out eight patrols, and although they only had limited success it showed the great potential of these boats, and the commanding officers were most enthusiastic about their performance. There is no doubt that had they become operational earlier in the war they would have been able to cause enormous damage and provided enormous problems for Allied escort forces.

Two variants of the Type XXI were designed in 1944, both increasing the number of torpedo tubes fitted. The Type XXIB had a second torpedo compartment fitted forward in the boat with the tubes firing astern angled out at 10° from the centreline. The Type XXIC had even more tubes fitted. None were built, and other variants were still in the design stage when the war ended. The Type XXI *U2518*, survived the war and served as *Roland Morillot* in the French navy, whilst *U2540* became the *Wilhelm Bauer* in 1960 in a reformed West German navy.

A number of other types and variants had been considered since 1935, but for various reasons were not proceeded with. These ranged from the Type III, which would have carried two MTBs in a special hangar aft of the conning tower, to the large Type XX transports. A Walter turbine version of the Type XXI was to be the Type XVIII; the Type XXXVI was to be a large ocean-going boat with a closed-cycle diesel engine.

U-2, Lockheed

US strategic reconnaissance and high-altitude research aircraft. Initiated jointly by the Central Intelligence Agency (CIA) and the US Air Force in the spring of 1954, the U-2 was evolved as a clandestine reconnaissance aircraft and flown at first by pilots working for the CIA. Two prototypes were hand-built in great secrecy at the Lockheed 'Skunk Works' at Burbank, California, the first one flying on or about August 1, 1955. Characterized by its light weight and huge wing span, the U-2 was, in effect, a powered sailplane, though an unusual one in that it had a remarkable rate of climb from an extremely short takeoff run. Forty-eight single-seat and five two-seat U-2s were ordered in February 1956. The initial U-2A had no ejection seat (the pilot wore an astronaut-type space-suit) and was powered by a 5080-kg (11 200-lb) st Pratt & Whitney J57-P-37A turbojet. Landing gear was of the bicycle type: two main wheels and two small tail wheels, retracting into the fuselage. In addition, small twin wheels or 'pogos' were attached under the outer wings for takeoff. They were then jettisoned, landings being made on the centre-fuselage wheels with the aircraft then settling gently on to one of the 90° turned-down wingtips. Landings turned out to be extremely critical, there being only one or

two knots difference between approach speed and stalling speed, and many U-2s were lost in landing accidents.

First operational deployment of the U-2A was from Lakenheath, England, where the first group of CIA pilots and aircraft arrived in 1956 under the cover title of the USAF's 1st Weather Reconnaissance Squadron (Provisional). Suspicions soon mounted as to the aircraft's true purpose, and the squadron was removed to Wiesbaden, Germany; when this base, too, attracted too much attention it was transferred again to more secure surroundings at Giebelstadt. A 2nd Weather Reconnaissance Squadron (Provisional) was formed at Adana, Turkey, and a 3rd at Edwards AFB in the US, the latter with a detachment at Okinawa. Other bases were established in Taiwan, Japan, the Philippines and Alaska, from which the U-2s performed their primary task of overflying Communist territories to monitor missile and other military activities, satellite launches, etc. From Cyprus other U-2s kept an eye on Suez in 1956, and in later years U-2s observed events in various Arab countries, Cuba and South-East Asia.

The first 'legitimate' US Air Force deployment was in 1957, with the 4080th Strategic Reconnaissance Wing of SAC at Laughlin AFB, Texas, and before long some genuine weather-research work was undertaken in Project HASP (High Altitude Sampling Program), gathering data on radioactive pollution from nuclear tests. But by 1959, after about 30 U-2As had been completed, the increasing weight of equipment being loaded into U-2s had so degraded performance that an uprated engine was needed. With a 7711-kg (17 000-lb) st J75-P-13 the aircraft became designated U-2B; all remaining examples, including most of the existing U-2As, were re-engined to this standard. The U-2A's internal fuel capacity of 3130 litres (689 Imp gal) gave it a range of only some 4185 km (2600 miles), and so two wing slipper tanks, each of 397 litres (87 Imp gal), were fitted to extend this to approx 6435 km (4000 miles). The two-seat U-2D was also given the J75 engine, but was distinguishable from the B by its tandem cockpits, between which projected two fairings for infrared spectrometers and radiometers. Used mostly by the 6512th Test Group of the USAF at Edwards AFB, the U-2D was employed for cosmic radiation detection and in connection with the Midas and Samos satellite programmes.

Despite the shooting down of Lieutenant Gary Powers' U-2 over Sverdlovsk in May 1960, photo-reconnaissance and elint (electronic intelligence) missions continued, and in 1962 it was the U-2 which alerted the US to the installation of Soviet missile sites in Cuba. Elsewhere the U-2 continued to attract only unfavourable publicity: by 1965 some two dozen had been lost in accidents or shot down over unfriendly territory—including all four U-2s operated by the Taiwan air force on behalf of the US, whose wreckage was displayed in Peking in June 1966. In Vietnam the U-2 started operating from Bien Hoa in 1964, later flying also from bases in Thailand and South Korea. Overflights of mainland China ended in 1974.

But the U-2 was still proving its worth, and high secrecy still surrounded the U-2C, an upgraded version with bulged intakes and a

long dorsal spine full of new and updated avionics. Most early U-2Cs were almost certainly conversions of earlier As or Bs, but in 1968 a fresh batch of 12 were ordered, originally with the weather designation WU-2C but since redesignated U-2R. These have a 31.39-m (103-ft) span fully 'wet' wing, eliminating the need for slipper tanks, a stretched fuselage of 19.2-m (63-ft) overall length, and no dorsal spine fairing. Also of relatively recent appearance is the U-2CT, a dual-control conversion trainer with an elevated second cockpit. Two have been produced, by converting one B and one D model, but there has been so much conversion from model to model that it is virtually impossible to delineate individual models properly. Moreover, there have been so many individually 'special' duties undertaken by U-2s that there are probably few aircraft which are not unique in internal equipment, external antennae and other features.

The production line is to be reopened in February 1980 to build 25 (possibly more) of the TR-1 version for the USAF. The new designation indicates that tactical reconnaissance is the role of this version, which will be based on the U-2R airframe and is intended primarily for use in Europe. The big difference will be an all-weather sideways-looking radar that will enable it to provide surveillance of battle areas without the need to overfly enemy territory.

(U-2C) Span: 24.38 m (80 ft) *Length:* 15.11 m (49 ft 7 in) *Gross weight:* 9980 kg (22 000 lb) approx *Maximum speed:* 850 km/h (528 mph)

Ugolini Vivaldi

Italian destroyer class, built 1927-31. Also known as the 'Navigatori' Class, 12 ships were ordered as scouts. Their role was to counter the French *contre-torpilleurs*, and to this end they were designed for 55 000 shp and 38 knots.

Alvise Cadamosto, Giovanni da Verazzano, Antonia Pigafetta, Nicolo Zeno—built by Cantiere Navale del Quarnaro, Fiume
Antonio da Noli, Leone Pancaldo—built by Cantieri del Tirreno, Riva Trigoso
Nicoloso da Recco, Emanuele Pessagno—built by Cantieri Navali Riuniti, Ancona
Lanzarotto Malocello, Luca Tarigo—built by Ansaldo, Genoa
Antoniotto Usodimare, Ugolino Vivaldi—built by Odero, Sestri Ponente

On trials *Alvise da Mosto* (ex-*Alvise Cadamosto*) developed 71 000 shp and exceeded 44 knots, but at full load they were only good for 32 knots. They were regarded as a disappointment, and in 1939-40 the whole class except *da Recco* and *Usodimare* were modified with a raised and raked bow to improve seaworthiness. The hull was also widened by 1 m (3 ft 4 in) to improve stability and allow more fuel to be carried. Despite these problems the ships had the reputation of being reliable steamers, and as the turbines and boiler were arranged on the unit system they were also more battleworthy than most foreign contemporaries.

From September 1938 the class was rerated as destroyers. *Alvise da Mosto* carried out some minelaying operations and

The Italian destroyer *Antonio Pigafetta*, one of the *Ugolini Vivaldi* class built in 1927-31. She was scuttled at Fiume on September 10, 1943, to avoid capture, but was refloated by the Germans

escorted convoys. On December 1, 1941, she was sunk off Kerkenah, north-west of Tripoli, by British cruisers and destroyers. *Antonio da Noli* survived until the armistice in September 1943, but on September 9, while trying to take action against German light craft, she was hit by shore artillery. She lost steerage way, drifted into a minefield and sank. *Nicoloso da Recco* was badly damaged in action off Gaudo, south of Crete, and her magazine exploded. She limped back to Trapani and was repaired to fight again. *Giovanni da Verazzano* was torpedoed and sunk on October 19, 1942, by HM Submarine *Unbending*. *Lanzarotto Malocello* was sunk by a mine on March 24, 1943. *Leone Pancaldo* was sunk in Augusta on July 10, 1940, by a Swordfish torpedo-bomber. She was refloated the following year but was sunk again by bombing on April 30, 1943. *Emanuele Pessagno* was torpedoed on May 29, 1942, by HM Submarine *Turbulent*. *Antonio Pigafetta* was scuttled at Fiume on September 10, 1943, to keep her out of German hands, but was refloated and recommissioned as *TA.44*. She was subsequently sunk by British bombers at Trieste on February 17, 1945. *Luca Tarigo* was sunk in action with British destroyers on April 16, 1941. *Antoniotto Usodimare* was regarded as an unlucky ship, being involved in three collisions before being torpedoed in error by the Italian submarine *Alagi* on June 8, 1942. *Nicolo Zeno* was damaged in a collision in February 1943 and was scuttled at Trieste on September 9, 1943, to avoid capture. *Ugolino Vivaldi* rammed and sank HM Submarine *Oswald* on August 1, 1940, and suffered damage off Pantelleria in June 1942. With *da Noli* she attacked German units north of Sardinia on September 9, 1943, but was hit by shore artillery; that night she was hit by bombs while trying to reach the Balearic Islands and sank next morning. *Nicoloso da Recco*, the sole survivor of the class, was used to repatriate Italian prisoners after September 1943, and was permitted to be retained by the postwar Italian navy. She was not discarded until 1954.

Displacement: 1900 tons (normal), 2580 tons (full load) *Length:* 107.28 m (352 ft) oa *Beam:* 10.2 m (33 ft 6 in) as built *Draught:* 3.63 m (11 ft 11 in) *Machinery:* 2-shaft geared steam turbines, 55000 shp=38 knots *Armament:* (As built) 6 120-mm (4.7-in)/50-cal (3×2); 2 2-pdr (40-mm)/39-cal AA (2×1); 4 13.2-mm (0.52-in) AA machine-guns; 6 53-cm (21-in) torpedo tubes; (From 1931-32) 6 120-mm (4.7-in [3×2]); 7/9 20-mm (0.79-in) AA (7/9×1); 4 53-cm (21-in) torpedo tubes (2×2) *Crew:* 173

UH-1, Bell US multipurpose helicopter
See **Iroquois**

UH-46, Boeing Vertol US assault and transport helicopter
See **Sea Knight**

Ukuru

Japanese escort class. The steadily increasing losses of her merchant fleet to US submarines forced Japan into convoying what was left of the fleet. The prewar attitude of ignoring the possibility of Japan being on the defensive had left the navy without an adequate escort force. Consequently, under the 1941 War Programme, designs were prepared for a new class of escorts, the largest to be ordered at that time. Eight of them, known as the Modified Type B, were ordered under the 1942-43 Estimates, with another 34 under the 1942 Modified Programme (1943-44 Estimates). Of these 34, a total of 18 were cancelled in the autumn of 1944 before they had been laid down. Under the 1943-44 War Programme (1944-45 Estimates) another 21 were planned, but 12 of these were also cancelled in the autumn of 1944. Under the 1944-45 War Programme 79 units were planned, but none was laid down before 1945.

These escorts were very similar to the *Mikura* Class, displacement and dimensions remaining the same. The hull form, however, was much plainer with flare, curves and sheer almost completely eliminated; with a much more basic hull form it was hoped that production could be speeded up. The hulls were prefabricated and by eliminating all but essential items the average construction time for units was reduced to four-five months. The bridge was enlarged to accommodate extra personnel for manning the radar and sonar equipment. The radar consisted of a Type 22 surface-warning set on the foremast and a Type 13 air-warning set on the mainmast. Armament was the same as in *Mikura* except that the light AA was increased to 16 25-mm (1-in) mounted as two triple mounts abreast the bridge, one mount aft of the mainmast and two triple mounts abreast the hexagonal funnel. On a bandstand in front of the bridge was mounted a single 25-mm gun superimposed over the mortar. A number of units were given in addition four single 25-mm mounts on the quarterdeck. Some early units were equipped with a paravane, but this was subsequently removed as it impeded the operation of the depth-charge throwers. The stowage of depth charges varied between units but was generally about 120. An electric lift from the depth-charge magazine carried the charges to the deck where some units were fitted with up to 16 depth-charge throwers.

Aguni, Amami, Okinawa, Ukuru—built by Tsurumi
Chikubu, Hodaka, Ikara, Ikino, Kozu, Murotsu, Shinnan, Urumi, Yaku—built by Uraga
Daito, Habuto, Hiburi, Ikuma, Kume, Mokuto, Otsu, Sakito, Shiskaka, Shonan, Tomoshiri—built by Hitachi
Habushi, Inagi, Kanawa, Oga, Takane—built by Mitsui
Iwo, Kuga, Shiga, Uku—built by Sasebo

Four of these were still under construction at the end of the war. *Murotsu, Otsu* and *Urumi* were very nearly complete, but work had only just begun on *Tomoshiri*. The remainder were all completed between June 1944 and the end of the war.

The following survived the war: *Aguni, Amami, Chikubu* (recommissioned into the new Japanese Self-Defence Force in 1948, renamed *Atsumi* in 1955), *Habushi, Habuto, Hodaka, Ikino, Ikuna* (as *Chikubu*, renamed *Ojika* in 1955), *Iwo, Kanawa, Kogu* (to USSR), *Kuga, Sakito, Shiga* (as *Chikubu*, renamed *Tusgaru* 1955), *Shisaka* (to China 1947), *Takane, Uku* (as *Chikubu*, renamed *Satsuma* 1955). Five were sunk by submarines: *Hiburi* (by *Harder* 8/44), *Kume* (by *Spadefish* 1/45, *Oga* (by *Springer* 5/45), *Shonan* (by *Hoe* 2/45), *Yaku* (by *Hammerhead* 2/45). Three were mined: *Daito* (11/45), *Ikara* (8/45), *Mokuto* (4/45). Two were sunk by aircraft: *Inagi* (8/45), *Okinawa* (7/45)

Displacement: 940 tons (standard) *Length:* 78 m (256 ft) oa *Beam:* 9 m (29 ft 6 in) *Draught:* 3 m (10 ft) *Machinery:* 2-shaft diesels, 4200 bhp=19.5 knots *Armament:* 3 4.7-in (120-mm) (1×1, 1×2); 16 25-mm (1-in); 1 3-in (76-mm) A/S mortar; 120 depth charges *Crew:* 150

Ulster

British destroyer class. The *Ulster* or 'U' Class destroyers were ordered in June 1941 as the 7th Flotilla of the Emergency War Programme. They were laid down during 1941-42, launched during 1942-43 and completed during 1943-44. In design they were repeats of the *Savage* or 'S' Class from which they differed in minor detail only. All completed with their designed armament, except *Undine* and *Urchin* which carried two twin 20-mm (0.79-in) mountings in place of their twin 40-mm (1.57-in) mounts which were not available at the time; *Undine* later received her twin 40-mm but *Urchin* did not. *Ulster* and *Grenville* completed with tripod foremasts, as designed, but these were later replaced by lattice masts while the rest of the class were similarly modified before entering service. Late in 1944 the four twin 20-mm mountings and the 44-in searchlight amid-

Umikaze

ships were replaced by single 40-mm guns except in *Ulster,* which remained unaltered, and *Urania,* which had her 20-mm guns replaced by the 40-mm weapons but retained the searchlight.

On completion *Grenville* and *Ulster* joined the Home Fleet but soon afterwards they were loaned to the Plymouth Command. In November both were damaged in action with German destroyers off the French coast. After repairs they transferred to the Mediterranean where they were joined by *Undine* and *Urchin,* the remainder of the class going to the Home Fleet. After covering the landings at Anzio, the Mediterranean vessels returned home and the entire class was brought together to cover the Normandy landings. In July 1944 *Urchin, Undaunted, Ulster* and *Undine* returned to the Mediterranean where they covered the landings in the south of France. At the end of 1944 all eight sailed for the Far East where they joined the British Pacific Fleet with which they operated until the end of the war. During the assault on Okinawa in April 1945 *Ulster* suffered a near miss by a kamikaze aircraft, and the explosion blew a hole 7.6 m (25 ft) long and 3.7 m (12 ft) deep in her side amidships causing extensive flooding. She was towed to Leyte, temporarily repaired by the US Navy and then taken home for full repairs between October 1945 and February 1946. In 1946 all except *Ulster,* which served as a training vessel until 1952, were placed in reserve. During the 1950s all eight were converted to Type 15 fast antisubmarine frigates and some survived into the early 1970s before being placed on the disposal list, the first to go being *Ulysses,* in 1962, and the last of the class, *Undaunted,* being sunk as a target in 1978.

See also *Rapid.*

Grenville, Ulster—built by Swan Hunter
Ulysses, Undaunted—built Cammell Laird
Undine, Ursa—built by Thornycroft
Urania, Urchin—built by Vickers-Armstrongs

Displacement: 1780 tons (standard), 2510 tons (full load) *Length:* 110.6 m (362 ft 9 in) oa *Beam:* 10.9 m (35 ft 8 in) *Draught:* 2.9 m (9 ft 6 in) *Machinery:* 2-shaft geared steam turbines, 40 000 shp=36 knots *Armament:* 4 4.7-in (120-mm) (4×1); 2 40-mm (1.57-in) (1×2); 8 20-mm (0.79-in) (4×2); 8 21-in (53-cm) torpedo tubes (2×4) *Crew:* 179

Umikaze

Japanese destroyer class. Authorized under the 1907 Programme, the plans for these two large destroyers were not finalized until some two years later. They were the first destroyers to be designed for the Imperial Japanese Navy after the Russo-Japanese War. Experience in conducting destroyer operations and the rapidly changing tactics and designs of warships caused the Japanese to give serious consideration to their staff requirement for their next destroyer design, and there was some delay over finalizing the design. The Japanese were careful to note what foreign navies were producing, particularly designs such as the British *Swift* and 'Tribal' designs. One of the obvious requirements was improved seakeeping qualities which would naturally accrue from a larger type of vessel.

By adopting a much larger design the vessels would be able to fit more powerful machinery and heavier armament. These vessels were therefore equipped with turbine machinery instead of the reciprocating machinery of previous vessels. The boilers were mixed-firing. Bunkerage consisted of 250 tons of coal and 180 tons of oil which gave the ships a radius of action of 2700 nautical miles at 15 knots. The main armament consisted of 4.7-in (120-mm) guns. The two vessels differed slightly in their armament, *Umikaze* being fitted with two twin torpedo tubes while the *Yamakaze* carried three single tubes.

The two vessels proved to be a successful design and were very popular. In 1929-30 they were converted to a minesweeping role when a number of boilers were removed, power being reduced to 11 000 shp and speed to 24 knots. Armament was reduced to a single 4.7-in gun on the forecastle and four 12-pdr guns. They were renumbered as *No 7* (ex-*Umikaze*) and *No 8* (ex-*Yamakaze*). They were removed from operational service in 1936 and scrapped.

Displacement: 1150 tons (normal) *Length:* 98.6 m (323 ft 6 in) *Beam:* 8.45 m (27 ft 9 in) *Draught:* 2.74 m (9 ft) *Machinery:* 3-shaft Parsons geared steam turbines, 20 500 shp=33 knots *Armament:* 2 4.7-in (120-mm); 5 12-pdr (80-mm); 3 (*Umikaze* 4) 18-in (46-cm) torpedo tubes *Crew:* 140

Undine

British submarine class. The 1937 Programme provided for the construction of three small submarines, *Undine, Unity* and *Ursula,* which were intended to serve as training vessels for submarine crews and to provide targets for A/S training. In wartime they were expected to undertake short patrols, but this was very much a secondary consideration. The three boats carried six bow tubes (four internal and two external) but only *Ursula* was fitted with a gun—a single 12-pdr. They were driven exclusively by electric motors, current being supplied by the batteries when submerged or by diesel-driven generators when surfaced. After the outbreak of war it was realized that these small vessels could be useful in the shallow waters of the North Sea where endurance was not a major problem, and as they could be built quickly 12 were ordered under the 1939 Emergency War Programme followed by another 22 under the 1940 Programme. The entry of Italy into the war gave the class another ideal area of operations in the Mediterranean, and a further 20 were ordered under the 1941 Programme and 34 under the 1942 Programme. Up to 1941 these vessels were repeats of the original trio except that they carried a 3-in (76-mm) gun and omitted the external bow tubes (*Unique, Upholder, Upright* and *Utmost* were fitted with six tubes like the originals) but the 1942 Programme boats were modified to part-welded construction which enabled them to dive to 91 m (300 ft) compared with 61 m (200 ft) in the earlier vessels. These latter boats were designated the 'V' Class although both the 'U' and 'V' Groups employed names beginning with both letters.

Despite their limited range and armament the class gave sterling service during the war and accounted for many thousands of tons of enemy shipping. In many ways their small size was an advantage as they were more manoeuvrable than larger boats, and the fact that they were available in large numbers made up for their individual inferiority. Seventy-two of the class entered service at regular intervals between 1941 and 1945, but after the end of hostilities in the Mediterranean their value diminished considerably and 20 of the 'V' Class ships were cancelled in 1944. All but two of the class (*Umpire* and *Una* constructed by Chatham dockyard) were built by Vickers-Armstrongs, a remarkable achievement although hardly comparable to German U-Boat production. The war-construction vessels, except for the 1939 Programme boats, were originally given numbers but those surviving until 1943 were given full 'U' or 'V' names.

As might be expected, war losses were heavy, particularly among the early units of the class. Eight were sunk by depth charging; *Undine* in 1940 in the North Sea, and *Union, Upholder, Urge, Utmost, P.38, P.48* and *Usurper* during 1941-43 in the Mediterranean. Also lost in the Mediterranean during this period were *Usk, P.32* and *P.33* which were mined, *P.36* and *P.39* which were bombed, and *Uredd* and *Undaunted* due to unknown cause. Four were lost by accident in Home Waters: *Unity, Umpire, Vandal* and *P.58,* but the last named was salvaged and re-entered service as *Vitality* in 1943. In addition to these, *Unique* disappeared in the Atlantic west of Gibraltar in 1942, and *Unbeaten* was accidentally sunk by RAF bombers in the Bay of Biscay in the same year. Several of the class were transferred to foreign navies both during and after the war. Most of the remaining vessels had been sold for scrap by 1950.

'U' Class
Undine, Unity, Ursula—1937 Programme
Umpire, Una, Unbeaten, Undaunted, Union, Unique, Upholder, Upright, Urchin, Urge, Usk, Utmost—1939 Programme
Uproar, P.32, P.33, Ultimatum, Umbra, P.36, Unbending, P.38, P.39, Uredd, Unbroken, Unison, United, Unrivalled, Unruffled, P.47, P.48, Unruly, Unseen, P.52, Ultor, Unshaken—1940 Programme
Unsparing, Usurper, Universal, Untamed, Untiring, Varangian, Uther, Unswerving, Vandal, Upstart, Varne, Vox—1941 Programme

Name	launched	completed	builder
Umikaze	10/10	9/11	Maizuru navy yard
Yamakaze	1/11	10/11	Mitsubishi

V' Class

Venturer, Viking, Veldt, Vampire, Vox, Vigorous, Virtue, Visigoth, Vivid, Voracious, Vulpine, Varne, Upshot, Urtica, Vineyard, Variance, Vengeful, Vortex, Virulent, Volatile, Vagabond, Votary—1942 Programme

Ursula, Unbroken and *Unison* were transferred to the USSR in 1944 and renamed *B.4, B.2* and *B.3*. They were returned 1949. *Urchin* and *P.52* transferred to Poland in 1941 and 1942 respectively and renamed *Sokol* and *Dzik*. They were returned 1946. *Uredd* transferred to Norway in 1941 and was replaced by *Ula* when lost in 1943; *Variance* transferred 1944 and was renamed *Utsira*. Norway also received *Venturer, Viking* and *Votary* in 1946 (renamed *Utstein, Uttaer* and *Utsira*); all these vessels were retained by the Norwegian navy. *Untiring, Upstart, Veldt, Vengeful, Virulent* and *Volatile* transferred to Greece during 1944-46 and renamed *Xifias, Amfitriti, Pipinos, Delfin, Argonaftis* and *Trianian* respectively. The first pair were returned in 1952 and the remainder during 1957-58. *Vox, Vineyard, Vortex* transferred to France during 1943-44 and renamed *Curie, Doris* and *Morse*; they were returned 1946-47. The Netherlands received *P.47* in 1942, *Dzik* (ex-*P.52*) in 1943 and *Vulpine* and *Morse* (ex-*Vortex*) in 1947. *P.47* was renamed *Dolfyn* in 1953; the *Dzik* became *U 1* on transfer then *Springeren* in 1948, while the last pair were renamed *Storen* and *Saelen* respectively.

Displacement: 545/735 tons (surfaced/submerged) *Length:* 60 m (196 ft 9 in) oa, ('V' Class) 62.3 m (204 ft 6 in) *Beam:* 4.9 m (16 ft) *Draught:* 3.9 m (12 ft 9 in) *Machinery:* 2-shaft diesel-electric 618 bhp ('V' Class, 800 bhp)/825 shp=11.75 (12.75)/9 knots (surfaced/submerged) *Armament:* 1 3-in (76-mm); 4 21-in (53-cm) torpedo tubes *Crew:* 33

Unebi

Japanese cruiser. *Unebi* was ordered from Forges et Chantiers at Le Havre and was laid down in May 1884. She was launched on April 6, 1886, and completed in October 1886. The steel-hulled cruiser was handed over to the Japanese in December 1886 having successfully completed her preliminary trials.

The heavy 18-ton guns were sited in broadside sponsons with the 5.9-in (150-mm) guns also mounted broadside, three on each beam with a fifth gun in the bow. The ship was designed with 74 watertight compartments.

Following further trials *Unebi* sailed for Japan, but she never completed the last leg from Singapore and was posted missing sometime in October 1887. As the cause of her loss was never established it cannot be said with certainty that it was as a result of faulty design, or perhaps poor workmanship, but the mounting of such heavy armament in broadside sponsons could not have improved her stability. The Japanese were very reluctant to order further vessels from French shipyards, and turned more and more to British yards for designs and construction.

Displacement: 3615 tons (normal) *Length:* 98 m (321 ft 6in) pp *Beam:* 13.1 m (43 ft) *Draught:* 5.7 m (18 ft 8 in) *Machinery:* 2-shaft horizontal triple-expansion, 6000 ihp=17.5 knots *Protec-*

tion: 60 mm (2.4 in) deck *Armament:* 4 9.4-in (240-mm); 7 5.9-in (150-mm); 2 6-pdr (57-mm) Nordenfeld QF; 10 1-pdr (25-mm) Nordenfeld QF; 4 10-barrel Gatling machine-guns; 4 17.7-in (45-cm) torpedo tubes (above water) *Crew:* 280

Unicorn

British maintenance carrier. The first ship designed to support distant operations by aircraft carriers, providing second-line maintenance and repair facilities, spares and reserve aircraft, was ordered in 1938 by the Admiralty. HMS *Unicorn* was to complement the *Illustrious* Class ships, of which two had been ordered in 1937 and one at the same time as herself. Laid down in June 1939, construction was suspended for a while in 1940 and she was not launched until November 1941.

Resembling a foreshortened fleet carrier, she had two hangar decks, each with clear height of 5 m (16 ft 6 in), so that she had a greater free-board than the 30.5 m (100 ft) longer front-line ship; the aerodynamic 'round-downs' of the latter were suppressed, however, so that the usable length of the flight deck was little less. When she was completed on March 12, 1943, she was equipped with the latest model of arrester gear, capable of stopping 9070-kg (20 000-lb) aircraft, and with the standard 66-knot catapult; full communications, air warning and fire-control radar and aircraft homing beacon were all fitted, giving her a potential not far short of that of the fleet carriers.

The staff requirement demanded that she should be equipped and manned to undertake the repair of eight aircraft simultaneously and that she should have all the necessary airframe, engine, radio, electrical and instrument workshops, up to the shore maintenance unit. The shape of the stern differed from that of the fleet carriers, being squared off to permit the slinging of an aircraft lighter under the after round-down.

Armament comprised four twin 4-in (102-mm) AA guns, two mountings on each side of the flight deck, four quadruple 2-pdr (40-mm) pom-poms and a total of 26 20-mm (0.79-in) Oerlikons. Like her larger contemporaries, she was armoured, with 51 mm (2 in) on her flight deck, but the hangar sides were not armoured and she had no waterline belt, the magazines being protected by internal plate on the crowns and sides and by a torpedo bulkhead.

As a high speed was not required of the ship, the machinery installed was similar to the current (1939) fleet destroyer plant: a maximum speed of nearly 24 knots was attained on trials.

The potential of the design for development as a combat carrier was recognised before *Unicorn* was completed and was realized in the '1942 Light Fleet' carriers, these ships being built along rather more utilitarian lines, with one hangar, no armour and no guns larger than 2-pdr. No 'Repeat *Unicorn*' was ordered, but two of the light fleets, *Pioneer* and *Perseus*, were completed as maintenance carriers.

Such was the shortage of British aircraft carriers, when *Unicorn* commissioned she did so as a front-line ship, beginning her work-up in March 1943 with two squadrons of Swordfish and one of Sea Hurricanes. Ten

Seafires replaced the Hurricanes in April and when the carrier accompanied a convoy to Gibraltar in May, to deliver RAF aircraft, the fighters were almost immediately in action, damaging a Focke Wulf Fw 200 shadower on May 24. The ship herself was near-missed by bombs from another Fw 200.

In August, *Unicorn* embarked two more squadrons of Seafires, for a total of 30 aircraft of this type, retained three Swordfish and joined four escort carriers to provide defensive fighter patrols over the Salerno invasion beaches. Her aircraft saw most of the limited combat between September 9-12, destroying two enemy fighters and damaging three others. One hundred and ninety-seven sorties were flown, but 19 Seafires were damaged beyond repair in landing accidents and the numbers had to be made good by the transfer of seven Seafires from *Illustrious* and eight Grumman F4F-4B Martlets from *Formidable*.

This was *Unicorn*'s last period as a full operational carrier, for on return to the United Kingdom she was re-equipped for her intended role and, at the end of 1943, despatched to Ceylon to support the carriers of the East Indies Fleet. She remained at Trincomalee from January to November 1944, sailing from time to time to provide a deck for continuation training of aircrew on the naval shore-based squadrons on the island. After a refit at Durban, *Unicorn* was allocated to the British Pacific Fleet, together with the Fleet carriers which she joined at Sydney in mid-February 1945.

In early March she moved up to the forward base at Manus, Admiralty Islands, and in April she proceeded to San Pedro Bay, Leyte to service the front-line carriers during their week-long break from interdicting the Sakishima Gunto. Returning to Manus in May, she remained there until the end of the war, while the fleet carriers joined the US Third Fleet in striking at Japan. After ferrying the aircraft from the reserve 'pool' at Manus back to Sydney and repatriating Commonwealth personnel, *Unicorn* left the Far East for home, arriving at Devonport in January 1946. She was almost immediately decommissioned and placed in reserve.

In the summer of 1949, *Unicorn* recommissioned for the Far East Fleet and sailed for Singapore in September with a load of aircraft and spares to support HMS *Triumph*. The commission was to have lasted a year, but the outbreak of the Korean war at the end of June 1950 led to her retention and she remained on the station until the end of hostilities, based mainly on Sasebo but returning to Hong Kong to collect material from time to time. Visiting the Yellow Sea in October 1953, she bombarded North Korean targets with her 4-in guns—her final combat.

Returning once again to Devonport on November 17, 1953, *Unicorn* was again placed in reserve. She was sold in 1959 and broken up on the Clyde.

Displacement: 14 750 tons (standard) 20 300 tons (full load) *Length:* 196.9 m (646 ft) oa *Beam:* 27.4 m (90 ft) *Draught:* 7.6 m (25 ft) *Machinery:* 2-shaft geared turbines, 40 725 shp=23.9 knots *Aircraft:* 28-33 (as operational carrier) *Armament:* 8 4-in (102-mm) DP (4×2); 16 2-pdr AA (4×4); 26 20-mm (0.79-in) AA *Crew:* approx 1200 (as maintenance carrier)

United Defense

The United Defense M42 submachine-gun, which had a 9-mm (0.354-in) Parabellum 20-round magazine

United Defense

US submachine-gun. The United Defense Supply corporation was set up under obscure circumstances in the US in 1940, and appears to have been a legal cloak to permit the US government to provide arms to friendly nations without jeopardizing the United States' neutrality.

In addition to its other sales, the company promoted two submachine-gun designs which had been submitted for military test. The first was the M42, designed in the late 1930s by Carl Swebilius of the High Standard corporation. Under contract from United Defense, numbers were made by the Marlin Firearms company for supply to the Dutch government for use in the Netherlands East Indies, but after the Japanese occupation the remainder of the contract was sent to the Office of Strategic Services for supply to various clandestine organizations in Europe.

The UD M42 was in 9-mm (0.354-in) Parabellum calibre, of the usual blowback type, and resembled the Thompson in having two pistol grips and a wooden butt. It fired from a box magazine and, from what accounts exist, was reliable and robust and one of the better wartime designs. Since it was made by traditional machining processes it was not cheap and could not compete for mass delivery with the Sten or US M3 designs.

In 1943 a fresh design was proposed and offered as an alternative to the M3. This used a tubular receiver and perforated barrel jacket and was almost entirely made by stamping, pressing and welding. An unusual design feature was the provision of two barrels; one in 0.45-in (11.4-mm) calibre and one in 9-mm. By changing barrels, the gun was immediately ready to fire the selected calibre, no change of bolt being required. When not in use, the spare barrel fitted into the rear of the receiver, was provided with a pad, and became the stock. It was a clever design but it failed to survive its trials, being particularly susceptible to mud and dirt.

(M42) *Calibre:* 9 mm (0.354 in) *Ammunition:* 9-mm Parabellum *Weight:* 4.14 kg (9 lb 2 oz) *Length:* 820 mm (32.3 in) *Barrel length:* 279 mm (11 in) *Magazine:* 20-round detachable box *Rate of fire:* 700 rds/min *Muzzle velocity:* 400 m/sec (1312 ft/sec)

Universal Carrier

British light armoured vehicle. Work on light armoured carriers had begun in the 1920s when designers saw two uses: as tractors for field guns and as mobile support vehicles mounting a light or medium machine-gun.

Some bizarre ideas were spawned, but it was the development of Hortsmann suspension which was fitted to the Dragon gun tractor in 1933 that led to the familiar Bren Gun Carrier and the Universal Carrier.

The suspension consisted of two coil springs on each side. For sharp turns one track was slowed down and the opposite speeded up, while on gradual turns both tracks could be disaligned by forcing the centre bogie wheels away from the hull to left or right. This system gave a smooth ride and also made the carrier very manoeuvrable.

When the BEF went to France in 1939 they were operating two types of carrier in addition to the Bren Carrier. The Scout and Cavalry Carrier were similar to the Bren Carrier, but the former had space for an extra man or a No 11 wireless set, a Boys antitank rifle and a Bren gun in the rear compartment. The Cavalry Carrier was designed to carry six men in a lightly armoured vehicle who could then keep pace with the tanks and vehicles of the Mobile Division. When the Mobile Division evolved into the Armoured Division the role for the Cavalry Carrier disappeared and only 50 were built.

The Bren Carrier like the Scout Carrier saw action in France in May 1940. It consisted of an armoured tracked vehicle with an open top with two compartments. The front housed a driver and machine-gunner and a third crew member was housed in the rear beside the engine. In winter they were open to the rain and wind, while in summer the unfortunate in the back seat was next to the engine. Overhead cover for the crew consisted of their helmets. The crew's stores were stowed in bins and on the decking to the rear of the driver. Armour was proof against small-arms and the carrier was capable of a speed of 48 km/h (30 mph).

After the withdrawal from France in 1940 it was decided to rationalize carrier development into a universal design. The Carrier Universal Marks I, II and III were born and remained the standard British and Commonwealth carrier during the war.

The Universal had armour plate on both sides (unlike the Scout and Bren) with bulletproof protection for the engine. There were mud guards at the front with a step at the rear for the crew. The Universal had a compartment for an extra crew member or stores to the rear of the driver. Armament consisted of either a 0.303-in (7.7-mm) Bren LMG or a 0.55-in (14-mm) Boys antitank rifle, while the Australians favoured mounting a Vickers 0.303-in MMG. When not in use the weapons could be stowed in clips with the crew's personal weapons. There were three positions for an AA mount for a Bren and boxes for two grenades in the driver's and rear compartments. Ammunition was stowed in the front two compartments as well as the rear right.

In the field the crew often rearmed their carrier with weapons like the 0.30-in (7.62-mm) Browning and 0.5-in (12.7-mm) Browning machine-gun or the German 20-mm (0.79-in) Solothurn antitank gun, PIAT antitank projector or 2-in (51-mm) light mortar.

In the Mk II Carrier a permanent mount for a 2-in mortar was incorporated while the mortar was fitted with sights for use from the

A Loyd tracked personnel carrier, one of the prewar carriers rationalized into the Universal

carrier. The Mk II had a welded waterproof hull. The Carrier, Universal No 1 Mk II had a crew of four, weighed 4.5 tons as against 3.75 tons but retained the same Ford V-8 engine. The Mk III was similar to the Mk II but had a modified air inlet and engine cover.

Some carriers were used for 3-in (76-mm) mortars, but though the mortar could be fired from the front gunner's position it was more common to dismount and assemble the weapon. Ammunition was carried stowed in racks inside the carrier.

A flame-throwing carrier was developed and by the end of the war four versions had been designed by the Petroleum Warfare Department. The Ronson had fuel tanks mounted externally with the flame gun mounted on top of the gunner's plate. The external tanks were not popular and the Wasp Mk I (FT, Transportable, No 2, Mk I) had two flame-fuel tanks (182 and 273 litres [40 and 60 Imp gal]), pressure bottles and fuel lines and gun inside the carrier. It had a crew of two and a flame range of 70-90 m (80-100 yards).

The Mk II Wasp had a superior flame gun and a profile which resembled an ordinary carrier.

The Mk IIC Wasp (C stood for Canada) was developed by the Canadians and first saw action outside Falaise in 1944. Though it had less fuel than the Mk II it could carry a Bren gun or 2-in mortar in the rear compartment since the fuel was carried externally.

The Mk IIC proved to be the most effective Wasp and after the production pro-gramme for the Mk II was complete all subsequent vehicles were built as Mk IICs. Some received plastic armour in the front. Wasps were issued on a scale of six per infantry battalion.

Universal carriers were built in consider-able numbers in Canada and the United States. Australia supplied its army with car-riers and even sent 1500 to China. In Canada and the United States there were a number of experiments to produce a model with a more powerful engine.

(Carrier Universal Mk I) *Weight:* 3.75 tons *Length:* 3.66 m (12 ft) *Width:* 2.06 m (6 ft 9 in) *Height:* 1.57 m (5 ft 2 in) *Armour thickness:* 10-70 mm (0.4-0.3-in) *Armament:* (various) 0.303-in (7.7-mm) Bren light machine-gun; 0.303-in Vickers medium machine-gun; 2-in (51-mm) mortar; 2 0.303-in rifles *Powerplant:* Ford V-8 85-bhp *Speed:* 48 km/h (30 mph) *Crew:* 3

Unryu

Japanese fleet carrier class. In 1941, well before the outbreak of the Pacific War, the Imperial Japanese Navy decided to order six 17000-ton fast carriers for the mobile fleet. The basic design chosen was that of the *Hiryu*, the principal differences being the positioning of the island on the conventional starboard side of the deck and the elimination of the third lift, amidships. The magazines were protected by 150-mm (5.9-in) belt armour but a deck only 55 mm (2.2 in) thick, so that the ships were no better protected against bombing attack than *Soryu*. The lower hangar was nearly 13 m (43 ft) shorter than *Hiryu*'s, so that aircraft complement was reduced from 64 to 57.

Three ships were laid down shortly after

the outbreak of war; *Unryu* was built by Yokosuka navy yard, *Katsuraoi* and *Aso* by Kure navy yard, *Amagi* and *Kasagi* by Mit-subishi, Nagasaki, and *Ikoma* by Kawasaki, Kobe. *Unryu* and *Amagi* were built with the intended 152 000-shp cruiser-type machinery, but the Japanese turbine industry could not provide a third installation in the time scale and so *Katsuragi* had to be fitted with two sets of destroyer turbines, with an output of 104 000 shp. The maximum speed was not lowered appreciably, for on trials *Katsuragi* made 32.7 knots—only slightly less than the 34-knot more powerful units.

Lack of shipyard capacity delayed the start of construction of the second batch of three until 1943, by which time 'Supplementary Programmes' had added another 11 ships of the class to the list of orders which could never hope to be fulfilled within the likely time-scale of this war, given Japan's acute lack of steel. The three ships laid down in 1943, *Kasagi, Ikoma* and *Aso*, were launched in late 1944, the last named being powered like *Katsuragi*, but none was completed before the end of the war, fitting-out being suspended during the spring of 1945.

Unryu and *Amagi* were completed on August 6 and 11, 1944 respectively. Both were allocated to the Carrier Division 1 and began to work up a new air group to replace the losses sustained two months earlier in the 'Marianas Turkey Shoot'. It was anticipated that they, and possibly the nearly complete *Katsuragi*, would be ready for action by mid-November but this plan was shattered by the opening moves in the Leyte campaign, a full month before the Japanese had expected the next US assault. The aircraft Carrier Division 1 were flown ashore to Formosa on October 10, 1944, where they were virtually wiped out four days later. Ironically, *Katsuragi* com-missioned on the latter date.

The three carriers were used to ferry aircraft between Japan, China and Luzon during the remainder of 1944. While engaged on this duty, *Unryu* was attacked by the submarine USS *Redfish* on the night of December 19; one hit was scored from the first salvo, setting the carrier on fire and stopping her. *Redfish* reloaded and hit *Unryu* again with a torpedo which caused a huge explosion, following which the ship sank rapidly, leaving few survivors.

Amagi and *Katsuragi* were restricted to home waters after the end of 1944: not only were there no aircrew available for training, but Japan was very short of oil fuel. After April 20, 1945, when Carrier Division 1 was disbanded, only *Katsuragi*, of all the Japan-ese carriers, remained in full commission, although still inactive. On July 24, both ships were hit by bombs in Kure harbour during a US Navy carrier strike: *Katsuragi*'s midship superstructure, including the flight deck, was wrecked by explosions in the hangars—*Amagi* sustained similar damage but was also holed below the waterline, causing her to flood and eventually capsize in shallow water.

The three incomplete ships, *Kasagi* (flight deck complete, armament not installed), *Aso* and *Ikoma* (complete only as far as the lower hangar deck), were also attacked and dam-aged; *Aso* had previously been used as a trials platform for shaped-charge warhead development. All three, and *Amagi*, were

scrapped in 1947, the only work on them subsequent to August 1945 being concerned with salvage. *Katsuragi* was patched up to make her hangars weatherproof, but was decommissioned on November 11, 1946, and broken up at Osaka.

Displacement: 17 460 tons (standard), 22 800 tons (full load), (*Katsuragi* and *Aso*) 17 260 tons (standard), 22 535 tons (full load) *Length:* 227.4 m (746 ft) oa *Beam:* 21.9 m (72 ft) wl, 27 m (88 ft 6 in) flight deck *Draught:* 7.8 m (25 ft 9 in), (*Katsuragi* and *Aso*) 7.8 m (25 ft 6 in) *Machinery:* 4-shaft geared turbines, 152 000 shp=34 knots, (*Katsuragi* and *Aso*) 104 000 shp=32.7 knots *Aircraft:* 57 *Armament:* 12 127-mm (5-in) DP; 89 25-mm (1-in) AA; 168 12-cm (4.7-in) AA rocket launchers (6×28) *Crew:* 1595 (*Katsuragi* and *Aso*) 1500

US-1, Shin Meiwa Japanese amphibious air-sea rescue version of PS-1 maritime patrol aircraft See **PS-1**

USGW, Hawker Siddeley Dynamics

British submarine-launched antiship missile. Under-Sea Guided Weapon, designated CR137 and known alternatively as Sub-Martel, was a proposed development of the Anglo-French Martel air-to-surface missile. The project was abandoned in September 1975 and the Royal Navy has since adopted Sub-Harpoon in its place, with the French (who were considering collaborating on USGW) concentrating on the SM.39 variant of Exocet.

USGW would have armed the RN's nuc-lear-powered attack submarines, allowing them to engage Soviet task forces from long range. Target information would be derived from the vessel's sonars, processed by a Ferranti FM 1600B computer, and passed to the missile's autopilot and inertial navigation system. USGW was to have been encased in a shroud and launched from standard torpedo tubes at considerable depths, being powered to the surface and then cruising at sea-skimming height before completing its attack under the control of an active radar seeker.

Uzi

Israeli submachine-gun. During the war of 1948 the newly emerged Israeli army felt the need for a standardized and reliable submachine-gun, and in 1949 Major Uziel Gal began work on a design. The Uzi, which appeared in 1952, borrows features from the Czech Model 26 which was common in the Middle East at the time, notably the use of an 'overhung' bolt, which is hollow at the face and wraps around the barrel when closed. This method of construction allows the receiver to be kept short and also allows the pistol grip to be placed at the point of balance and act as a magazine housing, giving very robust construction and simplifying the task of changing magazines in the dark. Wooden or folding metal butts can be used, the latter being the most common, and the whole design utilizes sheet-metal stamping and welding to the maximum.

The standard magazine holds 32 rounds,

Uzushio

Left: The Uzi with folding butt which was originally used by armoured or airborne troops but has become the most common pattern of SMG, being exported around the world

Right: The Uzi with the wooden butt fitted to the earlier versions of this SMG. It has 32 rounds of 9-mm (0.354-in) in a box magazine

The Uzi is one of the most successful postwar submachine-guns, and is not only robust and 'soldier-proof' but reliable under all conditions

Below: A section through the Uzi showing the magazine inserted into the grip which has a grip safety at the back for the firer's hand

but it had become the practice to weld two magazines together at right angles, so that when one magazine is entered into the housing, the other extends forward beneath the barrel. It is thus immediately available for reloading, and its weight helps to keep the muzzle down during automatic fire.

The Uzi has been widely exported, and in 1978 was in service in Belgium, Iran, West Germany, the Netherlands, Rhodesia, Thailand and Venezuela as well as in Israel itself. It has been manufactured under licence in Belgium by Fabrique National, and reputedly also in Rhodesia.

Calibre: 9 mm (0.354 in) *Ammunition:* 9-mm Parabellum *Weight:* 3.6 kg (7 lb 15 oz) *Length:* 640 mm (25.2 in) *Barrel length:* 259 mm (10.2 in) *Magazine:* 32-round box *Rate of fire:* 550 rds/min *Muzzle velocity:* 400 m/sec (1312 ft/sec)

No and name	laid down	launched	completed	builder
SS.566 *Uzushio*	9/68	3/70	1/71	Kawasaki
SS.567 *Makishio*	6/69	1/71	2/72	Mitsubishi
SS.568 *Isoshio*	7/70	3/72	11/72	Kawasaki
SS.569 *Narushio*	5/71	11/72	9/73	Mitsubishi
SS.570 *Kuroshio*	7/72	2/74	11/74	Kawasaki
SS.571 *Takashio*	7/73	6/75	1/76	Mitsubishi
SS.572 *Yaeshio*	4/75	5/77	3/78	Kawasaki
SS.573	12/76	3/78	1979	Mitsubishi

Uzushio

Japanese submarine class. Eight of these double-hulled submarines have been completed since 1971 for the Japanese navy. The hull is of teardrop design and constructed of high-tensile steel to enable a greater diving depth to be achieved. They are being refitted with a new bow sonar.

The last two vessels are of an enlarged and improved design. Displacement has been increased to 2200 tons and overall length by some 4 m (13 ft) and beam 0.9 m (3 ft). These improved submarines are expected to have much greater diving depth capabilities than the earlier *Uzushio* boats.

Displacement: 1850 tons (standard) *Length:* 72 m (236 ft 3 in) *Beam:* 9 m (29 ft 6 in) *Draught:* 7.5 m (24 ft 7 in) *Machinery:* 1 shaft, 2 Kawasaki-MAN diesels/1 electric motor, 3400 bhp/7200 hp=12/20 knots (surfaced/submerged) *Armament:* 6 21-in (53-cm) torpedo tubes (bow) *Crew* 80

V-1 Popular name for German flying bomb
See **FZG-76**

V.1

US submarine class. Three prototype submarines were built during the 1920s to experiment with various hull configurations and types of machinery to secure the best possible surface performance. The design was developed from that of the earlier 'S' Class, but displacement and dimensions were considerably increased to provide extra space for more powerful machinery and increased bunkerage. Advantage was taken of the increased space to provide quarters for the crew.

Torpedo armament differed from the 'S' Class in that two tubes were fitted in the stern instead of the single in the 'S' Class, but only 12 torpedoes were carried instead of the 14 in the 'S' Class. Two of the units mounted a 5-in (127-mm) gun instead of the 4-in (102-mm) of the 'S' Class but *V.2* carried only a 3-in (76-mm) weapon.

The machinery consisted of Sulzer and MAN diesels driving two shafts through a composite system; the MAN engines being coupled directly to the shafts and the two Sulzers driving generators which supplied power to the electric motor while surfaced.

The bunkerage of 364 tons of oil gave a surfaced range of 12 000 nautical miles, but they were unable to achieve their designed surface speed of 21 knots.

All three boats were built at Portsmouth navy yard, *V.1* being launched on July 17, 1924, *V.2* on December 27, 1924, and *V.3* on June 9, 1925. They were refitted in 1940, when the Sulzer diesels were replaced by MAN units of a higher rating.

During the war the boats were used for training purposes, a proposal to convert them to transport submarines being abandoned. *V.2* was seriously damaged by an engine-room fire in 1942 and was eventually used as a target in March 1945. The wreck was subsequently raised and scrapped. *V.1* and *V.3* were both sold for scrap after the Second World War.

Displacement: 2000/2620 tons (surfaced/submerged) *Length:* 104.1 m (341 ft 6 in) *Beam:* 8.4 m (27 ft 6 in) *Draught:* 4.4 m (14 ft 6 in) *Machinery:* 2 shafts, 4 diesels/2 electric motors, 6700 bhp/2400 hp=18/8 knots (surfaced/submerged) *Armament:* 1 5-in (127-mm); (V.2 only) 1 3-in (76-mm); 6 21-in (53-cm) (4 bow, 2 stern), 12 torpedoes *Crew:* 80

V-2 Popular name for German ballistic missile
See **A-4**

V-11, Vultee

US attack bomber. The Vultee V-11 was an all-metal low-wing cantilever monoplane powered by a single 850-hp Wright R-1820-F52 radial engine. It had an inward-retracting undercarriage and horizontal tailplane set forward of the single fin and rudder—a Vultee characteristic. The previous Vultee design was the commercial V-1A, but when US airlines abandoned the single-engined airliner concept the company turned to military aviation, specifically to export markets.

The V-11 was armed with four fixed 0.30-in (7.62-mm) wing guns and one flexibly mounted gun for the observer, who was seated at the end of the long glazed canopy. In attack configuration, the V-11 could accommodate 272 kg (600 lb) of bombs internally. With bombs carried externally a maximum 567 kg (1250 lb) was claimed.

The first prototype was lost in a fatal crash in September 1935, but was soon followed by a second prototype, which differed largely in having a 1000-hp G-2 Cyclone engine. The V-11G was a two-seater and the V-11GB had a crew of three, with a separate bomb aimer who was provided with glazed ventral and lateral panels and was also able to operate an additional 0.30-in machine-gun through a ventral hinged trap. China ordered 30 V-11Gs in 1935, but little is known of their operational record against the invading Japanese. A single V-11GB went to the Soviet Union and 31 were built there under licence, powered by Soviet M-62 radials. Lack of armour necessary for their intended ground-attack role led to their diversion to the national airline Aeroflot, where they served under the designation PS-43, largely on the Moscow-Kiev-Tashkent route. Survivors flew as liaison aircraft during the Second World War.

Forty V-11GBs were purchased by Turkey in 1937. They equipped that country's 2nd Air Regiment for a number of years. Brazil ordered 18 standard GBs and eight V-11TS aircraft with twin Edo floats for operation as torpedo-bombers.

The US Army Air Corps had tested and rejected the V-11 early on, but in view of such widespread foreign popularity seven YA-19s had been ordered in June 1938 powered by 1200-hp Pratt & Whitney R-1830-17 Wasp engines. Little use was made of the YA-19s, except as testbeds for new engines. In fact, two aircraft were delivered as testbeds from the outset as XA-19A and XA-19B respectively.

The V-12 development appeared in 1939. It had the 1200-hp Wasp engine and a number of refinements over its predecessor, the principal external difference being the raising of the rear fuselage decking to give an unbroken upper fuselage line from windscreen to tailplane. Twenty-five V-12Cs were bought by China and, after delivery of two sample machines, components for 50 V-12Ds powered by the more powerful 1600-hp Wright GR-2600 radial were shipped to that country.

Only a few had been assembled when the factory was bombed. Some parts were salvaged and sent to Bangalore in India, where a few V-12Ds were completed in 1941.

(V.11GB) *Span:* 15.24 m (50 ft) *Length:* 11.53 m (37 ft 10 in) *Gross weight:* 5188 kg (11 437 lb) *Maximum speed:* 369 km/h (229 mph) at 1980 m (6500 ft)

V/1500, Handley Page

British heavy bomber. The experimental heavy bombers ordered from Vickers and Handley Page in August 1917, which materialized as the Vimy and V/1500 respectively, were intended to carry out long-range bombing raids against Berlin and other targets in Germany during 1919. Consequently, although the V/1500 resembled Handley Page's earlier O/400 in configuration, but with equal-span wings, it was much larger, and the prototype, which first flew in May 1918, was powered by four 375-hp Rolls-Royce Eagles in tandem pairs mounted midway between the wings to drive two-blade tractor and four-blade pusher propellers, thus becoming the first British four-engined bomber as well as the largest aeroplane built in Britain up to that time.

Maximum endurance of the V/1500 was 14 hours; up to 30 113-kg (250-lb) bombs, or one or two of the new 1500-kg (3300-lb) bombs, could be carried for short-range flights, with a probable maximum of around 454 kg (1000 lb) for the projected raids on Berlin, and defensive armament consisted of single or twin Lewis guns in nose (production aircraft only) and dorsal cockpits, and a single Lewis in the tail-gunner's position—another innovation on a British aircraft. It would thus have proved a formidable bomber had the war continued, especially with the expansion of the RAF's Independent Force, begun in mid-1918, to include long-range night bomber squadrons based in England.

Unfortunately, after numerous modifications had been made to improve control, the prototype was destroyed in a crash in June 1918, and the second V/1500 was not completed until the following October. By this stage the Independent Force was preparing to receive the first production machines, but only six had been delivered by the Armistice, and the first three had reached 166 Squadron only three days before. Consequently, although a total of 255 had been ordered, the first of these before the type had even flown, only 33 were completed, the remainder being cancelled after the war.

The V/1500 did see action, however, when one which had made the first flight from England to India at the turn of the year was used to bomb Kabul in May 1919 during the Afghan war. One was used briefly by Handley Page on a London-Brussels commercial transport service, but an attempt to use one for a trans-Atlantic flight was forestalled by the success of Alcock and Brown.

Span: 38.4 m (126 ft) *Length:* 18.9 m (62 ft) *Gross weight:* 11 204 kg (24 700 lb) *Maximum speed:* 156 km/h (97 mph)

Val Allied codename for Aichi D3A Japanese bomber and trainer aircraft
See **D3A**

Vale

Swedish destroyer class, built 1906-10. Following the success of the British-built prototypes *Mode* and *Magne*, in 1905 the first Swedish design was prepared, following the lines of the Thornycroft-built *Magne*. They were very similar but had Yarrow boilers.

Six ships were built, the *Vale*, *Ragnar*, *Sigurd*, *Vidar*, *Hugin* and *Munin*, but progressive improvements were made. The *Vale*'s armament of two 75-mm (2.95-in) and four 6-pdr (57-mm) guns was increased to four 75-mm and no 6-pdrs in the *Ragnar*, *Sigurd* and *Vidar*, while the *Hugin* and *Munin* had Curtiss turbines in place of triple-expansion machinery.

In 1916, *Ragnar* and the four later vessels were rearmed with twin 45-cm (17.7-in) torpedo tubes. The *Vale* was scrapped in the late 1930s but the others were retained as escorts until 1945 when they were stricken.

Displacement: 460 tons (normal) *Length:* 65.8 m (215 ft 10 in) *Beam:* 6.3 m (20 ft 8 in) *Draught:* 2.6 m (8 ft 6 in) *Machinery:* (*Vale* group) 2-shaft reciprocating steam, 8800 ihp=30 knots, (*Hugin* group) 2-shaft steam turbines, 10 000 shp=31 knots *Armament:* 2/4 75-mm (2.95-in) QF (2/4×1); 4 6-pdr (57-mm) QF (4×1) *Vale* group only; 2 45-cm (17.7-in) torpedo tubes (2×1) *Crew:* 71

Valentine

British combat tank. In pre-1939 days the British Army considered that two types of tank were necessary, a fast cruiser and a slow-moving infantry tank. Others were not so convinced, among them Vickers who developed their own infantry tank which was moderately well armoured but faster than the War Office type. This was submitted for approval on February 14, 1938, from which came the name Valentine. The War Office did nothing for over a year but then, in July 1939, ordered Vickers to build 275 in the shortest possible time. The first tanks, officially designated Infantry Tank Mk 3, reached service in May 1940 and production continued until early 1944 by which time 8275 had been built. 1420 Valentines were also built in Canada by the Canadian Pacific Railway workshops, and most of these, together with 1300 British-made tanks, were sent to the USSR. In British hands the Valentine saw action in North Africa, in Madagascar and in the Burma and Pacific campaigns. After it was replaced as a battle tank the chassis continued in use as the basis for a number of specialist vehicles such as bridge-layers, flame-throwers and swimming tanks. It was also used for the Bishop self-propelled 25-pdr gun and the Archer self-propelled 17-pdr gun.

The Valentine layout was conventional, with the driver at the front, engine at the rear and fighting compartment in the middle. Suspension was unique to this design, using six road wheels on each side in two three-bogie units. The final-drive sprocket was at the rear and had a characteristic centre reduction unit which revolved backwards at high speed when the tank was moving. The turret varied: in early models it had a two-man crew, later a three-man crew; but whatever size of crew it held it was always cramped and inconvenient. The main armament was a 2-pdr gun,

though this was progressively improved, first to a 6-pdr and then to a 75-mm (2.95-in); in Soviet hands the 2-pdr was frequently removed, being considered by them as suited only to shooting sparrows, and replaced by a 76-mm (3-in) gun, a move which must have made the turret more cramped than ever.

The Valentine went through a succession of changes in specification:

Mark 1 AEC gasoline engine, 135 bhp; 2-pdr, 2-man turret
Mark 2 AEC diesel, 131 bhp; 2-pdr, 2-man turret
Mark 3 AEC diesel, 131 bhp; 2-pdr, 3-man turret
Mark 4 GMC diesel, 138 bhp; 2-pdr, 2-man turret
Mark 5 GMC diesel; 2-pdr, 3-man turret
Mark 6 GMC diesel; 2-pdr, 2-man turret; Canadian built
Mark 7 GMC diesel; 2-pdr, 2-man turret; Canadian
Mark 8 AEC diesel; 6-pdr, 2-man turret (modified Mk 3)
Mark 9 GMC diesel; 6-pdr, 2-man turret (modified Mk 5)
Mark 10 GMC diesel, 165 bhp; 6-pdr, 2-man turret
Mark 11 GMC diesel, 165 bhp; 75-mm (2.95-in) (improved Mk 10)

Weight: 16.26 tonnes *Length:* 5.41 m (17 ft 9 in) *Width:* 2.62 m (8 ft 7 in) *Height:* 2.26 m (7 ft 5 in) *Armament:* 1 2-pdr, or 1 6-pdr or 1 75-mm (2.95 in); 1 7.92-mm (0.312-in) machine-gun (omitted from some 6-pdr tanks) *Powerplant:* see text *Speed:* 25 km/h (15 mph) *Range:* 145 km (90 miles) *Crew:* 3 or 4

Valentine

British destroyer class. The *Valentine* or 'V' Class destroyers ordered in September 1941 were the 8th Flotilla of the Emergency War Programme. In design they were repeats of the *Savage* Class except in a few minor details. They were laid down in 1942, launched during 1942-43 and completed during 1943-44. All completed with lattice foremasts except *Venus*, which retained the original tripod mast, while *Volage* also differed from her sisters in having a quadruple pom-pom mounting amidships instead of the specified twin 40-mm (1.57-in). On completion *Valentine* and *Vixen* were transferred to the Royal Canadian Navy and renamed *Algonquin* and *Sioux* respectively.

The new ships were formed into the 25th Flotilla for service with the Home Fleet, the early units being employed mainly as escorts for Arctic convoys. *Virago* saw action very soon after completion when she took part in the sinking of the German battlecruiser *Scharnhorst* in December 1944. In the following month however the flotilla's leader, *Hardy*, had to be sunk by *Venus* after being seriously damaged by an acoustic torpedo, fired by the German submarine *U 278*. At the time *Hardy* was escorting the Arctic convoy JW56B.

In June 1944 all the remaining ships of the class, except *Volage*, formed part of the covering force for the Normandy landings. At the end of 1944 the class, with the exception of the two RCN ships, was refitted for service with the Eastern Fleet. The main

alterations were the addition of four 40-mm AA guns and the removal of the twin 20-mm (0.79-in) mountings (two of these were retained in *Verulam*), improvements in the radar and other electronic equipment and modifications to make them more suitable for a tropical climate. They sailed for the Far East early in 1945 together with the 'S' Class leader *Saumarez* as a replacement for *Hardy*. On the night of May 16, 1945, they became involved in their most famous exploit when *Saumarez, Verulam, Vigilant, Venus* and *Virago* intercepted the Japanese cruiser *Haguro* in the Straits of Malacca. In a perfectly executed night torpedo attack they scored no less than eight hits on the enemy ship which later sank. The only loss to the British vessels was superficial damage and two casualties in *Saumarez* which had been little more than grazed by three 8-in (203-mm) shells.

At the end of the war the class served for a short period in the Mediterranean, where *Volage* had her bows blown off by a mine in October 1946, and was then placed in reserve. During the 1950s all, including the RCN vessels, were converted into *Rapid* Class fast anti-submarine frigates, which extended their lives into the late 1960s/early 1970s.

Hardy, Valentine—built by John Brown
Venus, Verulam—built by Fairfield
Vigilant, Virago—built by Swan Hunter
Vixen, Volage—built by White

Displacement: 1800 tons (standard), 2530 tons (full load) *Length:* 110.6 m (362 ft 9 in) oa *Beam:* 10.9 m (35 ft 9 in) *Draught:* 3 m (10 ft) *Machinery:* 2-shaft geared steam turbines, 40 000 shp=36 knots *Armament:* 4 4.7-in (120-mm) (4×1); 2 40-mm (1.57-in) (1×2); 8 20-mm (0.79-in) (4×2); 8 21-in (53-cm) torpedo tubes (2×4) *Crew:* 180

Valiant

British submarine class. The Royal Navy's first nuclear-powered submarine, HMS *Dreadnought*, was virtually the seventh submarine of the US *Skipjack* Class, and included a US reactor. When it was announced on August 31, 1960, that a second nuclear submarine was to be built by Vickers at Barrow it was also stated that this would be of all-British design and would include a British reactor built by Rolls-Royce. *Valiant* and her four sisters (*Warspite, Churchill, Conqueror,* and *Courageous*) are similar to *Dreadnought*, though they are slightly larger and much quieter in operation. With powerful sonar for detecting and tracking other submarines they are armed with six 21-in (53-cm) bow torpedo tubes.

Displacement: 4400/4900 tons (surface/submerged) *Length:* 86.7 m (285 ft) *Beam:* 10.1 m (33 ft 3 in) *Draught:* 8.2 m (27 ft) *Machinery:* 1 Rolls-Royce pressurized water-cooled reactor, 1-shaft geared steam turbine=28 knots *Armament:* 6 21-in (53-cm) torpedo tubes (bow) *Crew:* 103

Valiant, Vickers

British long-range medium bomber. The Valiant was the first of the 'V' Class of four-jet bombers to enter service with Bomber Command, RAF. After the Second World War,

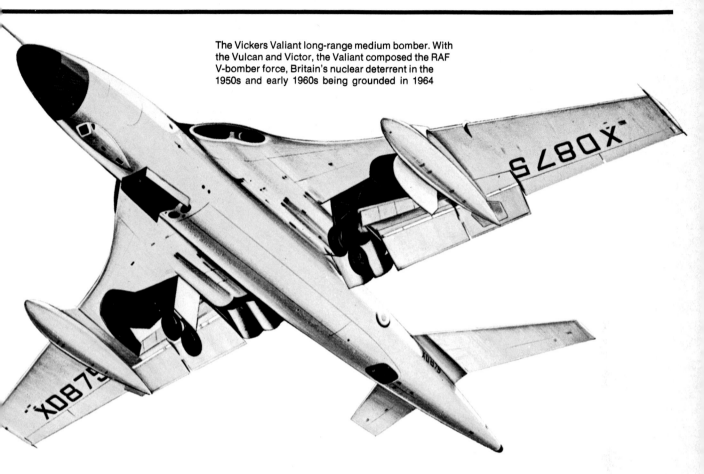

The Vickers Valiant long-range medium bomber. With the Vulcan and Victor, the Valiant composed the RAF V-bomber force, Britain's nuclear deterrent in the 1950s and early 1960s being grounded in 1964

Bomber Command was to be re-equipped with the Avro Lincoln and the Vickers Windsor. The Windsor was cancelled, and only the Lincoln entered service, reflecting the then-current operational philosophies of massed bomber raids. The swift development of the jet engine and nuclear weapons in the late 1940s soon altered RAF policy. It considered a smaller number of high-speed, high-flying jet bombers, which could deliver their weapons accurately with assistance from electronic devices, and not require defensive armament, was a more cost-effective solution. Vickers responded to an Air Staff requirement of 1947, and after some initial hesitation (as their solution was not quite as advanced as the Avro and Handley Page proposals, which later became the Vulcan and Victor) the air ministry drew up Specification B.9/48 around the Vickers design, Type 660. The prototypes were ordered in February 1949; the first was to be powered by four Rolls-Royce RA.3 Avon turbojets; the second was to have four Armstrong Siddeley Sapphire turbojets and was designated Type 667.

The first prototype made its maiden flight on May 18, 1951, and in June that year was named Valiant. Flight trials continued until January 1952, when the aircraft was lost. The second prototype flew on April 11, 1952, with RA.7 Avons installed in place of the Sapphires originally specified.

The Valiant was a cantilever shoulder-wing monoplane in conventional all-metal stressed-skin construction. The wings, which featured a compound leading-edge sweep, were of conventional two-spar construction with powered ailerons, double-slotted flaps and air brakes. The semimonocoque fuselage con-

tained a pressurized 'egg' for the crew of pilot, copilot, two navigators and air electronics officer; only the two pilots were equipped with ejection seats. Behind the crew compartment was the bomb bay. From the fuselage keel beam up to 21 conventional 454-kg (1000-lb) bombs or a single 4540-kg (10000-lb) bomb, plus various sized nuclear weapons, could be hung. The Blue Steel stand-off bomb was carried on a modified Valiant. A large dielectric panel was fitted aft of the nose radome, and the Valiant was equipped with an electrically operated tricycle undercarriage.

The early production Valiants were powered by four Rolls-Royce Avon 201 turbojets, each rated at 4310 kg (9500 lb) st, while later aircraft had the Avon 204 or 205 version, rated at 10000 lb st. Additional takeoff power could be provided by two underwing de Havilland Super Sprite rocket engines giving 8400 lb of extra thrust. Extra fuel could be carried in underwing tanks.

The single prototype Valiant B.2 featured a lengthened fuselage forward of the wings, and its main undercarriage retracted rearwards into fairings on the wing trailing edge.

The first production Valiant flew in December 1953, and was delivered to the RAF in January 1955. The main versions of the Valiant to enter RAF service were the Type 706 B.1 bomber (39 built, of which the first five were preproduction Type 674), Type 710 B(PR).1 bomber/photo-reconnaissance aircraft (eight built), Type 733 B.PR (K).1 bomber/photo-reconnaissance or tanker aircraft (13 built), and Type 758 B(K).1 bomber/tanker aircraft (44 built). With the 104 aircraft noted above, plus the two prototypes and the single prototype B.2 version, a grand total of

107 Valiants were built. Another 16 B(K).1s which had been ordered in the final batch were cancelled, and production ceased in August 1957.

The first unit to receive Valiants was 138 Squadron based at RAF Gaydon, who formed alongside 232 Operational Conversion Unit in early 1955; followed closely by 543 Squadron, flying in the strategic-reconnaissance role. Long-range deployments of the Valiant worldwide proved it to be a reliable aircraft. The Anglo-French Suez invasion in October-November 1956, with Valiants of 138, 148, 207 and 214 Squadrons operating with high-explosive bombs from an advanced base at Luqa, Malta, was the only occasion on which the V-bomber force dropped bombs in anger.

Valiants of 49 Squadron were used during the testing of British nuclear weapons. A B.1 (WZ366) dropped the first British operational atomic bomb to be carried by an aircraft, over Maralinga, South Australia, on October 11, 1956. Less than a year later, on May 15, 1957, a B(K).1 (XD818) dropped the first British thermonuclear bomb during Operation Grapple in the Pacific Ocean.

Valiants initially formed part of the strategic nuclear force of the RAF, maintaining a permanent quick-reaction alert, but by the early 1960s the Vulcans and Victors had assumed this role. Three squadrons of Valiants had replaced Canberras and were allocated to SACEUR as part of the UK's contribution to NATO, in the low-level tactical-bombing role; another two squadrons were maintained as tankers.

Following a series of accidents, it was discovered that the main wing structure of the Valiants had suffered from fatigue. The

Valkyrien

type was grounded in October 1964, being officially withdrawn from service in January 1965.

(B.1) *Span:* 34.85 m (114 ft 4 in) *Length:* 32.99 m (108 ft 3 in) *Gross weight:* 79 380 kg (175 000 lb) *Maximum speed:* Mach 0.84 at 9144 m (30 000 ft); 666 km/h (414 mph) at sea level

Valkyrien

Norwegian destroyer, built 1895-97. This large torpedo boat or torpedo gunboat was built by Schichau at Elbing, and was unusual in her day for her size and heavy armament. The hull was flush-decked with a turtleback forecastle, and the guns were mounted forward, abreast of the forefunnel and aft. Before the First World War the armament was increased to four 76-mm (3-in) quick-firers. The ship was scrapped in the early 1920s.

Displacement: 374 tons (normal), 415 tons (full load) *Length:* 57.9 m (190 ft) wl *Beam:* 7.4 m (24 ft 3 in) *Draught:* 2.8 m (9 ft 2 in) *Machinery:* 2-shaft reciprocating steam, 3300 ihp=23 knots *Armament:* 2 68-mm (2.7-in) QF (2×1); 2 37-mm (1.5-in) QF (2×1); 2 45-cm (17.7-in) torpedo tubes (2×1) *Crew:* 59

Vampire, de Havilland

British jet fighter aircraft. The DH.100 Vampire was the second type of jet fighter to enter RAF service, and was just too late to see action in the Second World War. With no radar, manually operated flying controls and

Vampire, with the cockpit, armament of four 20-mm (0.79-in) Hispano cannon and power-plant in a nacelle between the wings. This forward position of the cockpit gave the pilot an excellent field of view.

The construction of the Vampire around this fuselage nacelle was conventional. The nacelle was a monocoque shell of balsa wood sandwiched between two thin layers of plywood, built in two halves and split vertically. The wing was of all-metal stressed-skin construction, with manually operated ailerons, split flaps and aerodynamically balanced air brakes. The tail booms ended in a square-topped fin, with single tailplane between the two fins. The absence of a propeller allowed the Vampire to have a short undercarriage, which was of the tricycle configuration.

The first production Vampire F.I flew on April 20, 1945, with the first 40 aircraft being powered by the same engine as the proto-type. From airframe 41, the Goblin DGn2, rated at 1706 kg (3100 lb) st, was installed, and from airframe 51 the cockpit was pressurized. Later models were fitted with a

bubble canopy in place of the earlier three-piece type.

The Vampre F.I entered RAF service with 247 Squadron in March 1946 as an intercepter, and also equipped units of the 2nd Tactical Air Force in Germany, replacing Mustangs, Typhoons and Tempests. It entered service with the Auxiliary Air Force in July 1948, replacing the Mosquitos of 605 (County of Warwick) Squadron. Various versions were also supplied to Canada, Sweden and Switzerland, some examples of which found their way to Austria and the Dominican Republic.

The Vampire Mk II was the Nene-powered version which was not adopted in the UK. Three prototypes were built, one of which was shipped to Australia, where it performed much of the development work for their licence-built Nene-powered Vampire F.30, of which 80 were built. Later 29 were converted to F.31 (FB.5) standard and one to F.32 (FB.9) standard.

The Vampire F.III, which succeeded the F.I on the production lines, was an attempt to increase the effective range of the type. Increased wing tankage was introduced, and provision was made under the wing for the carriage of 455-909-litre (100 or 200 Imp gal) drop tanks. The tailplane was lowered and the characteristic pointed de Havilland fins of the prototype Vampire fitted. The changes increased the range from 1175 km (730 miles) to 2237 km (1390 miles). The Vampire F.3 (as it was designated after the change to arabic numerals in the official nomenclature) first flew on November 4, 1946, and was produced to Specification F.3/47. In July 1948 six

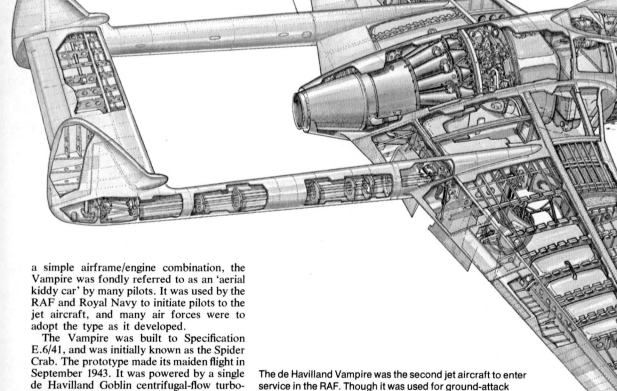

a simple airframe/engine combination, the Vampire was fondly referred to as an 'aerial kiddy car' by many pilots. It was used by the RAF and Royal Navy to initiate pilots to the jet aircraft, and many air forces were to adopt the type as it developed.

The Vampire was built to Specification E.6/41, and was initially known as the Spider Crab. The prototype made its maiden flight in September 1943. It was powered by a single de Havilland Goblin centrifugal-flow turbo-jet, rated at 2700 lb st. In order to minimize power losses from the jetpipe, a twin tail-boom configuration was adopted for the

The de Havilland Vampire was the second jet aircraft to enter service in the RAF. Though it was used for ground-attack work during the colonial counter-insurgency operations of the 1950s, it was principally of value as a jet trainer for RAF student pilots, and was known as the 'aerial kiddy car'

Vampire F.3s of 54 Squadron became the first RAF jet aircraft to cross the Atlantic, staging through Iceland, Greenland and Labrador to the United States.

Development of the Vampire's wing to carry drop tanks led to the carriage of other stores for ground attack. The wing was reduced in span and restressed to carry 907 kg (2000 lb) of bombs or rockets, and a longer-stroke undercarriage was developed. This became the Vampire FB.5, which first flew on June 23, 1948, and superseded the F.3 in Fighter Command, the RAuxAF and RAF Germany, helping the expansion of the RAF which was underway at the time. The FB.5 was also supplied to India (12), France (who later built 67 under licence), Australia (41) and New Zealand (47); while the FB.50 export model went to Sweden. Fitted with a Goblin DGn3 engine, rated at 1520 kg (3350 lb) st, the export model was designated FB.52 and was supplied to Egypt, Finland, Iraq, Italy (where 80 were built as the F.52A under licence), Lebanon, Norway and Venezuela. The Swiss licence-built 100 FB.6s.

The Vampire FB.9 was basically a 'tropicalized' version, being fitted with Godfrey refrigerator unit in the starboard wing intake fillet, and the uprated Goblin DGn3 engine. In RAF service they replaced FB.5s in the Middle and Far East, and FB.9s of 8 Squadron (usually based in Aden) were detached to Kenya where they took part in operations against nationalist guerrillas. Ex-RAF FB.9s were supplied to Southern Rhodesia (15), Jordan (10) and Ceylon (2). Production of single-seat Vampires ended in December 1953.

The first two-seat version of the Vampire with side-by-side seating flew on August 28, 1949, as a private venture, designated DE.113. It was equipped with AI Mk X radar in the nose and retained the four 20-mm (0.79-in) cannon of the single-seaters. Egypt ordered a quantity, but following an arms embargo the RAF took over the aircraft as the NF.10 pending the arrival of later marks of Meteor and Venom night fighters. It served in the night fighter role in 1951-54, and on training duties until May 1959. Some ex-RAF aircraft were later supplied to India.

Similar to the NF.10, the T.11 was the two-seat version of the Vampire, the first of which flew on November 15, 1950. Over 530 were produced and they saw wide-scale service within Training Command, entering service in 1952 and remaining in large-scale use until the arrival of the Gnat T.1 in 1962. A few remained in service after that date, and the type was finally withdrawn from service in November 1967. Most export users of Vampires had the trainer in service as well. The Royal Navy took delivery of 18 navalized FB.5s, known as Sea Vampire F.20s, for jet familiarization duties. A modified Vampire I became the first jet aircraft to land on and take off from a carrier on December 3, 1945, on HMS *Ocean*. An experimental version, the F.21, was also used for trials, landing with its undercarriage retracted on a rubberized deck on HMS *Warrior*. The Royal Navy also used the T.11, which was known as the Sea Vampire T.22, of which 74 were procured.

In all some 2800 Vampires of varied types were built, introducing the RAF and many other air forces to the jet age.

(F.1) *Span:* 12.19 m (40 ft) *Length:* 9.37 m (30 ft 9 in) *Gross weight:* 3891 kg (8578 lb) *Maximum speed:* 869 km/h (540 mph) at 6100 m (20 000 ft)

(FB.5) *Span:* 11.58 m (38 ft) *Length:* 9.37 m (30 ft 9 in) *Gross weight:* 5606 kg (12 360 lb) *Maximum speed:* 861 km/h (535 mph) at 9150 m (30 000 ft)

(NF.10) *Span:* 11.58 m (38 ft) *Length:* 10.54 m (34 ft 7 in) *Gross weight:* 5148 kg (11 350 lb) *Maximum speed:* 885 km/h (550 mph) at 6100 m (20 000 ft)

Vancouver, Canadian Vickers

Canadian patrol and general transport aircraft. The Canadian plant of Vickers (Aviation) was established in 1923 and formed the basis of the aircraft industry in that country. For the first few years it concentrated on the production of the Varuna and Vedette civil flying boats, but in the late 1920s the Forest Fire Protection Service issued a requirement for an aircraft to replace the Varuna. Powered by two Armstrong Siddeley Lynx IV radials, the prototype Vancouver I was deemed successful, and five of a Mk II production version were ordered. A change in powerplant caused some delay, but the first Vancouver II was completed in 1930, the others following shortly afterwards. The aircraft was a metal-hulled equal-span biplane, with stabilizing floats suspended from the lower wings. Powerplant consisted of two 240-hp Lynx IVC geared seven-cylinder radial engines, driving two-blade tractor propellers and positioned halfway between the two wings, just outboard of the fuselage. Vancouver IIs were used on forestry patrol, aerial survey and general transport duties until, in the mid-1930s, they drew the attention of the Royal Canadian Air Force, who decided to modify the aircraft for coastal-patrol use. Three gun turrets were installed, one in the forward fuselage and two behind the wings, each capable of carrying one or two Lewis machine-guns; there were stores points for small bombs under the lower wings. The number of crew members varied from three to five, and the military variant was designated Mk II/SW, indicating the use of two 300-hp Wright J6 Whirlwind nine-cylinder radial engines. Other alterations included the addition of a navigator's cabin and some redesigning of the tailplane surfaces. Experiments on two Vancouvers refitted with twin 380-hp Armstrong Siddeley Serval ten-cylinder engines (Mk II/SS) proved unsatisfactory; the projected Mk III photo-reconnaissance amphibian and Wasp-engined civil transport versions were not pursued.

(Vancouver II) *Span:* 16.76 m (55 ft) *Length:* 11.43 m (37 ft 6 in) *Gross weight:* 3447 kg (7600 lb) *Maximum speed:* 193 km/h (120 mph)

Van Ghent

Dutch destroyer class built 1925-29. Originally known as the *de Ruyter* Class the eight vessels of this class were built in collaboration with the Clydeside firm of Yarrow; they were laid down in pairs each year from 1925 to 1928:

de Ruyter—built by de Schelde, Flushing

Evertsen, Piet Hein, Kortenaer, Banckert, Van Nes—built by Burgerhouts, Rotterdam *Van Galen, Witte de With*—built by Fijenoord, Rotterdam.

The design was based on the Yarrow-built HMS *Ambuscade*, with slightly less power, speed and endurance but a heavier AA armament. A unique feature was a platform for a seaplane over the after bank of torpedo-tubes. The aircraft was intended for reconnaissance in the East Indies and was handled by a derrick on the mainmast. The ships proved too lively to make effective use of an aircraft, and the derrick was eventually removed.

Evertsen, Kortenaer, Piet Hein and *de Ruyter* had two 3-in (76-mm) AA guns sided between the funnels, but the later ships had one 3-in and two twin 40-mm (1.57-in) Bofors mountings. *de Ruyter* took the name *Van Ghent* to release the name for the new cruiser in 1935.

The entire class was based in the East Indies, but *Van Galen* was under refit in Rotterdam when war broke out in May 1940. She was bombed on May 10, 1940, raised in October 1941 and scrapped. *Van Ghent* struck an uncharted reef off Bangka on February 15, 1942, and had to be scuttled to prevent capture. On February 17, *Van Nes* was sunk by Japanese bombers south of Bangka, and two days later *Piet Hein* was sunk in Bandoeng Strait by gunfire from Japanese destroyers. *Banckert* was damaged by bombs at Soerabaya on February 24, and again four days later; she was finally scuttled on March 2. On February 27 *Kortenaer* was torpedoed and sunk south-west of Bawean Island in the Java Sea, and on the same day her sister *Evertsen* was driven ashore by gunfire in Sunda Strait and had to be abandoned the following day. *Witte de With* was damaged by bombs at Soerabaya on March 1 and was scuttled the following day. The Japanese raised and repaired *Banckert* and recommissioned her in 1944 as *Patrol Boat No 106*. She was returned to the Dutch navy in 1945 and was sunk as a target in Madura Strait in September 1949.

Displacement: 1310 tons (standard), 1640 tons (full load) *Length:* 98.1 m (322 ft) oa *Beam:* 9.5 m (31 ft 2 in) *Draught:* 3.2 m (10 ft 6 in) max *Machinery:* 2-shaft geared steam turbines, 31 000 shp=36 knots *Armament:* 4 4.7-in (120-mm)/50-cal (4×1); -1/2 3-in (76-mm) AA (1/2×1); 4 40-mm (1.57-in) AA (2×2) (later ships); 4 12.7-mm (0.5 in) machine-guns (4×1); 6 53-cm (21-in) torpedo-tubes (2×3) *Crew:* 120-129

Vanguard

British battleship. When naval rearmament began in 1937 one of the major problems encountered was that the ordnance manufacturing industry had become seriously run down. As warship guns, particularly those for battleships, took as long to produce as the ships themselves this seriously hampered the rate at which new ships could be built. Early in 1939 it was suggested that a new battleship might be built by utilizing four spare twin 15-in (381-mm) mountings originally manufactured for *Courageous* and *Glorious* during the First World War. From this suggestion a design for a 40 000-ton battleship was pro-

Vanguard, Vultee P-66

duced in which the weight saved by utilizing a comparatively light main armament was used to provide a speed of 30 knots. It was intended that the new ship should form the nucleus for a Far East Fleet, where her high speed and armament would be an ideal match for Japanese ships. Work on the design ceased on the outbreak of war but was resurrected soon after by the new First Lord of the Admiralty, Winston Churchill, and in February 1940 the design was continued. However, progress was slow owing to the heavy demands placed upon the available design facilities during 1940-41 and the ship was not ordered until March 1941. She was laid down at John Brown's yard, Clydebank, in October 1941. It was hoped she would complete in 1944, but with the shipbuilding industry already overloaded, mainly with escort vessels and merchant ships, this proved impossible. She was named *Vanguard* when launched in November 1944 and did not complete until April 1946. This long period of construction allowed for a continual revision of the details of the design in the light of war experience.

The main armament was both of the same design and the same layout as that of the *Queen Elizabeth* Class, designed in 1912, but prior to fitting in the ship the mountings were 'modernized', increasing the elevation of the guns to 30° and providing remote power control for training. Although the guns were of old pattern they were also one of the most efficient heavy ordnance types ever produced and this combined with new, modified ammunition, left them only marginally inferior in performance to more modern weapons. The rest of the ship was generally an enlarged and improved version of *King George V* with much the same secondary armament, armour arrangement and hull structure. The machinery was of higher power, to give 3 knots more speed, and as the *King George V* Class had proved very wet in heavy weather the sheer forward was substantially increased. The oil-fuel stowage was increased to improve endurance, which the war had demonstrated to be insufficient in existing British capital ships. The designed close-range AA armament was constantly changed while the ship was under construction, and she finally completed with a very modern uniform AA battery of 40-mm (1.57-in) Bofors, most of which were fitted in the

new six-barrelled Mk VI mounting. She also carried a twin 40-mm on the roof of B turret and a few single 40-mm. The completed ship was very impressive with heavy well-balanced superstructure and capped funnels but she paid the price of having so many additions made during building by being overweight and overcrowded. Nevertheless she was easily the best of Britain's battleships and was one of the most efficient and seaworthy vessels of her type ever produced. On trials she achieved 31.57 knots with 136000 shp on a displacement of 45720 tons.

Vanguard arrived too late to be of any practical use. She became known as the only British battleship that had never fired its guns in anger, and was employed on various duties until 1949 when she became a seagoing training ship, with occasional spells of service as a flagship. She was placed in reserve in the mid-1950s and sold for scrap in 1960.

Displacement: 44500 tons (standard), 51420 tons (full load) *Length:* 243.8 m (799 ft 11 in) oa *Beam:* 32.9 m (108 ft) *Draught:* 9.2 m (30 ft 3 in) *Machinery:* 4-shaft geared steam turbines, 130000 shp=30 knots *Protection:* 356-330 mm (14-13 in) sides, 305 mm (12 in) bulkheads, 330-279 mm (13-11 in) barbettes, 330-178 mm (13-7 in) turrets, 152-127 mm (6-5 in) decks *Armament:* 8 15-in (381-mm) (4×2); 16 5.25-in (133-mm) (8×2); 73 40-mm (1.57-in) AA (10×6, 1×2, 11×1) *Crew:* 1893 (2000 as flagship)

Vanguard, Vultee P-66

US intercepter fighter aircraft. In 1939 the Vultee aircraft company, after their successful V-11 series, turned out a further two private-venture prototypes. These were Models 48 and 48X, single-seat, single-engined fighters with a sliding transparent cockpit canopy and a fully retractable undercarriage. They were low-wing monoplanes powered by the 1200-hp Pratt & Whitney R-1830-S4C4-G engine, driving a spinnered propeller and very tightly enclosed within a metal cowling. In tests this posed weight as well as cooling problems, and a more normal and practical cowling was used on production machines which had a 1200-hp R-1830-33 Wasp and a shorter nose. Armament, too, had to be reduced. Initially it had been the intention to provide the aircraft with a selection of ten 0.30-in (7.62-mm) machine-guns,

two of which would be rearward-firing with aim assisted by an arrangement of mirrors. The eventual standard armament installation comprised two 0.5-in (12.7-mm) machine-guns in the nose and four of 0.30-in calibre in the wings. The Vanguard had a normal range of 1368 km (850 miles) at a cruising speed of 467 km/h (290 mph), with a service ceiling of 8595 m (28200 ft). The Swedish government ordered 144 Vanguards in February 1940, but some eight months later the US government placed a veto on the export of combat aircraft to Sweden and these machines were assigned subsequently to the RAF under the Lend-Lease programme. It seems doubtful that any of the Vanguards served with the RAF although its stablemate the Vengeance did. It was later decided to allocate the bulk of the Vanguard production to China, also under the Lend-Lease system, and that country took over 129 aircraft. It has also been suggested that some of the Vanguards were used in Canada as advanced trainers, but there is no recorded evidence of their ever having done so. Neither are there any details available as to the roles they fulfilled when in service with the Chinese air arm. The remaining 15 Vanguards from the original order were taken into the USAAF as P-66 fighter/trainers, but their useful lives were comparatively short.

Span: 10.97 m (36 ft) *Length:* 8.66 m (28 ft 5 in) *Gross weight:* 3349 kg (7384 lb) *Maximum speed:* 547 km/h (340 mph)

Vanneau, Morane-Saulnier M.S.470

French intermediate trainer aircraft. The Morane-Saulnier Vanneau (plover) had its beginnings during the Second World War when the head of the company's design bureau, M Gauthier, was allowed to develop

The attractive lines of HMS *Vanguard*, the Royal Navy's last battleship. She was known as the only British battleship that did not fire its guns in anger, for though she was launched in 1944 she did not complete until 1946. However, she was the most efficient and seaworthy vessel of her type to be produced

a design for a training aircraft for the French Vichy government. It was to be powered by a liquid-cooled Hispano-Suiza 12X engine of 690 hp driving a three-bladed Chauvière propeller. The M.S.470 No 01 was an all-metal low-wing monoplane with pupil and instructor seated under a continuous glazed canopy, the rear of which was faired into the fuselage decking. Leading-edge slots were soon discarded, but the inward-retracting main undercarriage legs, with wheels which turned through 90° during retraction to lie partially exposed in the fuselage underside, were retained throughout the Vanneau series. This method was used partly to avoid reducing the structural strength of the wings by having to provide for wheel wells, and partly to protect the main fuel tank in the event of an emergency landing. The fuel tank was immediately above the retracted wheels.

The first prototype flew on December 22, 1944, and tests proceeded successfully. After the war the Armée de l'Air decided to use the Vanneau to train pilots for its new rearmament programme. Three M.S.472 prototypes were ordered, M.S.472 No 01 flying on December 12, 1945. It incorporated a number of improvements, but the major change was the fitting of the 640-hp Gnome-Rhône 14M radial engine. Other engines were tested, among them the 860-hp Hispano-Suiza 12Y45 liquid-cooled engine. The 12Y45-powered prototype, designated M.S.475, flew on August 8, 1947. Modifications were made to the wings, and after protracted testing the type was ordered into production as the Vanneau V. Earlier, the French navy had taken an interest in the M.S.472 Vanneau II and had ordered the M.S.474, modified for deck landings.

In all 500 series versions of the Vanneau were delivered, comprising 230 M.S.472s, 70 M.S.474s and 200 M.S.475s. The M.S.475s were the most successful of all the variants,

and they achieved excellent manoeuvrability and were able to perform difficult aerobatics with ease.

The Vanneau served at a number of training schools specially established by the Armée de l'Air for reserve pilots. These included CEROs 301 at Le Bourget, 302 at Lille, 303 at Marignane, 304 at Bordeaux, 305 at Algiers, 306 at Lyons, 307 at Nancy, 308 at Toulouse, 309 at Oran, 310 at Casablanca and 311 at Tours. Elsewhere it was utilized at the Bases Écoles at Marrakesh and Meknès in French Morocco. The navy (Aéronautique Navale) M.S.474s were attached initially to the Ecole de l'Aviation Embarqué at Hyères on the Mediterranean coast of France, whence they made a number of practice landings on the aircraft carrier *Arromanches*. Later, M.S.474s were on the strength of Escadrille 52S at Kouriba in Morocco until retired from service in 1951.

(M.S.472) *Span:* 10.65 m (34 ft 11 in) *Length:* 8.6 m (28 ft 3 in) *Gross weight:* 2781 kg (6131 lb) *Maximum speed:* 468 km/h (291 mph) at 2000 m (6560 ft)

(M.S.475) *Span:* 10.65 m (34 ft 11 in) *Length:* 9.05 m (29 ft 8 in) *Gross weight:* 3125 kg (6889 lb) *Maximum speed:* 445 km/h (277 mph) at 4500 m (14 760 ft)

Vanoc/Wakeful

British destroyer class. These vessels, more commonly known as the 'V' and 'W' Class, are among the most famous of the British destroyer classes and were probably the best design of their type produced during the First World War. They originated in 1916 from a requirement for a new leader to accompany the destroyers of the 'R' Class, the existing leaders being too slow for this purpose. The design produced to meet this need was about half way in size between contemporary leaders and destroyers, dimensions having been restricted to provide the necessary speed while adopting the same machinery as in the 'R' Class. This resulted in their being designated half leaders but in the early 1920s they were rerated as destroyers. The great advantages of the new design were mainly in the provision of a high forecastle, for improved seaworthiness, and in fitting the second 4-in (102-mm) gun on a raised structure before the bridge, instead of between the funnels, where it had a wider arc of fire and a higher command. Five vessels of this design, *Valentine, Valhalla, Valkyrie, Valorous* and *Vam-*

pire, were ordered in April 1916 and constructed during 1916-17. Shortly after this order was placed various (false) reports were received that the Germans were constructing new, large, heavily armed destroyers and in searching for a reply the Admiralty decided that the new 'V' leader provided the ideal answer to this new threat. Therefore, in July, 25 vessels of the 'V' Class were ordered and, in December, 21 ships of the 'W' Class. These ships, which were constructed during 1916-18, were almost identical in design to the leaders but omitted the accommodation for the captain and his staff which allowed for some internal rearrangement. The 'W' Class also carried triple instead of twin torpedo tubes, a modification already applied to *Vampire.* Two of the 'V' Class and two of the 'W' Class were built to a personalized design by Thornycroft who fitted their ships with more powerful machinery and adopted a modified hull form which gave them a 1-knot advantage over the standard vessels. In 1918 another 48 were ordered of which 32 were cancelled at the end of the war while the remainder completed over an extended period from 1919-24. These were the Modified 'W' Class which were basically of the same design as the original 'W' except that 4.7 in (120 mm) BL guns were substituted for 4-in QF guns, while the 3-in (76-mm) AA gun was replaced by two 2-pdr pom-poms. In addition the boiler rooms were transposed, the double room being positioned aft and the single forward, so the bridge could be moved further aft where it would be dryer. Thus the new ships had the thin funnel forward and the thick one aft, the reverse of the arrangement in the earlier ships. Again the two Thornycroft vessels of this group were 'specials' with high power machinery and modified hull form and these, like the first four, had two large flat side funnels which served to distinguish them from the Admiralty vessels. At the time the Modified 'W' Class were the most powerful destroyers in the world and proved so successful that the basic design formed the pattern for future British destroyer design up to the mid-1930s.

Early in the 1920s, the twin tubes of the early vessels were replaced by triples but the class was otherwise little modified until late in the 1930s. Four of the class were lost during 1918-19— *Vehement* was mined in the North Sea in August 1918 and *Verulam* and *Vittoria* were sunk during the Baltic operations in September 1919. In 1933 *Vampire, Vendetta, Voyager,* and *Waterhen* were transferred to the RAN and another five,

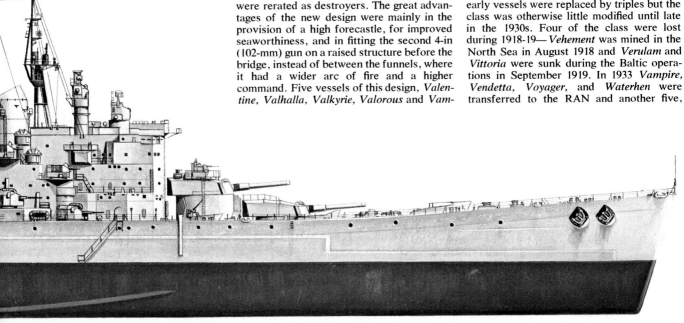

Van Speijk

Valhalla, Valkyrie, Violent, Walrus and Vectis, were sold for scrap during 1931-38.

In 1937 it was decided to reconstruct a large number of the surviving vessels to serve as AA escorts by removing the existing armament and fitting two twin 4-in HA/LA gun mountings, one forward and one aft, eight 0.5-in (12.7-mm) AA (2×4) and a new bridge structure surmounted by a new HA/LA director. These alterations were carried out in Whitley, Wolsey, Valorous, Vivien, Winchester, Valentine, Woolston, Vega, Vimiera, Wryneck, Verdun, Westminster, Vanity, Viceroy and Wolfhound during 1938-41. The heavy demands placed on construction and repair facilities from 1940 onwards prevented any further ships being so altered but a simpler reconstruction was applied from 1941 onwards when 20 of the class were converted to 'long-range A/S escorts'. This involved removing the forward boiler and converting the empty space for oil fuel stowage, thus enabling the ships to escort convoys all the way across the Atlantic. The remaining pair of boilers supplied 18 000 shp for 24.5 knots which, at this time, was quite sufficient for escort work. Other alterations included the removal of A gun, which was replaced by a Hedgehog, one set of torpedo tubes, which was replaced by a 12-pdr AA gun, and the fitting of additional depth-charge equipment, radar, HF/DF and AA guns. Some vessels also had Y gun and the second set of tubes removed. These conversions were spread over the period 1941-44, the ships involved being Vimy, Viscount, Vanessa, Winchelsea, Venomous, Whitehall, Volunteer, Vidette, Vanquisher, Vesper, Walker, Wrestler, Warwick, Wanderer, Vansittart, Versatile, Verity, Vanoc, Watchman and Velox. Apart from the ships that were early war losses the remaining vessels were reclassified as 'short-range escorts' and, apart from retaining their boilers, were modified along similar lines. These latter ships were employed mainly in Home Waters, particularly on coastal escort work, and several were fitted with a 2-pdr gun in the bow for use against E-Boats.

Sixteen of the class were lost during the Second World War—Valentine, Venetia, Wakeful, Wessex, Whirlwind, Whitley and Wren in 1940, Waterhen and Wryneck in 1941, Vampire, Vimiera, Vortigern, Voyager, Veteran and Wild Swan in 1942 and Warwick in 1944. However, on the credit side, ships of the class sank, or helped to sink, 38 enemy submarines during 1940-45 while Vanessa can actually claim credit for sinking a U-Boat in both World Wars, the UB 107 off Scarborough in July 1918 and the U 357 off Rockall in December 1942. The surviving ships of the class were sold for scrapping during 1945-48 except one, Wrestler, which was sold before the end of the war in 1944.

Admiralty 'V' Class
Valentine, Valhalla—built by Cammell Laird
Valkyrie, Valorous, Vehement, Venturous—built by Denny
Vampire, Vectis, Vortigern—built by White
Vancouver (renamed Vimy 1928), Vanessa, Vanity—built by Beardmore
Vanoc, Vanquisher—built by John Brown
Vega, Velox—built by Doxford
Vendetta, Venetia—built by Fairfield
Verdun, Versatile, Verulam—built by Hawthorn Leslie

Vesper, Vidette—built by Stephen
Vimiera, Violent, Vittoria—built by Swan Hunter
Vivacious, Vivien—built by White

Admiralty 'W' Class
Voyager—built by Stephen
Wakeful, Watchman—built by John Brown
Walker, Westcott—built by Denny
Walpole, Whitley—built by Doxford
Walrus, Wolfhound—built by Fairfield
Warwick, Wessex—built by Hawthorn Leslie
Waterhen, Wryneck—built by Palmer
Westminster, Windsor—built by Scotts
Whirlwind, Wrestler—built by Swan Hunter
Winchelsea, Winchester—built by White

Thornycroft 'V' and 'W' Classes
Viceroy, Viscount, Wolsey, Woolston

Admiralty Modified 'W' Class
Vansittart—built by Beardmore
Venombus, Verity, Veteran—built by John Brown
Volunteer—built by Denny
Wanderer—built by Fairfield
Whitehall, Whitshed, White Swan—built by Swan Hunter
Wren—built by Yarrow
Witherington, Wivern, Wolverine, Worcester—built by White

Thornycroft Modified 'W' Class
Wishart, Witch

Displacement: 1300-1345 tons (loaded) Length: 95.1 m (312 ft) oa Beam: 9 m (29 ft 6 in) (Thornycroft vessels 9.3 m [30 ft 6 in]) Draught: 3.2-3.4 m (10 ft 6 in-11 ft) Machinery: 2-shaft geared turbines, 27 000 shp=34 knots (Thornycroft ships 30 000 shp=35 knots) Armament: 4 4-in (102-mm) (4×1); 1 3-in (76-mm) AA; 6 21-in (53-cm) torpedo tubes (2×3); Modified 'W' 4 4.7-in (120-mm) (4×1); 2 2-pdr AA (2×1) Crew: 134

Van Speijk

Dutch frigate class. Four ships were ordered in 1962 (F.802-805) and two in 1964 (F.814-815).

Built to replace the six frigates of the Van Amstel Class (ex-US Cannon Class) the Van Speijk Class were based on the British Leander design. They incorporated a number of modifications dictated by the requirement to

install as much equipment of Netherlands manufacture as possible. To avoid unnecessary complication the basic weapons of Leander (the twin 114-mm [4.5-in] Mk 6; Seacat; Wasp helicopter; and the Limbo A/S mortar) were retained, but in those areas where physical dimensions were a less important consideration, such as the ships' sensors, Dutch equipment was used. The MRS-3 director of Leander was therefore replaced by an HSA M-45, while the Seacat director was the similar M-44. The small size and low weight of the latter enabled a second Seacat launcher and a second director to be worked in. Air search was provided by an LW-03 scanner, which replaced the Type 965 on the mainmast, and surface surveillance by a DA-02 antenna, mounted atop the foremast. The navigation radar platform which projects from the foremast is on the centreline, as in the earlier British Leanders. Van Nes and Evertsen are fitted with an HF/DF mast which is topped by a cone-shaped ECM jammer, similar to that on HMS Apollo. The other four units have a much taller version of the mast fitted to the middle Leanders. The sonars are a mixture of British and Dutch models.

In the mid-1970s it was decided that all six of the class should undergo 18-month refits; the first, that of Van Speijk herself, began in January 1977. It is intended to replace the 11-mm mounting by a single OTO-Melara 76-mm (3-in) gun and to install two quadruple launchers for Harpoon surface-to-surface missiles between the funnel and the mainmast. Two triple torpedo mountings will be fitted, and the Limbo A/S mortar will be removed, the well being plated over to provide an enlarged flight deck for a Lynx helicopter. In order to accommodate the latter a telescopic extension will be built into the hangar. New electronics and improved communications will be provided and the operations room updated. Increased automation is planned, and this will reduce the complement from 253 to 235.

Displacement: 2200 tons (standard), 2850 tons (full load) Length: 113.4 m (372 ft) oa Beam: 12.5 m (41 ft) Draught: 4.6 m (15 ft) Machinery: 2-shaft steam turbines, 30 000 shp=30 knots Armament: 2 114-mm (4.5-in) Mk 6 DP (1×2); 2 Seacat SAM quadruple launchers; 1 Limbo triple A/S mortar; 1 Wasp helicopter Crew: 253

No and name	laid down	launched	commissioned	builder
F.802 Van Speijk	10/63	3/65	2/67	Nederlandse DSM, Amsterdam
F.803 Van Galen	7/63	3/66	8/67	KM DeSchelde, Flushing
F.804 Tjerk Hiddes	6/64	12/65	8/67	Nederlandse DSM, Amsterdam
F.805 Van Nes	7/63	3/66	8/67	KM DeSchelde, Flushing
F.814 Isaac Sweers	5/65	3/67	5/68	Nederlandse DSM, Amsterdam
F.815 Evertsen	7/65	6/66	12/67	KM DeSchelde, Flushing

Varyag

Russian protected cruiser, built 1898-1900.
An order was placed with the US shipyard
William Cramp, Philadelphia as part of a
massive programme to increase the strength
of the Russian navy for the inevitable war
with Japan. She had 12 6-in (152-mm) guns
disposed in pairs on the forecastle, in casemates at the corners of the superstructure, in
open shields on the shelter deck, and on the
quarterdeck. In fact the design was a diminutive of the *St Louis* Class, built slightly later,
with fewer guns and increased speed.

The trials of the ship took place off the
New England coast at the end of July 1900,
and she maintained 23.6 knots for nearly
eight hours. She was sent out to Port Arthur
in 1903, and was the earliest casualty of the
war, being sunk by Japanese cruisers while
lying at Chemulpo on February 9, before war
had been declared.

The ship was raised in August 1905, and
was commissioned into the Japanese navy as
the training cruiser *Soya*. In March 1916 she
was sold back to Russia, taken over at
Vladivostok a month later and left for Great
Britain, en route to the Arctic. However, she
was still lying disarmed at Liverpool in
June 1917 and was seized after the October
Revolution. On February 15, 1918 she ran
aground on the coast of Ireland while in tow,
and was then laid up as a depot ship. In 1920
she was sold to a German shipbreaker and
became a total loss when she ran aground off
the coast of Scotland. The wreck was subsequently scrapped in 1923-25.

Displacement: 6500 tons (normal) *Length:* 126.8
m (416 ft) oa *Beam:* 15.84 m (52 ft) *Draught:* 5.94
m (19 ft 6 in) *Machinery:* 2-shaft reciprocating
steam, 20000 ihp=23 knots *Protection:* 76-38
mm (3-1.5 in) deck, 152 mm (6 in) conning tower
Armament: 12 6-in/45-cal (12×1); 12 75-mm
(2.95-in)/60-cal (12×1); 8 3-pdr (47-mm) QF
(8×1); 6 45-cm (17.7-in) torpedo tubes (bow,
stern, beam) *Crew:* 571

Vasco da Gama

Portuguese ironclad corvette, built 1874-78.
A small central battery ship for coast defence
was ordered from Thames Ironworks, Black-
wall and completed in 1878. As completed
she was barque-rigged but in 1902-03 she was
rebuilt at Livorno by Ansaldo with light pole
masts, two funnels and a ram bow. The old
vertical compound machinery was replaced
by modern triple-expansion engines and Yarrow boilers, and the armament, supplied by
Armstrongs, was modernized.

On October 9, 1917 during the revolution
she was badly damaged and ran aground.
Although refloated she was never seaworthy
again, and was scrapped in 1935.

Displacement: (as rebuilt) 2030 tons (normal)
Length: (as lengthened) 70.9 m (232 ft 9 in) oa
Beam: 12.2 m (40 ft) *Draught:* 5.6 m (18 ft 4 in)
mean *Machinery:* (as modernized) 2-shaft reciprocating steam, 6000 ihp=15.5 knots *Protection:* (as rebuilt) 229-178 mm (9-7 in) belt, 64 mm
(2.5 in) deck *Armament:* (as rebuilt) 2 8-in (203-
mm)/40-cal (2×1); 1 6-in (152-mm)/45-cal QF; 1
3-in (76-mm) QF; 6 3-pdr (47-mm) QF (6×1);
4 0.45-in (11.4-mm) machine-guns (4×1) *Crew:*
270

Vautour, Sud-Aviation SO 4050

French bomber, all-weather fighter and
ground-attack aircraft. Design of the SO 4050
Vautour began in 1951: originally conceived
as a twin-jet bomber, in 1953 it was ordered
by the Armée de l'Air in three versions, as an
all-weather fighter (Vautour IIN), single-seat
ground-attack type (Vautour IIA) and two-
seat bomber. The prototypes of these flew,
respectively, in October 1952, December
1953 and December 1954.

The prototype fighter was powered by two
2500-kg (5510-lb) st SNECMA Atar 101B
turbojets, while two of the three pre-
production IINs had Armstrong-Siddeley
Sapphires and the third a Rolls-Royce Avon,
but the production version, 70 of which were
delivered from 1956 out of an original order
for 140, like all production Vautours, had
3500-kg (7715-lb) st Atar 101E-3s. The IIN
was armed with four DEFA 30-mm (1.18-in)
cannon or up to 240 unguided rockets in the
fuselage, plus four pods, each containing

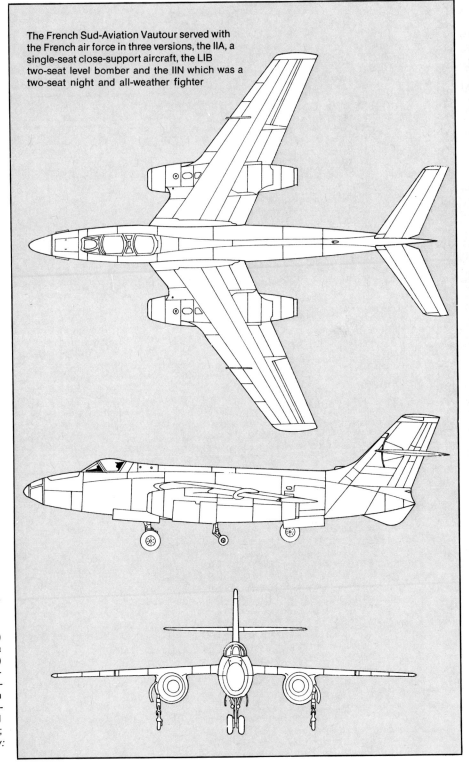

The French Sud-Aviation Vautour served with
the French air force in three versions, the IIA, a
single-seat close-support aircraft, the LIB
two-seat level bomber and the IIN which was a
two-seat night and all-weather fighter

VE-7, Vought

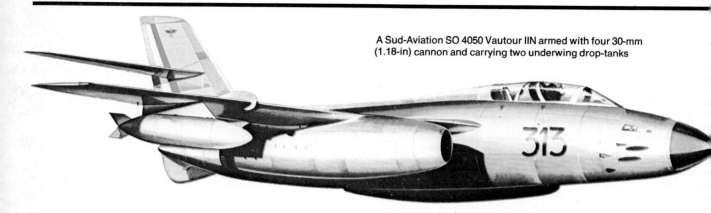

A Sud-Aviation SO 4050 Vautour IIN armed with four 30-mm (1.18-in) cannon and carrying two underwing drop-tanks

either 19 rockets, or guided missiles which were fitted under the wings. A nose radar was also carried.

The ground-attack version, with only a single cockpit and solid nose, was armed with four cannon plus up to six 450-kg (1000-lb) bombs in the fuselage bomb bay. Although 300 IIAs were ordered, only three pre-production and 30 production machines were actually built, and in 1960 25 of these were sold to Israel.

The prototype and one pre-production IIB were followed by 40 production bombers, with glazed nose for bomb-aiming, no cannon armament and provision for up to 2400 kg (5300 lb) of bombs; as with other versions of the Vautour drop-tanks could be carried under the wings. A 1958 prototype of the Vautour IIBR development, with nose radome and flight refuelling probe, was not pursued, and some IIBs were transferred to Israel in 1960 along with the 25 ground-attack machines.

Span: 14.94 m (49 ft) *Length:* 15.84 m (52 ft) *Gross weight:* 20700 kg (45635 lb) *Maximum speed:* 1160 km/h (720 mph)

VE-7, Vought

US Navy trainer and general-purpose aircraft. The prototype VE-7 two-seat two-bay biplane was built by the Lewis & Vought corporation in 1918 as an advanced trainer to take the licence-built French 150-hp Hispano-Suiza engine. By the time the firm had been renamed Chance Vought just after the end of the First World War the US Navy evinced interest in a version powered by the newly available 180-hp Wright-Hispano E water-cooled engine. In the early 1920s some 120 of all versions were built. As well as the original trainer, variants which saw considerable service with navy units include the VE-7G armed observation landplane, with a single synchronized 0.30-in (7.62-mm) Vickers gun plus a Lewis gun of the same calibre flexibly mounted for the observer. The VE-7H was an unarmed seaplane with an enlarged fin and a single central float plus two wingtip stabilizing floats.

When the first US carrier *Langley* was commissioned in 1922 it had two squadrons designed as single-seat fighters; these were VE-7s, selected because of their reliability and their availability. The single-seat fighter version which served with US Navy Fighting Squadron Two had the front cockpit faired over and a single synchronized machine-gun. A number of wheel-undercarriage VE-7s fitted with British-designed flotation gear were redesignated VE-7GF and VE-7SF respectively.

Twenty-one examples of the VE-9 development were built with the later Wright-Hispano E-3 engine. Like the VE-7Hs, the VE-9Hs served aboard battleships and cruisers, usually being launched by catapult. They were not withdrawn from service until the late 1920s.

(VE-7SF) Span: 10.39 m (34 ft 1 in) *Length:* 7.44 m (24 ft 5 in) *Gross weight:* 953 kg (2100 lb) *Maximum speed:* 188 km/h (117 mph)

(VE-9H) Span: 10.39 m (34 ft 1 in) *Length:* 9.17 m (30 ft 1 in) *Gross weight:* 1056 kg (2328 lb) *Maximum speed:* 187 km/h (116 mph)

Velos, Blackburn

British torpedo-bomber. The Velos was a two-seat development of the Blackburn Dart to meet a Greek navy requirement for a coastal-defence aircraft. It was essentially a seaplane, but could take the split-leg wheeled undercarriage when necessary, and could be used in the torpedo-dropping, bomber, reconnaissance and training roles. The Velos was powered by a Napier Lion IIB or V, rated at 450 hp.

The Velos was structurally similar to the Dart, which in turn was developed from the Swift. It was wired for night flying, and featured the following additional equipment: electric intercom between the pilot and gunner; W/T equipment, with a 320-km (200-mile) range; slings on the centre section of the upper mainplane and bomb racks under the centre fuselage with a capacity of four 104-kg (230-lb) bombs. A 0.303-in (7.7-mm) Lewis gun could be mounted on a Scarff ring in the rear cockpit, which was later raised on the Greek-built machines, which were designated T.3A.

The first four Velos aircraft were built at the Blackburn factory in Leeds and designated T.3, the first two (with wooden floats) flying from Brough on October 28, 1925. Blackburns also set up the Greek National Aircraft Factory at Old Phaleron, and the first of 12 T.3A Velos's, with wheeled undercarriage, made its maiden flight on March 17, 1926. The second aircraft, this time a seaplane, flew on March 31 the same year. By the end of 1930 the 12 aircraft had been built, and the factory had also reconditioned 13 Velos's including some of the Blackburn-built aircraft. They remained in Greek navy service up to about 1934.

One of the Leeds-built aircraft was retained by the company and used for demonstration purposes, while another was built to T.3A standards with metal floats for a South American tour, but no further military orders were received. It was later converted to a two-seat seaplane trainer, and together with another five aircraft registered to the North Sea Aerial and General Transport company. They were used by the RAF Reserve School at Brough until withdrawn from service in 1932. A total of 22 Velos's were built.

(T.3A seaplane) Span: 14.78 m (48 ft 6 in) *Length:* 10.82 m (35 ft 6 in) *Gross weight:* 3175 kg (7000 lb) *Maximum speed:* 161 km/h (100 mph)

Veltro, Macchi C.205V Development of Macchi C.202 Folgore Italian fighter aircraft **See Folgore**

Vengeance A-31/-35, Vultee

US dive-bomber. After the late-1930s V-11 and V-12 light-attack bombers which the Vultee company had produced for export, it produced a design intended specifically for the dive-bombing role. Since the outbreak of the Second World War, the German Luftwaffe had been enjoying considerable success with the Junkers Ju 87 dive-bomber in Poland and France. It was not surprising, therefore, that when the British Purchasing Commission visited the US in 1940 they were attracted to this new concept from Vultee. Designated V-72 by the company, the aircraft was an angular mid-wing all-metal monoplane, with retractable undercarriage, powered by a single 1600-hp Wright R-2600-19 engine. A central, elongated transparent cockpit canopy covered the pilot and gunner seated in tandem. Armament comprised four 0.30-in (7.62-mm) guns in the wings and two of a like calibre, firing rearwards, at the back of the cockpit; plus the capacity to carry 907 kg (2000 lb) of bombs. The RAF ordered 700 of these aircraft—400 as Vengeance Is and the other 300 as IIs. They were designated A-31 by the US authorities. Due to the size of the order and the need for its urgent delivery the Northrop company built 200 Vengeance Is as well as an equivalent amount of Mk IIs. Of this number about half were sent to Britain under the Lend-Lease plan with the designation Vengeance IA.

The first flight was made in July 1941 and after further testing modifications were made for the production model; a revised fin and rudder layout, plus dive brakes fitted on the top surface of the wings. A production Vengeance made its first flight in June 1942, but it was another year before they began to enter RAF service. By this time the US had been forced into the war after the attack on Pearl Harbor in late 1941 and 243 aircraft of the British order were retained by the USAAF as V-72s, a few also being sent to the army for trials. A further Lend-Lease quota of 100 Vengeance IIIs was built by Vultee for the RAF. Unfortunately, by this time—1943—it had been realized that dive-bombers could only be used effectively under ideal conditions and needed fighter escorts. So they were used in service with the RAF in Burma and India, where they proved very effective, in conjunction with Hurricanes for fighter cover, as a replacement for Blenheims, in the Arakan campaign. They also served with the Royal Australian Air Force in some numbers.

One A-31 was constructed by Vultee in 1942 as the XA-31A, later a testbed for the 3000-hp XR-4360-1 Wasp Major engine; for the latter purpose it was known as the XA-31B. Five more Vengeances were used as engine testbeds for the 2200-hp Cyclone R-3350-13 and -37 powerplants destined for use in the B-29. These were designated YA-31Cs.

These were followed by the Vengeance IV or A-35A, equipped with five 0.5-in (12.7-mm) guns; two in each wing and one in the rear of the cockpit. Ninety-nine of these were built by Vultee, together with 831 A-35Bs, powered by the 1700-hp Wright R-2600-13 radial and armed with six 0.5-in guns in the wings and one in the cockpit. The RAF received a total of 562 from the run of these two models under Lend-Lease and 29 were sent to Brazil. Apart from the six squadrons in service in Burma and India, most other RAF machines were relegated to the role of target tug and designated Vengeance T.T. Mk IV, and the same fate awaited those in use with the USAAF. Total production of all models when building finished in September 1944 was 1931, the RAF having received 1205 aircraft.

(Vengeance IV—A-35B) *Span:* 14.63 m (48 ft) *Length:* 12.12 m (39 ft 9 in) *Gross weight:* 7439 kg (16 400 lb) *Maximum speed:* 449 km/h (279 mph)

Venom, de Havilland

British jet fighter. The DH.112 Venom was the logical development and improvement of the Vampire. Similar in layout to its predecessor, it was a new design introducing a new wing with moderate sweepback on the leading edge and reduced thickness-to-chord ratio, wingtip fuel tanks and the de Havilland Ghost 103 jet engine, rated at 2200 kg (4850 lb) st. It retained the same armament of four 20-mm (0.79-in) Hispano cannon and 907 kg (2000 lb) of weapons under the wings. The Venom prototype first flew on September 2, 1949, and the aircraft inherited the high-altitude manoeuvrability and easy low-speed handling of the Vampire, while giving a much better performance, the rate of climb being 2204 m/min (7230 ft/min). The Venom was produced to Specification F.15/49.

The first production Venom FB.1 left de Havilland's factory at Hatfield in 1951. Bulk production was transferred to Chester, delaying large-scale deliveries, and the first Chester aircraft flew in June 1952. Marshall of

Cambridge and Fairey at Stockport also built the Venom, but large-scale manufacture by Bristol at Filton was cancelled.

The first RAF units to receive the Venom FB.1 were 11, 16 and 266 Squadrons in RAF Germany in August 1952. The Middle East air force received their first FB.1s in February 1954, when 6 Squadron at Amman, Jordan, re-equipped. It soon succeeded the Vampire all round the Middle and Far East, including 14 Squadron, RNZAF, at Singapore. The last unit to re-equip was 28 Squadron in Hong Kong in February 1955.

By 1955 a refined Venom had appeared, designated FB.4, which featured a redesigned tail, power-operated ailerons and an ejection seat. The first Venom FB.4 flew on December 29, 1953, but was not in RAF service until summer 1955, 5 Squadron in Germany being the first unit to receive the type. During the 1956 invasion of Suez, FB.4s of 6 and 249 Squadrons were in action attacking Egyptian airfields, while in summer 1957, 8 and 249 Squadrons were used during the Oman rebellion. Most Venom FB.1 units re-equipped with the FB.4, serving in the ground-attack role until the early 1960s. The last RAF Venom FB.4s on the strength of 28 Squadron were replaced by Hunter FGA.9s in 1962.

In Switzerland the licence-built Vampires were followed by the Venom FB.50, an export version of the FB.1. Some 250 were produced, the last 100 to FB.4 standard, most of which remained in service through the late 1970s, though due to be replaced by the F-5E/F. Iraq received some 30 FB.50s in 1954-56, while 22 FB.4s were ordered by Venezuela in December 1955, and although withdrawn from front-line duties in 1968, are still understood to be used for various second-line tasks.

Like the two-seat Vampire before it, the two-seat Venom was produced as a private venture, the first aircraft flying on August 22, 1950. Like the Vampire NF.10, the Venom NF.2 (as the type was designated following its procurement by the RAF) housed a two-man crew side by side. Production problems delayed introduction into service, and the only Venom NF.2 unit, 23 Squadron, got their aircraft in November 1953. As the design was refined to NF.3 standard, some NF.2s were updated and redesignated NF.2A.

The two-seat Venom NF.3 incorporated the features of the FB.4 and carried improved AI.21 radar and a clear-view canopy with a power-operated jettison. Both the NF.2 and NF.3 were powered by the de Havilland Ghost 104, rated at 2245 kg (4950 lb) st. The first NF.3s were delivered to 141 Squadron RAF in June 1955. Seven RAF Squadrons were equipped with the Venom NF.2, NF.2A and NF.3 variants; the last unit, 89 Squadron, giving up their Venom NF.3s in favour of the new delta-wing Javelin in October 1957.

Although the RAF operated the largest number of Venom night fighters it was an export version, the NF.51, built for Sweden, which was first in service. These aircraft were powered by a licence-built version of the Ghost, shipped to the UK for installation in the 62 NF.51s built. The first 30 aircraft equated to the NF.2, and entered service in August 1953. All the aircraft were eventually brought up to NF.3 standard, and were

phased out of Flygvåpnet service in 1960. A total of 838 Venoms were produced in the UK, in addition to the 250 FB.50s built in Switzerland.

(FB.1) *Span:* 12.73 m (41 ft 9 in) *Length:* 10.06 m (33 ft) *Gross weight:* 7080 kg (15 610 lb) *Maximum speed:* 1030 km/h (640 mph)

(NF.3) *Span:* 13.06 m (42 ft 10 in) *Length:* 11.18 m (36 ft 8 in) *Gross weight:* 6632 kg (14 620 lb) *Maximum speed:* 1014 km/h (630 mph)

Ventura, Lockheed B-34

US light patrol/bomber aircraft. A twin-engined mid-wing monoplane of all-metal stressed-skin construction, the Ventura was ordered initially by the British Purchasing Commission in the summer of 1940. It was intended as a replacement for the Lockheed Hudsons then in service with RAF Coastal Command, which had been based on the civil Model 14. The Model 18 Lodestar transport was now to serve as a basis for the Ventura, which did resemble the Hudson in design, although the dorsal gun turret was fitted further forward to give a clearer field of vision for the gunner, and a 'stepped' ventral gun mounting was fitted in the underside of the fuselage. A crew of five was carried, including the pilot. It had been intended to use Twin Wasp powerplants, but this was altered to two 2000-hp Pratt & Whitney GR-2800-S1A4-G Double Wasps. The internal bombload was 1360 kg (3000 lb), and standard armament comprised eight 0.30-in (7.62-mm) guns, two in the dorsal turret, two in the ventral mounting and four in the nose position.

The first flight took place on July 31, 1941, the RAF having ordered 675 Ventura I and IIs. The Mark IIs had a different armament layout of two fixed 0.5-in (12.7-mm) guns, two vertically movable 0.303-in (7.7-mm) in the nose, two 0.303-in in the dorsal turret and two 0.303-in in the ventral bay. Bombload and powerplants remained the same as the Mark I. Eighty-eight Ventura Is were produced before the configuration was changed to the Mark II version.

Deliveries to the RAF commenced in the summer of 1942, although an earlier date had been expected, and the first operational flight was with 21 Squadron of Bomber Command on November 3 of that year. The Venturas were found to be unsatisfactory for daylight raids; they were withdrawn from Bomber Command in 1943 and transferred to Coastal Command, where they equipped two squadrons as Ventura G.R.Is.

Although these aircraft were not very popular with Bomber Command pilots, the RAF order was increased by 200 Ventura IIAs through the Lend-Lease system. This version had been given the designation B-34 by the USAAF, and as the US was involved in the war by the end of 1941 over 200 aircraft of the earlier Ventura II type were retained as such by the USAAF, which employed most of them on land-based over-water patrol duties as B-34As or, with navigational training equipment, as B-34Bs.

A further modified version, the Ventura III (O-56) had 1700-hp Wright R-2600-31 engines, its original designation in the O (observation) series indicating that it was

Verité

intended only for patrol and not for bombing. But, from an order for 550 only 18 were built and they were allocated to the USAAF as B-37s.

Meanwhile, the US Navy had already received 27 Ventura IIs (also from the British contract) in September 1942; these were designated PV-3. All were utilized as land-based patrol bombers, equipped with two 0.5-in guns in the nose, two 0.5-in in the dorsal turret and two ventral 0.30-in guns. Provision was also made for six depth charges, 227-kg (500-lb) bombs or a torpedo in the bomb bay (total capacity 1360 kg [3000 lb]); 907 kg (2000 lb) of stores, or two additional drop tanks could be fixed in the underwing position. Some were modified to carry Mk IV radar in the nose, with the armament reduced to six 0.5-in guns, and the R-2800-31 engines were retained. Deliveries to VP-82 Squadron of the USN commenced in December 1942. From then onwards the navy had priority for the entire PV-1 production run of 1600 aircraft, but nevertheless, 388 were supplied to the RAF under Lend-Lease, where they were known as Ventura G.R.Vs, serving with Coastal Command in Britain and overseas. Venturas of various models served also with the Canadian, South African (approx 270), Australian (75) and New Zealand (139) air arms.

Another variant appeared in 1944, the PV-2 Harpoon, with increased span, larger fins and rudders, internal improvements, and an armament of five forward-firing guns in the nose and two in the dorsal turret.

Some RAF Venturas also served in the Middle East on mine detection patrols and with one squadron of Transport Command. Those with Coastal Command undertook basic meteorological patrols during the war. The total number of Venturas built in the series was 2475; production ended in May 1944.

(Ventura I) *Span:* 19.96 m (65 ft 6 in) *Length:* 15.67 m (51 ft 5 in) *Gross weight:* 11 793 kg (26 000 lb) *Maximum speed:* 502 km/h (312 mph)

(PV-1) *Span:* 19.96 m (65 ft 6 in) *Length:* 15.77 m (51 ft 9 in) *Gross weight:* 14 096 kg (31 077 lb) *Maximum speed:* 476 km/h (296 mph)

Verité

French battleship class, built 1903-08. Four ships were laid down in 1903 as improved editions of the *Republique* Class. *Démocratie* was launched in April 1904 at Brest arsenal, followed by *Justice* in September at La Seyne, Toulon, *Liberté* in 1905 at St Nazaire, and *Verité* in May 1907 at Chantiers de la Gironde, Bordeaux. The same 12-in (305-mm) gun, the 45-calibre Model 1902, was used, but the secondary armament was increased to ten 194-mm (7.6-in) guns in six single turrets at forecastle-deck level, and four in casemates at main-deck level forward and lower-deck level aft. Although considered the best French battleships of their day, they appeared a year after *Dreadnought* and were hopelessly outclassed by most foreign contemporaries. They were reliable steamers, and could maintain 17 knots for three days. All exceeded the designed speed on trials. On September 25, 1911, *Liberté* blew up at Toulon when defective cordite

The French *Verité* Class battleship *Démocratie*. She was built at Brest and launched in 1904

exploded spontaneously. Following the loss of *Iéna*, the disaster revealed grave shortcomings in French ammunition and led to an overhaul of manufacturing standards.

The three survivors served in the Mediterranean in 1914-18, and took part in operations against the Greeks at Salamis in September 1916. *Justice* served in the Black Sea in 1919 against the Bolsheviks and towed the damaged *Vergniaud* back to Toulon. In 1921 all three were stricken and scrapped.

Displacement: 14 900 tons (normal), 15 800 tons (full load) *Length:* 134.8 m (442 ft 3 in) wl *Beam:* 24 m (78 ft 9 in) *Draught:* 8.4 m (27 ft 7 in) *Protection:* 180-280 mm (7.1-11 in) belt, 60 mm (2.4 in) deck, 320 mm (12.6 in) turrets *Machinery:* 3-shaft reciprocating steam, 17 500 ihp=18 knots *Armament:* 4 305-mm (12-in)/45-cal Model 1902 (2×2); 10 194-mm (7.6-in)/45-cal Model 1902 (10×1); 13 65-mm (2.8-in) QF (13×1); 10 3-pdr (47-mm) Model 1902 (10×1); 4 45-cm (17.7-in) torpedo tubes (2 submerged, 2 above water; all broadside) *Crew:* 809 as flagship

Vesely

British machine-gun. Joseph Vesely was a Czech citizen who assisted in the manufacture of the British BESA machine-gun just before the Second World War. In 1940 he submitted two sets of drawings of a sub-machine-gun that he had designed, but it was turned down as the decision had just been taken to go ahead with the Lanchester and there was neither time nor any capacity for other models. Two years later Vesely tried again, this time with a prototype which he called the V 42. It was fairly conventional in appearance, being long and fitted with a wooden butt with a semipistol grip. A folding bayonet was permanently attached to the muzzle and lay back above the barrel jacket when not in use. It operated by simple blowback, but there was no suggestion of Advanced Primer Ignition and the bolt closed on the breech before the spring-loaded firing pin struck the cap. To accommodate the extra power of the recoiling bolt the return spring was very robust.

The general construction was of sheet metal, stamped, wrapped and welded, but the memorable feature of the Vesely was the magazine. It held 60 rounds of 9-mm (0.354-in) Parabellum in two columns, one behind the other each in a separate compartment. The front row fired first, and while holding down the platform on the rear column. When the last round was fed from the front, the rear column was allowed to come up far enough to engage the bolt, and this column was then fed. There was thus no pause in the loading and feeding and the rear column came into use without any action on the part of the firer. Quite naturally there were difficulties with this at first, and the sand and mud tests of the Ordnance Board proved it to be troublesome, but in the end it was perfected and rarely jammed. The Ordnance Board were not sufficiently impressed to recommend a change of weapon from the Sten, which in 1942 was well under way, and despite a 1943 version the Vesely passed out of sight in favour of other, more promising designs. The double magazine has not been used since.

Calibre: 9 mm (0.354 in) *Ammunition:* 9-mm Parabellum *Weight:* 4.17 kg (9 lb 3 oz) *Length:* 813 mm (32 in) *Barrel length:* 254 mm (10 in) *Magazine:* 60-round detachable double-compartment box *Rate of fire:* 750 rds/min (cyclic) *Muzzle velocity:* 411 m/sec (1350 ft/sec)

Vettor Pisani

Italian armoured cruiser class, built 1892-99. Two medium-sized cruisers with 6-in (152-mm) guns were laid down in 1892 to a design by Engineer-Director Edoardo Masdea. *Carlo Alberto* was launched on September 23, 1896, by La Spezia arsenal, and *Vettor Pisani* on August 14, 1895, by Castellamare di Stabia.

The ships were almost at the end of their useful lives when war broke out in 1915. *Vettor Pisani* was retained on the active list but her sister was disarmed in 1917 at Venice arsenal. Her armour was removed, a new deck was added to provide accommodation for troops in the waist, and the finishing touches were completed by Taranto arsenal. Under the new name *Zenson* she recommissioned in April 1918 for service as a troop transport. She and *Vettor Pisani* were discarded in 1920.

Displacement: 6500 tonnes (normal) *Length:* 105.7 m (346 ft 9 in) oa *Beam:* 18.04 m (59 ft 2 in)

Draught: 7.2 m (23 ft 8 in) *Protection:* 150 mm (5.9 in) deck, 50 mm (2 in) gun shields *Machinery:* 2-shaft reciprocating steam, 13 000 ihp=19 knots *Armament:* 12 6-in (152-mm)/40-cal (12×1); 4/6 4.7-in (120-mm)/40-cal QF (4/6×1); 14 6-pdr (57-mm)/43-cal QF (14×1); 6/8 1-pdr (37-mm)/20-cal (6/8×1); 2 machine-guns; 4 45-cm (17.7-in) torpedo tubes (above water) *Crew:* 600

Vickers British aircraft See **F.B.9, Gunbus, Vildebeeste, Vimy, Vincent, Virginia, Warwick, Wellesley, Wellington**

Vickers

British machine-guns. The firm of Vickers began in Sheffield as steel-makers and from this it moved into shipbuilding and opened yards on the Tyne and in the north-west of England. A factory was built at Erith on the Thames and it was here that the Maxim gun was built. Hiram Maxim needed a partner with a manufacturing base for the production of his gun, and in 1883 he entered into an agreement with Albert Vickers. In time the firm became Vickers, Son and Maxim and Maxim's connection with Nordenfelt was severed. The Erith factory was largely concentrated on the Maxim gun, though there were other products too. Vickers-built Maxims were sold all over the world, and were accepted into the British Army in 1891. At the same time as the rifle-calibre guns were being made, the factory also built another

"*Carlo Alberto*"

The Italian armoured cruiser *Carlo Alberto* which was used as a troopship from 1918 to 1920

Maxim design, the 1-pdr pom-pom. The name pom-pom was an onomatopoeic derivative of the distinctive sound of its slow and rhythmic rate of fire. The pom-pom was adopted by several nations mainly because the idea of a shell-firing machine-gun was extremely popular at that time.

The pom-pom was a large machine-gun of 37-mm (1.46-in) calibre firing explosive shells weighing 0.45 kg (1 lb) which were the smallest allowed by the Convention of St Petersburg. It was not a complete success, but several were bought by the Boers and used against the British Army in the war of 1899-1901. It was not capable of sustained fire like the smaller gun, and its bulk was not

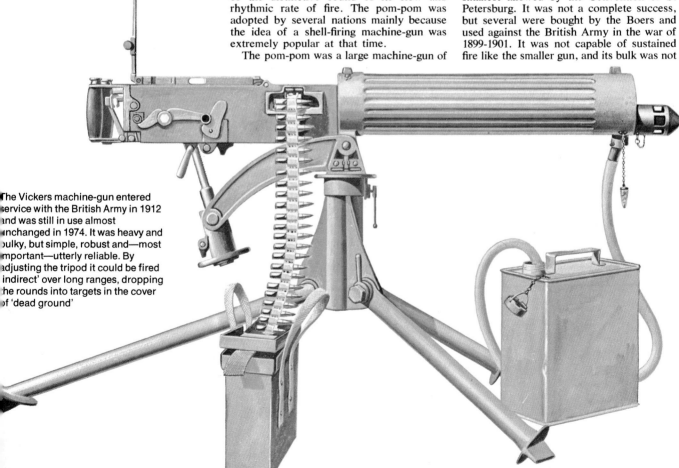

The Vickers machine-gun entered service with the British Army in 1912 and was still in use almost unchanged in 1974. It was heavy and bulky, but simple, robust and—most important—utterly reliable. By adjusting the tripod it could be fired 'indirect' over long ranges, dropping the rounds into targets in the cover of 'dead ground'

Vickers

easy to hide, but a burst of pom-pom shells could do plenty of damage to unprotected troops in the open.

Vickers saw that the Maxim gun was capable of improvement and development and they brought out their first developed version in 1904. Much weight was saved by careful stress calculations since the Maxim had been designed by more or less empirical methods and was needlessly heavy, but the use of high grade steels and aluminium also brought the weight down. The toggle action was turned upside down which reduced the depth of the receiver by nearly half, and in the end the Vickers-Maxim was roughly 25% lighter than the original gun. It was adopted by the British Army in 1912 and in the First World War earned an enviable reputation for reliability and effectiveness. Complete battalions were formed, armed with nothing else but the Vickers, and the idea was revived in the Second World War. It remained the standard support machine-gun of the British Army until the mid-1960s and is still in use in small numbers in ex-Commonwealth countries. It was also mounted in aircraft, where it was air-cooled, in ships and in armoured vehicles. A heavy version was made in 0.5-in (12.7-mm) for tank use in the 1920s and 1930s and in the First World War a few were made to take the French 11-mm (0.43-in) cartridge for use in shooting observation balloons from scout aircraft.

Despite its advantages of reliability and long life there were drawbacks to the Vickers; it was heavy and demanded a crew of three men to move it, as well as a supply of water and men to make up belts of ammunition, so the company purchased the Berthier design for a light machine rifle and developed it into a light machine-gun. This appeared in 1930 and was advertised as a general-purpose machine-gun, for use in the front-line in direct support and also as a support gun in place of their belt-fed gun. The Vickers-Berthier was a simple gun, magazine fed and in many ways not unlike the Bren which the British Army chose in its stead. But the VB was adopted by the Indian army and was used quite widely in the Second World War where it fulfilled all the promises made by its designers. It was adaptable as an aircraft gun for use by the observer from an open cockpit. From this idea arose the notion of increasing the rate of fire and giving it a larger magazine. It was fitted with a flat round pan magazine in which the rounds were pushed round by a clock spring, so that the pan itself did not rotate, and the rate of fire went up to 900 rds/min. The pan magazine held 100 rounds, though there was a 60-round version, and this gave a useful number of bursts. Unfortunately this version, which became known as the Vickers Gas-Operated gun, or VGO, fared little better than the VB since soon after it came into service open cockpits went out and turrets were introduced, armed with belt-fed Brownings.

Some VGOs were given to the army and mounted on vehicles for SAS work in the desert. In this role they were highly successful and there were still some in use in the early 1960s. The VB and VGO were light gas-operated machine-guns with air-cooled barrels and the usual variety of accessories such as a tripod and spare barrels. Very few were sold abroad and the venture must have lost

money. At the time Vickers tried to interest their clients in the Pedersen rifle which was to be made under licence. Nothing came of that and the firm then gave up the idea of designing and making small-arms, except for a trickle of orders for the water-cooled gun.

In other armament fields the firm was much more active. Warships were built by Vickers from the late nineteenth century onwards and the firm's drawing office took a large part in the design of the famous 18-pdr field gun together with its ammunition and fuzes. After the First World War attention was turned towards antiaircraft gunnery and resulted in the British 3.7-in (94-mm) AA gun which was used throughout the Second World War and up to very recent times. Vickers played a major part in the design and manufacture of the Abbot SP gun and the 105-mm (4.13-in) Light Gun. Directly after the First World War a design office for tanks was set up and there were several successful models which the firm built and sold, both to the British Army and to foreign countries.

In the late 1920s the idea of the pom-pom was revived for antiaircraft use and for possible mounting in aircraft also. The latter idea led to the Vickers S gun which never got the recognition it deserved, but the pom-pom was developed into a 40-mm (1.57-in) automatic weapon firing a 0.9-kg (2-lb) shell fed by a belt. The rate of fire was fairly low and the army bought a few for defence of fixed installations such as dockyards, but it was not a success in this role. However, when clustered into groups of six or nine it proved to be a most effective AA weapon against low-flying aircraft and it was adopted by the navy for warship defence. The normal grouping was nine guns in one large mounting which produced a rate of fire of over 1000 rds/min. The only drawback was the limited range of the short-cased round.

(Vickers machine-gun, Mks 1-7) *Calibre:* 0.303 in

Norwegian troops training in England in 1940, armed with a Vickers medium machine-gun

(7.7 mm) *Ammunition:* 0.303-in SAA *Weight:* 18.1 kg (40 lb) *Length:* 115.6 cm (45.5 in) *Barrel length:* 724 mm (28.5 in) *Magazine:* 250-round cloth belt *Rate of fire:* 450 rds/min (aircraft versions 700 rds/min) *Muzzle velocity:* 747 m/sec (2450 ft/sec)

(Vickers-Berthier light machine-guns) *Calibre* 0.303 in *Ammunition:* 0.303-in SAA *Weight:* 9.5 kg (20 lb 14 oz) *Length:* 118 cm (46.5 in) *Barrel length:* 607 mm (23.9 in) *Magazine:* 30-round box *Rate of fire:* 450-500 rds/min *Muzzle velocity:* 747 m/sec (2450 ft/sec)

(Vickers-Berthier aircraft observer's automatic gun) *Calibre:* 0.303 in *Ammunition:* 0.303-in SAA *Weight:* 8.3 kg (18 lb 4 oz) *Length:* 106.7 cm (42 in) *Barrel length:* 607 mm (23.9 in) *Magazine:* 100-round horizontal drum *Rate of fire:* 900 rds/min *Muzzle velocity:* 747 m/sec (2450 ft/sec)

Vickers

British tanks. During and immediately after the First World War, British tank production was a government responsibility, but in the postwar reduction of military establishments the tank design department was severely curtailed and Vickers were asked to undertake the design of a light tank. Work began in 1922 and the first vehicle was delivered in 1924, being taken into service as the Light Tank Mk 1. In appearance it was a complete change from the lozenge-shaped wartime tanks; the hull rose above the tracks and was surmounted by a revolving turret carrying a 3-pdr gun and four Hotchkiss machine-guns; two Vickers guns were mounted in the hull sides. It was powered by an air-cooled V-8 engine and had a specified speed of 24 km/h (15 mph) on firm ground—in fact it was capable of almost twice that. All in all it was a good design for its time, and with slight modifications remained in service until 1939.

Shortly after the delivery of the Mark 1, a Mark 1A version appeared with heavier armour, better vision arrangements, and a mounting for an AA machine-gun in the turret. Further similar improvements led to the Mark 2 in 1925 and this remained the standard tank until the late 1930s. In 1930, with the advent of an even lighter design, these tanks were reclassified 'Medium'.

In 1930 a Medium Mark 3 was developed, with a larger turret to take extra radio equipment, antigas protection and new steering and transmission features. It also had two auxiliary turrets mounting machine-guns at the front corners of the hull. However, shortage of money and indecision resulted in only three pilots being built, and the Mark 3 never attained service status.

Having produced a successful design, Vickers produced a number of private-venture tanks which they offered for sale overseas. Probably the most significant of these was the Six-Ton or Model E, designed in 1928. Two models were produced, the A with two machine-gun turrets side by side on the hull, and the B with a single turret mounting a 47-mm (1.85-in) gun. This tank was sold to many countries and had a considerable influence on design; it was built under licence, and from it came a number of local variations which led to national designs. Among these were the Soviet T-26, the Polish 7TP and the US T1E4 patterns. Light tanks, similar to those built for the British Army, were also exported.

In 1925 Vickers produced the famous Independent tank to meet a War Office specification. The name arose from the tank's capability to operate independently instead of being tied to the infantry as had previously been the accepted custom. The Independent was a large vehicle, and its most significant feature was the use of five turrets; the principal, central turret mounted a 3-pdr gun, and it was surrounded by four smaller turrets each with a Vickers machine-gun. Weighing 32 tonnes, it required a crew of eight, and the commander was kept at full stretch trying to control five turrets and the driver and make decisions at the same time. Although not adopted by the British Army, the design was copied by both the USSR and Germany in later years.

In 1930 Vickers began production of the British Army Light Tank Mark 1, a two-man vehicle mounting a single machine-gun in the turret. This was gradually improved, notably in the suspension, over the next few years and eventually reached the Mark 6 variant. In the course of these improvements the turret increased in size and mounted both a 0.5-in (12.7-mm) Vickers and a 0.303-in (7.7-mm) Vickers machine-gun side by side. Power was increased and the final models had a commander's cupola. With the adoption of twin machine-guns a three-man crew was introduced. Many of the Mark 6 light tanks were employed in France in 1939-40, but their agility and speed were small compensation for their thin protection and lack of firepower, and it was this experience which led to the abandonment of light tanks in British service.

In the latter part of the 1930s tank designs once more began to flow from the military research establishments, and from that time the private-venture tank became less common. Vickers did, however, produce some of their own designs; the Valentine and Tetrarch tanks were entirely designed and produced by Vickers, while several other tanks owed part of their design to the Vickers experts.

In postwar years the company has been primarily concerned with the construction of military vehicles to official designs, such as the Abbot self-propelled gun, though even these have shown evidence of Vickers influence. More recently the company have designed a complete main battle tank which was selected by the Indian Government for production as their Vijayanta. It is a sound compromise between armour, firepower and mobility; it mounts the British 105-mm (4.1-in) gun and uses the same engine and transmission as the Chieftain MBT. While the basic specification is kept simple, optional additions allow for more sophisticated fire control, CBW protection, wading equipment, or virtually any other refinement a purchaser may require. The first tanks of this type were completed in 1963. By 1969 production in India had begun, and by the late 1970s almost the whole of the Indian tanks were Indian built. It has also been sold to Kuwait in small numbers.

(Medium Mk 2) Weight: 13.67 tonnes Length: 5.33 m (17 ft 6 in) Width: 2.79 m (9 ft 2 in) Height: 3 m (9 ft 10 in) Armour thickness: 12-8 mm (0.5-0.3 in) Armament: 1 3-pdr; 3 0.303-in (7.7-mm) machine-guns Powerplant: Armstrong-Siddeley V-8 air-cooled, 90 bhp Speed: 26 km/h (16 mph) Range: 200 km (125 miles) Crew: 5

(Light Mk 6) Weight: 5.28 tonnes Length: 3.94 m (12 ft 11 in) Width: 2.06 m (6 ft 9 in) Height: 2.24 m (7 ft 4 in) Armour thickness: 14 mm (0.55 in) Armament: 1 0.5-in (12.7-mm) Vickers machine-gun; 1 0.303-in (7.7-mm) Vickers machine-gun Powerplant: Meadows 6-cylinder gasoline, 88 bhp Speed: 56 km/h (35 mph) Range: 200 km (125 miles) Crew: 3

(Independent) Weight: 32 tonnes Length: 7.75 m (25 ft 5 in) Width: 3.2 m (10 ft 6 in) Height: 2.69 m (8 ft 10 in) Armour thickness: 28-13 mm (1.1-0.51 in) Armament: 1 3-pdr; 4 0.303-in (7.7-mm) machine-guns Powerplant: Armstrong-Siddeley V-12 air-cooled, 398 bhp Speed: 32 km/h (20 mph) Range: not known Crew: 8

(Six-Ton) Weight: 7.12 tonnes Length: 4.57 m (15 ft) Width: 2.41 m (7 ft 11 in) Height: 2.08 m (6 ft 10 in) Armour thickness: 14-5 mm (0.6-0.2 in) Armament: 2 0.303-in (7.7-mm) machine-guns Powerplant: Armstrong-Siddeley 4-cylinder air-cooled, 80 bhp Speed: 35 km/h (22 mph) Range: 150 km (95 miles) Crew: 3

(Main Battle Tank; Vijayanta) Weight: 38.6 tonnes Length: 7.92 m (26 ft) Width: 3.17 m (10 ft 5 in) Height: 2.64 m (8 ft 8 in) Armour thickness: 80 mm (3.1 in) Armament: 1 105-mm (4.1-in); 1 0.5-in (12.7-mm) machine-gun; 2 0.30-in (7.62-mm) machine-guns Powerplant: Leyland 6-cylinder multifuel, 650 bhp at 2670 rpm Speed: 56 km/h (35 mph) Range: 480 km (300 miles) Crew: 4

'Victor'

Soviet nuclear-powered attack submarine class. The first boat was laid down in 1965 and was completed in 1968. By 1979 15 further boats had been completed to this design at the Admiralty yard, Leningrad, at a rate of about two per year. The only known name is 50 Letya SSSR.

The first 'Victor' Class boat appeared at about the same time as the first of the 'Charlie' Class, to which they bear a close resemblance. They have the same teardrop hull form and streamlined conning tower, and dimensions (at first thought to be very different) have turned out to be identical. The only distinguishing features externally are the gently sloping bow, the angled front of the conning tower (compared with the vertical front in the 'Charlie' Class), and its proximity

A Soviet 'Victor' Class nuclear-powered attack submarine photographed by the RN in 1975

Victor, Handley Page

to the bow. Whereas the 'Charlie' Class carry antiship missiles, the *Victor* Class appear to have been designed as hunter-killer submarines, a role in which they succeed the 'November' Class. Improvements over the latter include a much quieter propulsion system, a more streamlined hull form, and more horsepower in a hull which is a full 15 m (50 ft) shorter, giving them five knots more speed surfaced or submerged. Unlike the 'November' Class, all eight 53-cm (21-in) torpedo tubes are in the bow; 64 mines can be carried in place of the torpedoes. The 'Victor' Class are thought to have acquired the SS-N-15 antisubmarine missile which, like the equivalent US Subroc missile, can be fired from torpedo tubes.

In 1973 a new submarine type was observed in the waters of the Northern Fleet. It was at first given the code name 'Uniform', but because of its resemblance to the 'Victor' Class was redesignated 'Victor II', the earlier boats being reclassified 'Victor I'. Two further boats of this type are known to have been completed. Apart from a slight increase in length, displacement and speed there is little to distinguish the two versions in shape or performance.

('Victor I') *Displacement:* 4300/5100 tons (surfaced/submerged) *Length:* 94 m (308 ft 6 in) oa *Beam:* 10 m (32 ft 9 in) *Draught:* 8 m (26 ft 3 in) *Machinery:* 1 pressurized water-cooled reactor, 2-shaft steam turbines, 24 000 shp=26/30 knots (surfaced/submerged) *Armament:* 8 53-cm (21-in) torpedo tubes; mines; SS-N-15 SSMs *Crew:* 100

('Victor II') *Displacement:* 4700/6000 tons (surfaced/submerged) *Length:* 88.5 m (290 ft 4 in) oa *Machinery:* 30 000 shp=33 knots (submerged) (Other specifications as for 'Victor I')

A Handley Page Victor drops 35 454-kg (1000-lb) iron bombs from its capacious bomb bay

Victor, Handley Page

British long-range medium bomber. The crescent-winged Victor was the third and final V-bomber to enter service with the RAF. Designed to the same specification as the Vulcan, B.35/46, it represented a new approach to the problem of carrying a large weapon load for great distances at high altitude at high subsonic speeds. The first Handley Page HP.80, as the type was designated by the manufacturers, made its first flight on December 24, 1952.

The Victor is of conventional all-metal stressed-skin construction. The angle of sweep on the crescent-wing is in three separate stages, with the thickness-to-chord ratio graduated along the span to ensure a constant critical Mach number over the whole wing. The lift capacity of the wing is further increased by leading-edge flaps and Fowler-type flaps on the inboard trailing edge. The semimonocoque fuselage houses a compartment for the five crew (pilot, copilot, two navigators and an air electronics officer) plus a large bomb bay capable of carrying (in its B.2 version) up to 35 conventional 454-kg (1000-lb) bombs or a Blue Steel missile

A Victor K Mk 2 tanker refuels a Hawker Siddeley Buccaneer. *Inset:* The pilot's eye view from a Phantom FCR 2 refuelling from a Victor with the probe inserted into the drogue

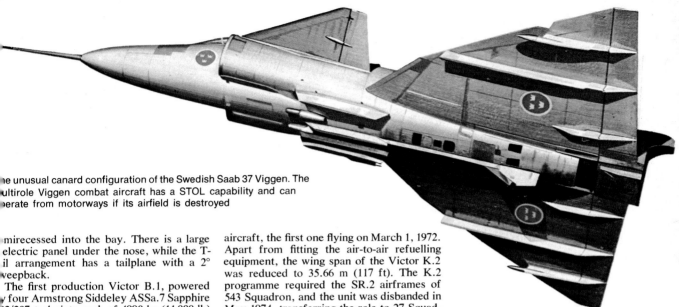

The unusual canard configuration of the Swedish Saab 37 Viggen. The multirole Viggen combat aircraft has a STOL capability and can operate from motorways if its airfield is destroyed

...mirecessed into the bay. There is a large ...electric panel under the nose, while the T-...il arrangement has a tailplane with a 2° ...veepback.

The first production Victor B.1, powered ...y four Armstrong Siddeley ASSa.7 Sapphire ...02/207 turbojets each of 4990 kg (11 000 lb) , flew on February 1, 1956, and the last of 50 ...rcraft was delivered in February 1961. The ...1 entered RAF service with 232 OCU on ...ovember 28, 1957, and the first operational ...nit, 10 Squadron, received its Victors in ...pril 1958. Three more units, 15, 55 and 57 ...quadrons, were equipped with the B.1.

Some 24 B.1s were converted to B.1A ...andard with more sophisticated ECM ...quipment, while a flight-refuelling tanker ...ersion was also produced as a conversion. ...leven B.1s were converted to K.1 config-...ration (with two-point later increased to ...ree-point refuelling facilities), six B(K).1As ...tained bombing capability with a two-point ...cility, and 14 K.1As were converted to ...ree-point tankers. The Victor tanker force ...onsisted of 55, 57 and 214 Squadrons, the ...rst of which to become operational, in ...ebruary 1966, being 57 Squadron.

The Victor's basic design was refined to ...roduce the B.2 version. This featured an ...ncreased wing span, four Rolls-Royce ...Co.11 Conway 103 bypass turbojets, ...325 kg (17 250 lb) st, in place of the Sap-...hires, a more comprehensive ECM suite ...cated in trailing-edge 'speed-pods' and a ...ilcone, and provision for underwing fuel ...nks. Like the Vulcan B.2, the Victor B.2 ...ould be armed with the Blue Steel weapon.

The first production Victor B.2 made its ...aiden flight on February 20, 1959, and the ...rst RAF unit to receive the type was 139 ...quadron in February 1962. The only other ...ictor B.2 unit, 100 Squadron, formed in ...ay 1962. A total of 34 B.2s were built, 21 of ...hich were immediately uprated to B.2R ...tandard with provision for Blue Steel and ...e RCo.17 Conway 201 turbojets rated at ...344 kg (20 600 lb) st.

A strategic-reconnaissance conversion of ...e Victor, designated SR.2, and fitted with a ...ariety of camera and other sensor options in ...e bomb bay, was flown on February 23, ...965. Some 10 B.2s were converted and were ...perated by 543 Squadron, which received its ...rst aircraft in May 1965. A conversion ...rogramme of B.2s to K.2 tanker configura-...on was begun during 1968 by Handley Page. ...ollowing the demise of the company in ...970, Hawker Siddeley at Woodford com-...leted the modification programme of 24

aircraft, the first one flying on March 1, 1972. Apart from fitting the air-to-air refuelling equipment, the wing span of the Victor K.2 was reduced to 35.66 m (117 ft). The K.2 programme required the SR.2 airframes of 543 Squadron, and the unit was disbanded in May 1974, transferring the role to 27 Squadron flying Vulcan SR.2s. The first Victor K.2s arrived on 57 Squadron in July 1975, and later joined 55 Squadron in April 1976; 214 Squadron with K.1/1As disbanded during the changeover. The Victor K.2 is expected to continue to serve the RAF well into the 1980s.

(B.1) *Span:* 33.53 m (110 ft) *Length:* 35.03 m (114 ft 11 in) *Gross weight:* 81 645 kg (180 000 lb) *Maximum speed:* 1045 km/h (650 mph)

(SR.2) *Span:* 36.58 m (120 ft) *Length:* 35.03 m (114 ft 11 in) *Gross weight:* 101 150 kg (223 000 lb) *Maximum speed:* 1045 km/h (650 mph)

Viggen, Saab 37

Swedish multipurpose combat aircraft. Prior to the introduction of the Viggen, Sweden, as other countries, had used different types of aircraft to fulfil different roles. In order, partly, to cut down costs of their defence system, the Swedish authorities decided to try for one aircraft that could meet the four basic requirements—low-level attack, high-altitude interception, strategic/tactical recon-naissance and training. This was to be designed on the principle of having inter-changeable equipment and armament. The Saab (Svenska Aeroplan Aktiebolaget—Swedish aircraft company) design team, under the direction of Erik Bratt, was given the task of creating this aircraft in 1952. It was to be ready to enter service in the 1970s, replacing both the Draken and Lansen in Flygvåpnet (Royal Swedish Air Force) ser-vice. The aircraft was required to have a speed of just under Mach 1 at sea level, but the ability to reach Mach 2 in a supersonic dash—similar to that of the Draken. What was demanded, also, was a full STOL facil-ity, plus higher rates of climb and accelera-tion, carrying a heavy weapon load. This was so that the aircraft could be used from temporary short airstrips, including the 500 m (550 yards) lengths of the main trunk roads that are part of Sweden's defence system. Over 100 design configurations were discus-sed between 1952-58, several utilizing the double-delta wing of the Draken. This, how-ever, did not give the required performance

and a 'canard' layout was decided upon. The main delta wing is set low and towards the rear of the fuselage, with a smaller delta 'nose-wing' or foreplane fitted at a higher level on the fuselage above the engines. These are situated side by side in the fusel-age, having the air intakes in line with the rear of the cockpit.

The engines helped solve the STOL prob-lem. After careful consideration of available powerplants, a military version of the Pratt & Whitney JT8D turbofan was selected. This RM8A has a rating of 6700 kg (14 770 lb) st and is fitted with afterburning, which gives 11 800 kg (26 015 lb) st, and a thrust reversal system. One other distinctive feature of the Viggen is the hinged vertical tail which folds downwards for stowage purposes. Many of Sweden's hangars are underground, and others are hollowed out of the sides of cliffs.

The first of six Saab 37 Viggen single-seat prototypes made its maiden flight on Feb-ruary 8, 1967; a seventh aircraft was a two-seat prototype for the SK 37 trainer variant. First flight of a production Viggen (from an initial order of 175) was on February 23, 1971, and by 1978 five different models had been ordered by the Flygvåpnet—the AJ 37 for the attack role to replace the Lansen A 32A, deliveries of which commenced in June 1971; the SK 37 two-seat operational trainer; the SF 37 tactical reconnaissance type to replace the Lansen S 32C; the SH 37 for maritime reconnaissance to take over from the Lansen S 32C; and the AJ 37 intercepter to eventually take over from the Draken J 35F. All versions of this aircraft are equipped with a Saab-Scania CK-37 miniaturized digital computer, which may be programmed to perform a multiplicity of tactical functions according to requirement. It also operates the autopilot, navigation, fire control and armament equipment, monitors fuel consumption, and is linked to Sweden's STRIL 60 ground-defence network.

One hundred Viggens were completed by the beginning of 1976 and a further five AJ 37s ordered. By spring 1978, AJ 37s equipped F6 and F7 Wings (two squadrons each) of the Flygvåpnet. Armament on this model and the

Vigilant, Vickers

SK 37 trainer (which can be used in the secondary attack role) is the same. All hardware is carried on seven external permanent stores points, three beneath the fuselage and two under each rear wing; two additional underwing points may also be fitted if required. Basic equipment is the Swedish RB04E air-to-surface missile for use against naval targets, or the Saab RB05A air-to-surface type which can also be used against ground and air intruders. Additional pods of 13.5-cm (5.3-in) Bofors rockets, bombs or 30-mm (1.18-in) Aden cannon can be carried. With the use of RB24 Sidewinder or RB28 Falcon missiles this version can be used in the intercepter role. The trainer version has a taller tail fin of increased area, a bulged second cockpit canopy, and is fitted with twin periscopes. Deliveries began in June 1972.

A total of 149 Viggen AJ 37s, from an anticipated total of 160-180 aircraft, had been ordered by mid-1978, and deliveries began at the end of that year. These have a more powerful (12 750-kg [28 108-lb]) st RM8B engine; a permanent external pack housing one 30-mm Oerlikon KCA long-range cannon, to port of the under-fuselage centreline; and nine external stores points, fitted with medium and short-range air-to-air missiles. Improved fire-control equipment is standard and advanced radar for target search and retention is installed. The SF 37 was ordered and flown for the first time in 1973, deliveries commencing in April 1977. These have modified camera noses and can carry external pods of photographic equipment. Viggen model SH 37 was ordered at the same time and although for use mainly to survey, register and report incidents occurring around the Swedish borders, can also be used in the attack role. Deliveries commenced in June 1975 and were continuing through 1978. Both these variants are similarly armed with two air-to-air missiles on the outboard wing points and an active or passive ECM pod on the inboard points, with drop-tanks on the under-fuselage positions. Internal equipment of the SF 37 includes a special optical sight, data camera, tape recorder, four vertical low-level cameras and two long-range ones in the nose. The SH 37 carries nose-mounted surveillance radar (as does the AJ 37), plus camera and registration equipment. External stores may also include a long-range cannon and day or night reconnaissance pods. The Saab 37X projected export model is based on the AJ 37.

(AJ 37) *Span:* 10.6 m (34 ft 9 in) *Length:* 16.3 m (53 ft 6 in) including probe *Gross weight:* 16 000 kg (35 275 lb) approx, normal armament *Maximum speed:* over 2125 km/h (1320 mph) or Mach 2 at 11 000 m (36 090 ft)

Vigilant, Vickers

British antitank missile. Vickers began work on guided weapons in the early 1950s, and when the Red Dean radar-guided air-to-air missile was cancelled in 1957 the company's board voted £400 000 of the compensation money to keep its missile design team intact. A light antiaircraft weapon was considered initially but was rejected since no suitable radar was available. Attention then turned to an infantry-portable ATGW which could also be mounted on reconnaissance vehicles. The

A North American A-5 Vigilante carrier-based reconnaissance aircraft takes off during trials

army had no requirement for such a weapon, so development was financed by Vickers.

Vigilant was demonstrated to representatives of the United States and other NATO members in 1959, and in August 1960 the British Army ordered 100 rounds for evaluation. Further demonstrations to 22 countries in July 1961 were very successful and the British Army ordered its first production batch in mid-1962, by which time Kuwait had already signed a contract. The British Army eventually took nearly 12 000 rounds for infantry use and to equip Ferret 2/6 scout cars, with another 2500 or so missiles going to Kuwait, Finland, Saudi Arabia, Libya and Abu Dhabi. The missile is being replaced by Milan in the British Army.

Vigilant is fired from a simple box launcher which can be placed on the ground or mounted on a vehicle. The operator tracks the target through an optical sight and issues steering corrections by means of a joystick; these commands are transmitted down trailing wires to operate flap surfaces (rather than the more conventional spoilers) which gives the missile high manoeuvrability. Vigilant was advanced for its time in that it contains an autopilot to keep it on course until commanded to change direction by the operator. One man can control up to six fixed launchers or three two-round launchers which can be remotely trained through 340°.

Length: 1.07 m (3 ft 6 in) *Span:* 28 cm (11 in) *Diameter:* 13.2 cm (5.16 in) *Weight:* 14.7 kg (32 lb 8 oz) *Speed:* 560 km/h (350 mph) *Range:* 1600 m (1 mile) *Warhead:* 6-kg (13 lb 3-oz) hollow-charge

Vigilante, North American A-5

US Navy carrier-based reconnaissance aircraft. Designed to meet a US Navy requirement in 1955 for an all-weather high-performance attack aircraft, the Vigilante was the heaviest machine to serve on a US carrier, except for the Douglas A-3 Skywarrior. Two prototypes were ordered from North American Aviation, designated YA3J-1. First flight was made on August 31, 1958, the name Vigilante having been adopted by then. The aircraft was a tandem two-seat shoulder-wing monoplane, with low aspect ratio swept back wings, typical of most North American designs at the time. There were no ailerons on the wings, which were fitted with blown flaps for low-speed control. Spoilers in the wing upper surface combined with all moving differential tailplanes ('tailerons') and a slab-type fin and rudder to give control in roll, pitch and yaw axes. For the first time in a US production aircraft the two side-by-side engines were fed through variable-geometry intakes, the initial production powerplant being General Electric J79-GE-2, -4 or -8 turbojets of 7711 kg (17 000 lb) st with afterburning. A novel innovation was the 'linear bomb bay'. This consisted of a tunnel running half the length of the fuselage from the central weapons bay, down between the tailpipes of the engines. It was intended that nuclear or conventional bombs should be ejected rearwards. The main armament was to be a free-falling nuclear weapon, attached to which were two fuel tanks—only part of the internal load carried. This fuel was used first and when the bomb was dropped the empty tanks acted as stabilizers.

Production aircraft began delivery in 1960 as A3J-1s and VAH-7 Squadron, which became operational in June 1961, embarked in the USS *Enterprise* in August the following year, the aircraft now being redesignated A-5A. The 57 A-5As built were equipped with the REINS (radar-equipped inertial navigation system) bombing navigation system and provision was made for fuel tanks, bombs or rockets to be carried on two underwing pylons. Six A-5Bs (later redesignated YA-5C Limited]) were built next, with extra fuel stored in a 'saddle' tank over the fuselage, enlarged wing flaps, better boundary-layer control (air being blown over the total wing area) and four underwing pylons as standard. Initial flight of the first aircraft was made on April 29, 1962, but about this time the US Navy, under government directive, was relieved of its strategic nuclear bombing role and the six aircraft in this batch, together with 43 existing A-5As, were converted to unarmed reconnaissance RA-5C configuration. Ninety-one more were built as RA-5Cs, the first flight by one of these being made on June 30, 1962. These Vigilantes incorporated the modifications introduced on the B model, with the exception of the saddle tank. The switch to this new role was somewhat expedient, since difficulties had been experienced with the bomb bay's operation. As RA-5Cs the Vigilantes entered service in June 1964 with RVAH-5 on board the USS *Ranger*. All carriers of the *Forrestal* Class were allocated six aircraft and two of the *Midway* Class ships were refitted to accommodate the type.

RA-5Cs carried a vast range of electronic and visual reconnaissance equipment in what had previously been the bomb bay; this included sideways-looking airborne radar, vertical, oblique and split-image cameras, plus active and passive ECM systems. They had a wide speed range, and could operate in all weathers at both high or low altitudes carrying a pilot and observer/radar operator. The underwing pylons could be fitted with additional fuel tanks for extra range and Vigilantes could also be re-equipped for the secondary attack role by the attachment of napalm canisters, 454-kg (1000-lb) or 907-kg (2000-lb) bombs, or Bullpup air-to-surface missiles to the four pylons. Powerplants were two J79-GE-10 turbofans of 8100 kg (17 860 lb) with afterburning, which gave a maximum range of 4830 km (3000 miles)—with internal fuel tanks only—and a cruising speed of 901 km/h (560 mph). Vigilantes served with RVAH-1, RVAH-5, RVAH-7, RVAH-9 and RVAH-11 Squadrons into the mid-1970s.

(RA-5C) Span: 16.15 m (53 ft) *Length:* 23.11 m (75 ft 10 in) *Gross weight:* 36 100 kg (79 588 lb) *Maximum speed:* 2230 km/h (1385 mph)

Vigneron

Belgian submachine-gun. The Vigneron was a well designed submachine-gun which originated from a retired Belgian army officer, Colonel Vigneron. It was adopted in the early 1950s and has been the standard submachine-gun of the Belgian forces ever since. Much of the gun is common to many others of that period, and it is primarily made from simple steel stampings with plastic furniture and a telescoping wire stock. The barrel is longer than with most designs and it appears to have required rather more machining than would seem necessary. There are elementary cooling rings cut into it near the breech and a simple form of compensator on the muzzle. The foresight stands up with no protection, though at least one version has been seen in which there was a hood around it.

There is a grip safety in the pistol grip which locks the bolt in the closed position and there is a second safety in the selector lever. An unusual feature is that the gun will fire semiautomatically even when the selector lever is in the auto position. A slight pull on the trigger will fire a single shot; a longer pull will fire automatic.

The whole gun is quite light and well made. One arm of the wire stock is longer than the other and can be used as a cleaning rod, but in all other respects the Vigneron is much like many more submachine-guns which have been in service in NATO since the mid-1950s.

Calibre: 9 mm (0.354 in) *Ammunition:* 9-mm Parabellum *Weight:* 3.29 kg (7 lb 4 oz) unloaded *Length:* 889 mm (35 in) extended *Barrel length:* 305 mm (12 in) *Magazine:* 32-round detachable box *Rate of fire:* 620 rds/min (cyclic) *Muzzle velocity:* 365 m/sec (1200 ft/sec)

Viking, Lockheed S-3A

US carrier-based antisubmarine aircraft. It is almost ten years since Lockheed received a contract from the US Navy on August 4, 1969, to produce a new antisubmarine aircraft. Development began under the designation S-3A and Lockheed acquired the services of other manufacturers to help produce the prototype and production models. Design and construction of the wings, engine pods, tail unit and landing gear was assigned to the Vought company; Sperry's Univac division produced the digital computer for the weapons system, vital for the high-speed processing of information on a modern type of ASW aircraft. The Lockheed company was responsible for building the fuselage, integrating the electronics, and final assembly. A prototype was ready on the set date of November 8, 1971, the first flight being made on January 21, 1972. Further funds were received to produce eight pre-series test aircraft over a five-year period. In the following May the US Navy ordered 13 production S-3As; in April and October 1973 batches of 35 and 45 were contracted, plus other subsequent orders over the next year or so.

The production S-3A Viking is a high-wing cantilever monoplane, of all-metal construction, with a capacious fuselage which incorporates fore and aft weapons bays fitted with clam-shell doors, with a battery of 60 sonobuoy launchers between them in the centre section. The all-metal cantilever-swept vertical tail unit can be folded downwards for on-board stowage purposes—the wings fold upward and inward on hydraulic jacks. Also operated hydraulically is the retractable tricycle undercarriage, with main units similar to those of the Vought Crusader and nose unit to that of the Corsair II. A catapult towbar (retractable) and an arrester hook are also fitted. A crew of four is carried, the pilot and copilot sitting side by side on the flight deck, which has a tinted canopy; the other two being situated in the rear cabin, with side windows. All are equipped with McDonnell Douglas ejector seats; both crew areas are pressurized and air-conditioned.

The two 4207-kg (9275-lb) st General Electric TF34-GE-2 turbofan engines are suspended on pylons, one under each wing. Fuel is contained in wing tanks, one either side of the fuselage inboard of the wing folding section. Normal capacity is 7192 litres (1582 Imp gal); two extra 1136-litre (250-Imp gal) drop-tanks can be attached to underwing pylons if required. There is an illuminated in-flight refuelling probe situated in the top fuselage. Vikings are equipped with highly sophisticated search and forward-looking infrared radars, electronics and communications systems as well as an automatic carrier landing system, retractable magnetic anomaly detector (MAD) tail boom, and passive ECM. Armament can comprise, internally, four MK-36 destructors, four MK-46 torpedoes, four MK-82 bombs, two MK-57 or four MK-54 depth charges or four MK-53 mines. The two underwing pylons can, instead of fuel tanks, be used alternatively to carry flare launchers, cluster bombs, rockets or practice bombs.

Following the delivery of the first Viking to the US Fleet on February 20, 1974, further batches began arriving at North Island, California, for pilot training with VS-41 Squadron. One hundred and eighty-seven aircraft had been delivered by mid-1978, this being the total number ordered up to the beginning of 1979. The first operational assignment for the Vikings was with VS-21 Squadron on board the USS *John F Kennedy* in July 1975 and they served with about a dozen squadrons on service in the Pacific, Atlantic and Mediterranean waters in 1979. The S-3A has been constructed with future development in mind as improved equipment becomes available. A US-3A utility transport version was first flown in 1976 and was still under test in 1978. Designs for a tanker variant (KS-3A) together with plans for an ES-3 electronics patrol model are currently being considered by the US Navy.

(S-3A) Span: 20.93 m (68 ft 8 in), 8.99 m (29 ft 6 in), folded *Length:* 16.26 m (53 ft 4 in) *Gross weight:* 23 831 kg (52 539 lb) *Maximum speed:* 834 km/h (518 mph)

Vikrant

Indian navy light fleet carrier. Laid down as a *Majestic* Class light fleet carrier at the Tyneside yard of Vickers-Armstrongs, in October 1943, and launched on September 22, 1945 as HMS *Hercules*, the ship which was to become the Indian navy's first aircraft carrier was purchased on January 1, 1957. At this time she was structurally complete and fitted out, apart from armament, electronics and internal communications, having been laid up since May 1946, when construction had been suspended.

Renamed *Vikrant*, she was taken in hand in April 1957 at Belfast and completed by Harland & Wolff. The work involved the replacement of the original hydraulic catapult by a longer, more powerful steam catapult, more modern arrester gear, improved air conditioning in living spaces and extended aircraft-control facilities. An angled deck was, of course, featured, necessitating an extension of the flight deck on the port side, abreast the island. As completed, she closely resembled HMAS *Melbourne*.

Vikrant was accepted by the Indian navy on March 4, 1961, the conversion having taken an inordinately long time, for reasons which are not clear. She worked up in British waters with an air group which included ex-Royal Navy Hawker Sea Hawks and new-built Breguet Br.1050 Alizé antisubmarine aircraft; these continued to serve aboard her

Vilar Perosa

until 1979, with the number of types of potential fixed-wing aircraft available to replace them limited by the carrier's small size and relatively slow speed. The Indian navy was given a demonstration of VTOL operations and a Hawker-Siddeley Harrier flew to and from *Vikrant*'s deck in 1972.

Vikrant was based at Cochin, near the Indian navy's main air station. Her one combat operation was in 1973, during the second Indo-Pakistan war: she served in the Bay of Bengal, where her aircraft effectively blockaded the East Pakistan coast between Chittagong and Cox's Bazaar, the Sea Hawks undertaking successful strikes against naval and military targets.

Displacement: 16 000 tons (standard), 19 500 tons (full load) *Length:* 213.4 m (700 ft) oa *Beam:* 24.4 m (80 ft) wl, 39 m (128 ft) over sponsons *Draught:* 7.3 m (24 ft) *Machinery:* 2-shaft geared turbines, 40 000 shp=23 knots approx *Aircraft:* 23 *Armament:* 17 40-mm (1.57-in) Bofors *Crew:* 1400 approx

Vildebeest, Vickers

British torpedo-bomber. The Vildebeest was begun in 1926 as a specialized replacement for the Hawker Horsley, which had been adapted as a torpedo machine. A two-seat single-bay biplane with spatted wheels on a split main undercarriage, to enable a 46-cm (18-in) torpedo to be carried below the fuselage, the prototype Vildebeest was tested with a Townend ring cowling, but all production aircraft except the Mk IV dispensed with cowlings. The pilot had a high-set cockpit and operated a Vickers machine-gun in the port side of the forward fuselage, while the gunner in the rear cockpit was armed with a ring-mounted Lewis. On production models accommodation for a third crew member could be provided just behind the pilot's cockpit.

The first prototype flew in April 1928 powered by a 460-hp Bristol Jupiter VIII and was followed by 22 production Vildebeest Mk Is with 600-hp Bristol Pegasus IM3 engines, 30 Mk IIs with 635-hp Pegasus IIM3s, 111 Mk IIIs and 18 Mk IVs with closely cowled 825-hp Bristol Perseus VIIIs —the RAF's first sleeve-valved engine— driving three-blade propellers.

Deliveries of the Mk I to RAF Coastal Command began in 1932, and the type was still in service in the Far East at the start of the Second World War; a number were destroyed during the Japanese invasion of Singapore at the end of 1941. The Spanish navy bought the original prototype, re-engined with a 600-hp Hispano-Suiza 12 Lbr, as the Vildebeest VII, which could be fitted with a twin-float undercarriage. CASA built 25 with this powerplant under licence. These six floatplanes and 20 landplane Vildebeests saw action on the Republican side in the early stages of the Spanish Civil War, but few remained in service by the end of 1936 and only two survived the conflict. Another 27 Mk IIIs were supplied to the Royal New Zealand Air Force. The Vildebeest was later developed as the general-purpose Vincent.

Span: 14.94 m (49 ft) *Length:* 11.48 m (37 ft 8 in) *Gross weight:* 3856 kg (8500 lb) *Maximum speed:* 251 km/h (156 mph)

Despite its age, the Vildebeest saw some action during the Second World War in the Far East

Vilar Perosa

Italian machine-gun. The Vilar Perosa is frequently cited as the first submachine-gun, on the grounds that it is the first recorded automatic weapon firing pistol ammunition. While the mechanics are not in doubt, the tactical function of the Vilar Perosa excludes it from consideration as a submachine-gun and places it as a light machine-gun. It was designed by Revelli and patented in 1915. The patent was assigned to a company known as the Officine Vilar Perosa, from which the gun takes its name. It was also manufactured by Fiat, and in Canada by the Canadian General Electric company. Manufacture ceased in 1918.

The VP was designed to fill a demand by Italian mountain troops for a light machine-gun, an equipment which did not exist in 1915 in the Italian army. The mechanism is a delayed blowback type, though there is room for doubt as to whether Revelli meant it to be. The bolt moves back and forth in the receiver, controlled by a lug riding in a helical groove, so that as the bolt closes it is rotated through 45°. This rotation does not lock the bolt to the breech; it merely ensures that a straight groove inside the bolt is aligned with a lug on the firing pin so that the firing pin can pass through to strike the cartridge; this ensures that the gun cannot fire until the bolt is closed. However, since the recoiling bolt has to 'unwind' through 45°, there is an element of delay in its action. The bolt, however, is light and the return spring stiff,

so that the rate of fire is extremely high at 1500 rds/min.

In order to obtain maximum firepower, the design called for two of these guns to be mounted side by side and controlled by a single spade grip and trigger at the rear. Feed was from box magazines inserted into the top of the actions, and the assembly was carried on a platform suspended from the firer's neck by a strap, rather like a matchseller's tray. The tactical proposal was that he should then walk forward in the assault, firing the guns from the hip and spraying the target with high-speed fire. Since the two magazines held only 25 rounds each, the rate of fire meant that both were empty in less than a second, so the firer would have spent more time changing magazines than actually firing. An alternative method was to put a bipod on the barrels and use it as a ground gun. It was also tried as an aircraft weapon, but the range was insufficient.

By 1918 the Italian army had had enough, and withdrew the guns for them to be split and each weapon mounted into a wooden stock to become a submachine-gun. These became the OVP and Beretta M1918 models, and as a result of this move very few original twin Vilar Perosa guns can be found today.

Calibre: 9 mm (0.354 in) *Ammunition:* 9-mm Glisenti *Weight:* 6.48 kg (14 lb 5 oz) *Length:* 535 mm (21.1. in) *Barrel length:* 320 mm (12.6 in) *Magazine:* 2 25-round boxes *Rate of fire:* 3000 rds/min *Muzzle velocity:* 400 m/sec (1310 ft/sec)

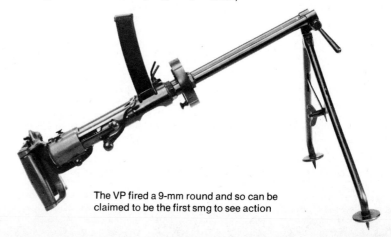

The VP fired a 9-mm round and so can be claimed to be the first smg to see action

There is no difference in basic features between naval ordnance and land service ordnance; they both have rifled barrels, breech mechanisms and recoil systems. The differences arise in the manner of employment. The first fundamental which has to be grasped is that naval guns are invariably fired from a moving platform and generally against a moving target; the only land service gunnery which approximates to this is tank gunnery, and it is notable that much of tank gunnery, in its early days, was derived from naval practice. The second point is that the moving platform is moving in several directions at once; not only is the ship steaming ahead, it is also pitching and rolling with the motion of the sea. A third feature is that by the nature of the targets envisaged—armoured ships—the naval gun needs to be a high velocity weapon firing on a relatively flat trajectory in order to deliver a substantial blow at the target end; with rare exceptions, howitzers and low velocity weapons are not found in naval inventories.

By the time of the First World War naval guns had been categorized into two broad classes; the primary armament of battleships and heavy cruisers, which consisted of heavy, large calibre guns mounted in turrets, their prime task being the bombardment of enemy ships at as long a range as practicable, and the secondary armament, which consisted of medium and small-calibre weapons in broadside mountings intended for the protection of the ship against smaller types of attacker such as destroyers and torpedo boats.

The turret, and its related gun mountings, was a masterpiece of naval engineering. Into this restricted space had to go two or three major-calibre guns, their loading apparatus—which had to handle shells weighing up to one ton in weight—sights, communications, ammunition supply, fire-fighting equipment and the men to operate it. Moreover this mass of machinery had to be so balanced that it could be trained round to point accurately at a target irrespective of how the ship was rolling or pitching; it is relatively easy to construct a 1500-ton mass which will rotate smoothly on a firm base, but to make the same mass rotate equally smoothly and accurately when the base is tipped sideways by several degrees is a formidable engineering problem.

Having developed the upper section of the turret to mount the desired guns, the structure then had to be continued down into the ship in order to provide a shaft up which the necessary ammunition could be supplied, and supplied at a rate capable of keeping the guns firing at the maximum rate of fire. In addition, the supply system had to be developed with an eye to safety, so that in the event of an explosion in the turret, due to an enemy shell or an accident, the resulting flash would not pass down the supply system and ignite the contents of the ship's magazine. That such disasters did happen from time to time is indicative of the difficulties encountered in trying to solve the problem.

The secondary armament was less of a mechanical problem. The general standard was the 6-in/152-mm gun, mounted so as to be able to pivot and cover as wide an arc as the ship's structure permitted, and protected by a simple shield. Ammunition supply was

Batches of 5-in (127-mm) shells being loaded aboard USS *Hull*, a *Forest Sherman* Class destroyer

to some convenient nearby point and did not involve having to deliver shells right onto the gun platform. Below the 6-in level came the 3-in/76-mm class, used for defence against light vessels where a high rate of fire was more necessary than a formidable armour-piercing performance.

The First World War made few changes to this. The first problem to arise was the provision of special weapons to fight submarines, and the first thoughts on this subject were to fight the submarine on the surface or as it began to submerge. For this purpose various specialized weapons were developed, the most usual being forms of diving shell. These were normal small-calibre piercing shells with discs attached to the nose to prevent the shell ricocheting on striking the surface of the water, so that it would continue on an underwater course and strike the hull of the submarine.

These were moderately successful, but another line of approach was to rely less upon a direct hit than upon pitching a heavy charge of explosive into the water and trusting to the subsequent blast pressure to damage the target. This led firstly to the adoption of heavy 'stick bomb' projectiles, cylindrical charges on the end of rods which were inserted into the muzzle of a light gun and fired by a blank cartridge. Then came the adoption of howitzers firing heavy shells armed with depth-sensitive fuzes. All these, however, gradually died out after it was realised that the best answer to the submarine was to get above it and drop depth charges. If a submarine was met on the surface, then it became a conventional surface target.

More portentous for the future was the arrival of aircraft, though very little was done about this threat during the war apart from the provision of machine-guns and modifying the light guns then in existence.

In general terms the First World War might be said to have reinforced prewar trends of naval thinking, and as the war ended plans were afoot in most maritime nations for bigger and more powerful naval guns for primary armament, calibres of 18-in (460-mm), 20-in (510-mm) and even 21-in (533-mm) being proposed. The 1921 Washington Conference on Naval Limitations, however, put a stop to these extremes, which allowed naval ordnance designers to stay in an area with which they were familiar, while allowing them scope to set to work on the question of antiaircraft guns. Here the solution was to develop dual purpose weapons, guns of small and medium calibre on mountings which allowed them to fire in the surface role or, without delay, elevate so as to be able to engage flying targets. At the same time there was a move towards the development of light fast-firing weapons in the 20-mm (0.79-in) to 40-mm (1.57-in) class, as exemplified by the German Solothurn cannon and the British pom-pom, weapons which could put up a stream of small projectiles in a short time to keep close attackers at bay.

The Second World War saw the decline of the capital ship with large-calibre armament, and postwar years have brought a general reduction in the size of warship which has, in turn, led to the development of smaller calibre guns as main armament. Today the accent is on fast-firing medium-calibre weapons, using mechanical ammunition supply and full automation to extract the highest rate of fire with the use of the minimum number of men. Current designs tend towards gun mountings which are completely automated, being aimed and fired by remote control from a central control point and merely requiring the minimum number of men to keep ammunition moving into the supply system, after which loading, firing, and disposal of the empty case is done entirely without human intervention.

The principal revolution in naval gunnery, which has made it possible to develop automated weapons, has been the progress made in the techniques of fire control over the last 40 years. In the early 1930s naval gunnery relied entirely on optical acquisition of the target, optical rangefinding, and subsequent correction of the fall of shot by optical methods. This was allied to some fairly simple calculating devices which, fed with such parameters as the relative speed and course of the ship and its target, the wind speed, temperature, and muzzle velocity of the guns, would deduce the future position of the target and the gun data required to hit it. In the late 1930s radar observation and rangefinding began to appear, first in the German and then in the British and US navies, and by the end of the war it was sufficiently accurate to permit engagements in darkness with some degree of accuracy. The last engagement between battleships with heavy guns was fired by radar when, on October 25, 1944, the USS *Mississippi* sank the Japanese *Yamashiro* by salvoes of 16-in (406-mm) shells at 17.6 km (11 miles) range in darkness.

Since then radar has improved in accuracy and discrimination, and it has been allied to electronic computing systems which are capable of doing far more involved calculations

at far higher speeds than were the old pattern of mechanical calculator. Current naval fire-control systems can detect targets, assess their relative importance, allocate armament to them in order of priority, transmit firing data to the guns which then elevate and train automatically and fire when precisely aligned. The radar will then detect and analyse the fall of shot, produce corrections, give fresh data to the guns, and continue until the target is destroyed, moves out of range, or is abandoned in favour of some other target.

For long-range work the gun is rapidly giving way to various forms of surface-to-surface missile, while the antiaircraft field is also yielding to the missile. Nevertheless, there is still a place for the gun in naval thinking. The US Navy had to hurriedly recommission gun-armed ships in order to provide their fleet with a shore bombardment capability during the Vietnam war, and this led to a reassessment of the place of guns followed by development of several medium-calibre, automated weapon systems. The gun now has several competitors in various roles, but its prime advantage is its versatility, ensuring its survival for a long time to come.

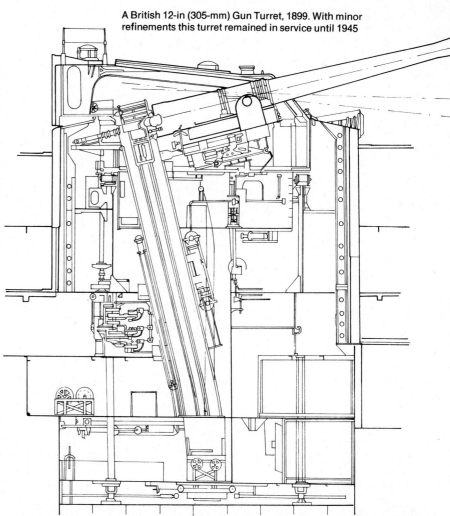

A British 12-in (305-mm) Gun Turret, 1899. With minor refinements this turret remained in service until 1945

Loading a shell in the 6-in (152-mm) turret of HMS *Orion*. The crew have antiflash hoods

Above left: A WRNS Fleet Analysis Unit Officer checks the recording camera installation sited on a ship's gunnery direction system. *Above right:* Loading belts of 2-pdr shells into the pom-pom AA guns of the cruiser HMS *Shropshire*. The pom-pom was an excellent short-range AA gun. *Below left:* The local control console with TV monitor, track ball and instruments and controls on the OTO Melara 76/62. The gun's fixed structure ammunition hoist can be seen to the left of the picture. *Below right:* The OTO Melara 76/62 with TV/Optical sighting hood on a coastal range

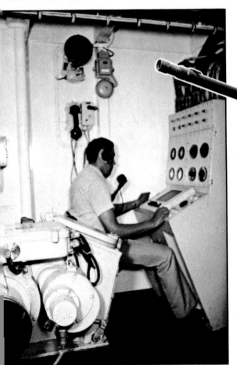

Naval Ordnance

Machine-guns

From the turn of the century until well into the Second World War machine-guns were mounted in most warships, either as part of the antiaircraft armament or for use by landing parties. Calibre and type usually corresponded to those in use on land in the country concerned, but not always. In the Royal Navy the .45-in (12-mm) Maxim had ousted the earlier Nordenfelt types, although the 1-in (25-mm) was still in use in older ships and many .45-in 5-barrelled Nordenfelts were still around. When the British Army changed to .303-in (7.7-mm) the navy followed suit.

The US Navy retained the Gatling gun long after it had disappeared elsewhere, in a .30-in (7.62-mm) version. The French used the 2-barrelled Gardner gun but later adopted the Hotchkiss 8-mm (0.315-in).

After the First World War the heavy machine-gun came back into favour as an antiaircraft weapon. The British adopted the Vickers .5-in (12.7-mm), a scaled-up version of the .303-in, and in 1937 a quadruple version was tried in HMS *Aberdeen*. Although a cumbersome and ineffective weapon it was widely used. The US Navy was equally dazzled by the supposed killing-power of the .5-in, and single water-cooled mountings were standard in prewar ships. The French adopted a 13.2-mm (0.52-in) in twin and quadruple mountings.

20-mm (0.79-in)

The best-known in this series was the Swiss Oerlikon. The German navy used the Solothurn variant in single and quadruple mountings (the well-known flak vierling), but the Danish Madsen single was also popular.

25-mm (1-in)

The best-known gun in this calibre was the Hotchkiss automatic, developed for the French navy but made under licence in Japan. The Japanese decided on this calibre rather than a mixture of 20-mm (0.79-in) and 40-mm (1.57-in), which proved a mistake as it had neither the handiness of the Oerlikon nor the weight of shell of the Bofors. It was used widely in a triple mounting, either in an open 'tub' or in enclosed blast-proof mountings.

28-mm (1.1-in)

Known also as the Hudson machine-gun, this was adopted as the US Navy's standard close-range AA weapon shortly before the Second World War in quadruple side-by-side mounting in an open tub. It proved unreliable and clumsy, and was quickly superseded by the 40-mm (1.57-in) Bofors, although many ships continued to mount it until supplies of the Bofors became available. The Soviet navy introduced a Gatling type in this calibre, in low-level barbette mountings similar to the older twin 30-mm (1.18-in). It is presumably an equivalent of the Vulcan Phalanx intended as a Close In Weapon System (CIWS).

30-mm (1.18-in)

A modern calibre, this was introduced by the Hispano division of the Oerlikon group as the 831. It is used in a twin power-operated

Above: Soviet sailors with a twin water-cooled Browning .5-in (12.7-mm) M2 AA machine-gun on a Mk 21 mount. *Below:* The USS *King* with her 20-mm Vulcan Phalanx close-range AA gun

Left: A depth-charge explodes astern of a Soviet warship. In front of the depth-charge racks is an 'over-and-under' 37-mm (1.46-in) AA gun. *Below:* A Soviet warship with quad 37-mm (1.46-in) guns. The chain-feed ammunition system gives a very high rate of fire, and has been adopted by numerous navies

Soviet sailors manning 45-mm (1.77-in) guns possibly aboard *Voroshilov* during AA training; this was a compact and useful AA gun

mounting (A32 type) for small warships. The same barrel is used in a single CAS 62 mounting by the French navy and in the US Emerlec 30 twin-automatic mounting made by Emerson Electric. A 65-cal automatic version is used in Soviet warships, as a remotely-controlled AA weapon. It is in a distinctive conical barbette-type mounting, and is used in the *Osa* Class missile boats among others.

35-mm (1.38-in)

The GDM-A twin automatic mounting is electrically driven for AA defence and can be used against sea-skimming missiles. It is used in the Greek *Combattante* Class fast patrol boats whose armament differs from the French and German boats of the same class.

37-mm (1.46-in)

As the 1-pdr this was a popular calibre at the turn of the century, in the British, French, US and Soviet navies. It was used as a semiautomatic, single-shot piece, or as a revolving gun designed by the Colt company in the French and US navies. In the Soviet navy it re-emerged in 1943 when an army AA gun was adopted. Both single and twin mountings were produced and many are still in service in older Soviet warships. It was the standard close-range AA weapon for the German navy as well, in a twin mounting.

40-mm (1.57-in)

The first guns in this calibre were Vickers 2-pdrs, developed from the original pom-pom which existed as a land weapon at the end of the nineteenth century. Essentially a scaled-up Vickers-Maxim machine-gun, complete with water-cooling, it was used in destroyers from 1913 onwards, first as a close-range weapon and then as a primitive AA gun. The existence of about one and a half million rounds for this gun led to its choice as the basis for a new multiple AA mounting developed by Vickers for the Royal Navy during 1921-27. The 8-barrelled pom-pom was a fearsome weapon capable of delivering half a ton of shells per minute, firing each barrel with a slight delay to distribute the stress evenly over the whole mounting. It was so big that it could only be mounted in battleships, carriers and heavy cruisers, but in 1937 a 4-barrelled version appeared, suitable for light cruisers and destroyers. The drawbacks to both types were the low muzzle velocity of the 2-pdr shell and the vulnerability of the base of the mounting to blast, but it was far and away the best defence against dive-bombers in 1940, and remained in front-line service until 1945.

The need for more close-range defence led to the wartime design of single mountings. These were used in destroyers against aircraft and fast surface targets, in MGBs and landing craft. A variant was the air-cooled Metrovick 2-pdr, but the most successful was the power-operated 2-pdr Mk XV. This was initially intended for MGBs, and was essentially a 2-pdr barrel mated to a power mounting for the twin 20-mm (0.79-in) Oerlikon. It became very popular in 1944-45 when kamikaze attacks showed that the twin Oerlikon lacked stopping power, and British destroyers going out to join the Eastern and Pacific Fleets were hurriedly rearmed with them in place of the Mk V twin 20-mm. The single 2-pdr was made under licence in Italy and served from 1914 to 1943.

The most famous 40-mm gun was the Bofors. It emerged first as a single-barrelled gun but was turned into a quadruple mounting by the US Navy to replace the 28-mm (1.1-in) Hudson, despite the fact that it weighed more than twice as much. The next step was to break down the quadruple Mk 2 into two twins, and these 'utility' mountings were used as the basis for the British Mk V mounting. The British also used the Mk IV Hazemeyer, with its own radar tracker, as an AA mounting in destroyers.

Other variants of the Bofors included the British 6-barrelled Mk 6, with autofeed, the single Mk VII and Mk IX and the Boffin,

Buster and STAAG mountings. Boffin was a Canadian variant of the power-operated 2-pdr, using a Bofors barrel with the 20-mm Mk V mounting as a lash-up AA mounting in 1944-45. Buster was a 22-ton monster with only two barrels, designed by Rose Brothers, but it never went into production. The Stabilized Tachometric AA Gun (STAAG) was made in two marks, with its own fire-control radar on the mounting, and was fully automatic. The 'antlered beast' was complex, heavy and expensive, but when it appeared in 1947 it was the most advanced weapon afloat. It was used on B turret in the modernized cruiser HMNZS *Royalist* and the 'Battle' and *Daring* Class destroyers, and finally disappeared in the 1960s.

Today the 40-mm Bofors is still in service in many navies, and with the advent of proximity-fuzed, pre-fragmented ammunition it has greatly enhanced effectiveness.

45-mm (1.77-in)

The 45-mm single was the standard AA weapon of the Soviet navy in the Second World War, in all categories of ships.

47-mm (1.85-in)

As the 3-pdr this was a popular gun in most navies at the turn of the century, either as a single-shot Hotchkiss semiautomatic or as the Vickers automatic, and was used as a close-range weapon. In the First World War both types were used as AA guns by the Royal Navy, becoming the HA IC and HA III mountings, and although virtually useless no doubt improved morale by the noise they made.

50-mm (2-in)

Known in contemporary British sources as the 4-pdr, this was a German light gun used in torpedo boats and in older cruisers.

57-mm (2.24-in)

Otherwise known as the 6-pdr, this was the most popular of the Hotchkiss semiautomatic guns in service early in the century. It was used in the first British Mk I Male tanks and was used on the HA IC and HA IV high-angle mountings. With its short recoil and shoulder piece it could be aimed and laid quickly, making it suitable for rapid firing. It formed the armament of destroyers up to about 1904, and after 1914 was used to arm trawlers and merchantmen. The same barrels were modified in 1943, for use against U-Boats when it was discovered that splinter hits could prevent them from diving, and several escort destroyers were given two 6-pdrs forward of the bridge.

The final use of the 6-pdr was the twin Mk I mounting introduced in 1943, for use on the east coast against schnellboote. It was a navalized version of the coast defence 6-pdr twin, and its use in destroyers was suggested by its success in a slaughtering attack on Malta by MAS-boats in July 1941. With a normal rate of fire of 72 rds/min, a mounting with a rapid rate of slew plus radar-tracking it was very effective against fast-moving surface targets.

Today 57-mm guns are widely used. The

Soviet navy has several versions in service, a twin automatic, a twin semiautomatic and a quadruple mounting. The Bofors company has also produced several versions, a twin AA enclosed mounting for the secondary armament of the *Halland* Class destroyers and the cruiser *Gota Lejon*, and two marks of single mounting for the *Spica* and *Jagaren* Class fast patrol boats. Barrels for the 60-cal pattern Model 1950 were supplied to Creusot-Loire for installation in a twin mounting used in the *Surcouf* and *le Corse* Classes in the French navy.

75-76-mm (2.95-3-in)

Known principally as the 12-pdr, but with minor variants known as the 12½-pdr, 13-pdr, 14-pdr and 15-pdr to give various buyers the impression that they were getting tailor-made guns, this was a standard light gun at the turn of the century. It was used as the tertiary battery in battleships and cruisers and as the main gun in destroyers, and remained in service in various forms until 1945.

After the outbreak of war in 1914 many were removed from old warships; many went into new escorts and merchant ships and many were converted to AA guns. In 1915 the Royal Navy bought a large number of what it thought were 12-pdr Elwick pattern guns from the Japanese, but found that they were old Obuchov 75-mm guns stripped from Russian ships surrendered and captured in 1905. The French *soixante-quinze* field gun was used in similar fashion by the French navy.

In the Second World War both the Royal Navy and the US Navy used 3-in AA guns, the former retaining the term 12-pdr for them. The US developed a new rapid-firing 3-in/50-cal twin to replace the quadruple 40-mm (1.57-in) Bofors. Later a 70-cal version, known as the 'broomstick', was developed but it did not last long. A single-barrel version was also developed called Mk 34, as against Mk 27 and 33 for the twins, for use in light warships. The 3-in round was chosen for development in an automatic AA mounting because at the time it was the smallest round which could be given a proximity or Variable-Time (VT) fuze.

The British Mk 6 3-in twin was a development of the 70-cal barrel design by the US

A Bofors 57-mm (2.24-in) AA gun. It is secondary armament for the *Halland* Class destroyers and the cruiser *Gota Lejon*, with single barrel guns on the *Spica* and *Jagaren* Class fast patrol boats

Bureau of Ordnance, and was manufactured by Vickers. It was credited with a rate of fire of 120 rds/min and was fitted with water cooling, but this phenomenal rate of fire was never used operationally, 60 rds/min being the more usual rate. It is mounted in the *Tiger* Class cruisers and some Canadian DDEs.

In 1964 NATO gave a development contract to the Italian OTO-Melara company to develop a new dual-purpose rapid-fire shipboard gun, using the standard US Navy 3-in round, and in 1969 the first production units appeared. With its 80 rds/min and exceptional reliability this has now become virtually a standard gun in NATO and many Western navies. It is built under licence in the United States and Japan, and may soon be built by Vickers in England. It is light enough to be used in patrol boats, and is the normal gun armament of the *Combattante* and similar classes of fast patrol boats, in addition to being used in the *Oliver Hazard Perry* Class frigates of the US Navy. Sweden has a 50-cal single for use in fast patrol boats, while the Soviet Union has a twin 75-mm dual-purpose mounting in the *Kashin* and *Kynda* Classes. The so-called 80-mm AA gun used by the Japanese in the Second World War was a 76-mm piece.

Sailors of the Royal Navy on gunnery drill with a 12-pdr 3-in gun mounted on a submarine

84-85-mm (3.30-3.35-in)

Used in the Soviet navy, this calibre exists in two forms, the elderly twin AA mounting in the *Skory* Class destroyers, and a new water-cooled single mounting in the latest of the *Krivak* Class. In the 1950s a version of the 20-pdr (84-mm) gun, which was fitted as the main armament in Centurion tanks until 1957, was fitted in the fast patrol boat *Bold Pioneer* for a short while.

88-mm (3.46-in)

The standard German light weapon from the turn of the century to the end of the First World War, this was the equivalent of the 12-pdr and was used as a tertiary gun in cruisers and capital ships, or as main armament in torpedo boats. From 1914 it was progressively stripped for larger ships and replaced by AA versions.

90-mm (3.54-in)

The Model 1926 was used as an AA weapon (twin-barrelled) in the French cruisers *Colbert*, *Foch* and *Dupleix*, and the tender *Jules Verne*, but was not continued.

100-102-mm (3.9-4-in)

The 100-mm has always been a favourite calibre in the French navy, first as a low-angle gun, and since 1925 as an AA weapon. The Model 1925 and Model 1936 is used in 1st Class submarines and the Model 1931 in cruisers and battleships. A new model which came into service in 1939 was a copy of the successful British Mk 16 twin 4-in AA, adopted to try and make up for lost time. Since the war Creusot-Loire has produced the Model 53 and Model 68, externally identical and differing only in that the Model 68 is lighter. A new model, the Compact, is reported to be lighter still, but barrel and ammunition remain the same.

The British 4-in has an equally long history, being used for the first time in destroyers in the *Beagle* Class of 1910, but much earlier in cruisers. It formed the secondary armament of battleships from the *Bellerophon* Class, and was used as the standard gun

Above: A Vickers 4.5-in (113-mm) Mk 8 gun on HMS *Ambuscade*. It has a fume extractor and muzzle brake and the ballistically shaped turret found on most modern gun mounts. *Below:* Twin 4.5-in Mk VI aboard HMS *Leopard*. After the war its first installation was in HMS *Saintes*

Below left: Soviet sailors manning 102-mm (4-in) guns on the after deck of an old DD. *Below right:* The standard French 100-mm (3.9-in) DP gun

in destroyers, sloops and sweepers. It was used as an AA gun after 1918, first in single mountings, but from 1937 in the famous Mk 16 mounting, which with modifications is still in use in many navies.

A 4-in gun was used in US First World War destroyers, while the Soviet navy also used a 4-in in the *Novik* and her successors. Most navies found guns in this bracket useful for many years. The most advanced 4-in is the automatic dual-purpose single designed by Vickers-Armstrongs in the 1950s for the Chilean *Almirante Riveros* and *Almirante Williams*. Based on a British army project for a land-mobile AA gun, later cancelled, it had a continuous feed and radar control.

105-mm (4.1-in)

This was the German equivalent of the 4-in, used first as a cruiser-gun before the First World War, and then as the principal destroyer-gun through to 1945. It was also produced in twin high-angle mountings in the 1930s for capital ships and cruisers. After

1945 captured mountings were used in French ships until such time as indigenous weapons could be developed.

4.5-in (114-mm)

Originally developed to allow the provision of common ammunition with the army's AA guns, the Royal Navy's 4.5-in rapidly developed on separate lines. By 1943 it was in production as the new destroyer-gun, first in a single Mk V mounting with 55° elevation and then in a twin Mk IV between decks (BD) high-angle mounting with 85° elevation. The mounting for the single was identical to the 4.7-in mounted in the *Saumarez* Class, and was first mounted in HMS *Savage*. The twin appeared in the 'Battle' Class.

In 1943 a new twin, the Mk VI, was planned, and it appeared in 1948, first in HMS *Saintes* in B position and then in the *Daring* Class. It was used in subsequent classes, the *Devonshire* Class DLGs and the *Whitby, Rothesay, Leander, Leopard* and *Salisbury* Class frigates.

The latest 4.5-in gun is the Vickers Mk 8 Single, which is a robust mounting capable of firing automatically. It is mounted in modern British DDGs, frigates and the DLG *Bristol*, as well as the Brazilian *Niteroi* Class.

4.7-in (120-mm)

Another popular calibre from before the turn of the century, by 1910 the 4.7-in was in service in the Japanese navy's destroyers, but did not appear in the Royal Navy until 1916, when it was specified for the *Shakespeare* Class leaders. It was in fact a naval version of the army's 4.7-in field gun, itself a derivative of the old 4.7-in naval guns landed from cruisers for service on wheeled carriages in the Boer War, in place of the 5-in (127-mm) proposed for the new ships. The 4.7-in thereafter became the standard destroyer-gun in the RN until supplanted by the 4.5-in, which had slightly superior ballistics. The final mark of 4.7-in, the Mk XX, fired a 29-kg (64-lb) shell, putting it on a par with foreign destroyer-guns of up to 5.9-in calibre.

Sailors in foul-weather clothing prepare to load a 4.7-in (120-mm) gun on board the destroyer HMS *Hesperus* during the Second World War